PATON'S *CRY, THE BELOVED COUNTRY:*
The Novel, The Critics, The Setting

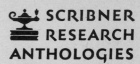 SCRIBNER
RESEARCH
ANTHOLOGIES

Martin Steinmann, Jr., GENERAL EDITOR

SHERIDAN BAKER
University of Michigan

PATON'S *CRY, THE BELOVED COUNTRY:*
The Novel, The Critics, The Setting

SCRIBNER
RESEARCH
ANTHOLOGIES

CHARLES SCRIBNER'S SONS   New York

Preface

Each Scribner Research Anthology is a collection of written sources upon a single historical, political, literary, or scientific topic or problem—the Hungarian Revolt, Shakespeare's *Julius Cæsar,* or extrasensory perception, for example. In addition to these sources, it contains (1) "Guide to Research," an account of the rationale and the methods of research and of research-paper writing, (2) an introduction to the topic of the anthology, (3) suggested topics for controlled research, and (4) suggested sources and topics for library research.

Each anthology is designed to serve two purposes. First, each gives the student access to important sources—texts, documents, letters, diaries, essays, articles, reports, transcripts of hearings, for instance —on a given topic. Some of these sources are otherwise available in only a few libraries, some (manuscripts and historical and government documents) in only one. In any case, the collection as a whole is not otherwise available in one volume. Second, each anthology gives the student either all his sources for a controlled-research paper or some of them for a library-research paper. Each anthology can be valuable either for readings in courses in history, literature, science, or humanities or as the basis for a research paper in these or in other courses.

A controlled-research paper—a paper in which the student's search for sources is limited to, and in certain ways controlled by, those sources contained in one anthology—is not so noble an undertaking as a library-research paper. But it is often more successful—more rewarding for the student and easier for his instructor to teach effectively and judge fairly. Its advantages for both student and instructor are often considerable.

For the student, it sometimes provides sources unavailable in his school library. And it enables him to learn a good deal about research (selection, interpretation, and evaluation of sources; quotation and paraphrase; and documentation) without prior instruction in use of the library (and, incidentally, without overtaxing the facilities and the resources of his library and without loss of, or damage to, sources either irreplaceable or difficult and expensive to replace).

For the instructor, it permits focus of class discussion upon a limited set of topics. It enables him to track down the student's sources conveniently. And—perhaps the greatest advantage of all—it enables him to judge both conveniently and exactly how well the student has selected, interpreted, and evaluated his sources and how well he has quoted and paraphrased them.

In many schools, a controlled-research paper is either a preliminary to or a part of a library-research paper. A library-research paper is probably the most difficult paper that the student can be assigned to write. The problems that confront him are not simply those common to any paper —organization, paragraphing, and transitions, for instance—and those (already mentioned) common to all research papers. He has, in addition, the problem of using the library well—of, for example, using the card catalogue, periodical indexes, and other reference works. But, if the instructor assigns a controlled-research paper as a preliminary to or, as it were, an early part of a library-research paper, the student need not come to grips with all these problems at once.

Each Scribner Research Anthology is compiled according to the following editorial principles. Each source that is not anonymous is prefaced by a biographical note on its author. At the foot of the same page is a bibliographical note. Each source is reprinted exactly as it appears in the original except for (1) some typographical peculiarities, (2) explanatory notes, given in brackets, and (3) omissions, indicated by ellipses (". . ."). And, finally, for each source that has pagination in the original, page numbers are given in brackets within the source itself—thus: "[**320/321**]," where everything before the slash (and after the preceding slash, if any) is from page 320, and everything after the slash (and before the next slash, if any) is from page 321. For a source hitherto unpublished, no page numbers are given; and the student who uses it should cite the page numbers of the Scribner Research Anthology. Footnotes to a source are given as in the original. Where the original pagination of a footnote is not evident, its page number precedes it in brackets.

MARTIN STEINMANN, JR.

Bingham Bay
Lake Gogebic
August, 1960

Guide to Research

THE IDEA OF RESEARCH

Research is the organized, disciplined search for truth; the aim of all research is to discover the truth about something. That thing may be a historical object like the Stonehenge monuments or a historical event like the Hungarian Revolt or the Battle of Waterloo. It may be a work of literature like Shakespeare's *Julius Cæsar* or Miller's *Death of a Salesman*. It may be a recurring event like the motions of the planets or the circulation of the blood. It may be an experimentally repeatable phenomenon like behavior of rats in a maze or perception apparently unaccounted for by the five senses. Or it may be a political problem like the decision to use the atomic bomb in World War II. Archeology, history, political science, literary criticism and scholarship, astronomy, physiology, and psychology—these are some of the many divisions of research. Indeed, all the sciences—physical, biological, and social—and all other scholarly disciplines share this organized, disciplined search for truth.

The search for truth has often been confused with such aims as confirming prejudice, instilling patriotism, and praising friends and blaming enemies. The attempt to prove the preconceived conclusion *that* one college is superior to another, for example, is not research (though the attempt to discover *whether* one college is so superior is). Research is hostile to prejudice.

General Methods of Research. The best general method of research is first-hand observation. But this method is not always possible and, when it is possible, not always practical.

The best method to begin discovering the truth about something is to observe that thing and the circumstances surrounding it. To discover the truth about *Julius Cæsar* or *Death of a Salesman*, get the play and read it, or go to the theatre and watch a performance. To discover the truth about the planets, observe them through your telescope. To discover the truth about the intelligence of rats, build a maze and run some rats through it.

This first-hand observation is not always possible, however. To discover the truth about the Battle of Waterloo, you can't observe the battle. The best that you or anyone else can do is to observe other persons' observations, the recorded observations of eye-witnesses: diaries, letters, and memoirs, for instance, of soldiers and generals who were in the battle. With more recent historical events—for example, the Hungarian Revolt—you are better off. You can watch films and listen to tape recordings. You may be able to interview people who were there. But these observations are still second-hand; and, on the whole, history can be observed only at second-hand. The sole exception is history that you have been part of. You may have fought in the Hungarian Revolt—though, if you did, you may be prejudiced.

Even when first-hand observation is possible, it is not always practical. You may have a copy of or tickets to *Julius Cæsar* or *Death of a Salesman* but not know enough about the principles of dramatic criticism to interpret the play unaided. You may have a telescope but not know how to use it or, if you do, not know what to make of what you observe through it. You may have some rats but not know how to build a maze or, if you do, not know enough about animal psychology to run your rats through it properly. The best that *you* can do under these circumstances is to supplement whatever first-hand observations you can make with observations of the first-hand observations of other people better-trained or better-equipped than you. Read *Julius Cæsar* or *Death of a Salesman* and also critics' interpretations of the play. Observe the planets, if you can, and read treatises on astronomy. Do what you can with your rats, and read reports of experiments with rats. After all, no one can master the special methods and come by the special equipment of all scholarly disciplines. Indeed, few people can do this with more than one discipline, and then not before they're thirty. But all people who want a liberal education should try to discover as much of the truth about as many scholarly disciplines as their abilities and their circumstances permit. Indeed, the achievement of this is what is meant by "a liberal education."

Primary and Secondary Sources. As the foregoing account of the general methods of research suggests, there is, ultimately, only one source of the truth about something—the thing, the event, or the phenomenon itself: the Stonehenge monuments, the Hungarian Revolt, or the Battle of Waterloo; the text of *Julius Cæsar* or *Death of a Salesman;* Robert Oppenheimer's testimony on the use of the atomic bomb against Japan; the motions of the planets or the circulation of blood; extrasensory perceptions or rats running in a maze. Such a source is a *primary* source. And, in historical research, where the thing itself (the Hungarian Revolt or the Battle of Waterloo) cannot be observed at first hand, a report of an eyewitness or a film or a tape recording is also counted as a *primary* source. But any other second-hand source (an interpretation of *Julius Cæsar* or *Death of a Salesman,* a treatise on astronomy, a report of an experiment with rats) is a *secondary* source.

A primary source is, of course, better. But, if a primary source is unavailable to you (if it is a book, perhaps your school library does not have it) or if you are not trained or equipped to use it (you don't know how to run rats through a maze or you have no telescope), then a secondary source must do. In any case, except for the most mature scientists and scholars, a good

secondary source is useful and often indispensable.

It is worth noticing that being primary or being secondary is not an intrinsic characteristic of the source itself. It is, rather, a relationship that either exists or does not exist between a given source and a given topic of research. Consequently, a given source may be primary in relation to one given topic but secondary in relation to another. Two examples may serve to make this important point clear. Edward Gibbon's *The Decline and Fall of the Roman Empire* (1776-1788) is a secondary source in relation to the topic of the Roman Empire but a primary source in relation to that of eighteenth-century English prose style or that of eighteenth-century historiography. Samuel Taylor Coleridge's *Lectures on Shakespeare* (1811-1812) is a secondary source in relation to the topic of Shakespeare's plays but a primary source in relation to that of nineteenth-century principles of dramatic criticism or that of Shakespeare's reputation.

It is worth noticing also that a given source may be primary or secondary in relationship to more than one topic. James Joyce's novel *A Portrait of the Artist as a Young Man* is a primary source in relation not only to the topic of the structure of *A Portrait of the Artist as a Young Man* (and dozens of other topics on the novel itself) but also to the topic of use of the stream-of-consciousness technique in twentieth-century fiction.

THE RESEARCH PAPER

A research paper is a paper giving the results of research, the methods by which they were reached, and the sources, primary or secondary, which were used. A research paper attempts to tell the truth about a topic, and also tells how and where this truth was discovered. As we have seen, the sources of a research paper may be either written sources (literary texts and historical documents, for example) or sources of other kinds (experiments, for example). Since a research paper written in school is almost always based upon written (printed) sources, we shall here discuss only that kind. A research paper based upon written sources may be either a library-research paper or a controlled-research paper. A library-research paper is a research paper for which your search for sources is limited to those sources contained in the libraries available to you; a controlled-research paper, to those sources contained in one anthology —to those contained in this volume, for example. Here we shall emphasize the latter kind.

Finding Your Topic. The first step in writing a research paper based upon written sources, whether a library-research or a controlled-research paper, is finding a topic. We say "finding a topic" rather than "choosing a topic" because the process is more like finding a job than choosing a sandwich from a menu. Unless your instructor assigns you a topic, which he may do, you must look for one; and the one you find may not be just what you want but the best one that you can find. But, if you look long and carefully, you may find a topic that so well suits your interests, your capacities, and the time and the space at your disposal that your paper will almost surely be a success.

Finding a topic is the most important single step in writing a research paper, and the things that you should have in mind when looking for a topic are (1) your interests, (2) your capacities, and (3) the time and the space at your disposal. If you are interested in a topic, if you know something about the special methods of research that the topic requires, and if your topic is narrow enough to require no more time than you have for research and no greater development than you can give it in a paper of the length assigned you, then the paper that results will probably be satisfactory. For example, the topic of figures of speech in *Julius Cæsar* may interest you greatly. But, if it does, you must ask yourself whether you know enough about figures of speech to do research on them

and, if you do, whether this topic is narrow enough. Even the topic of metaphors in the play would be too broad for most papers; metaphors in Brutus' soliloquies might be about right. In any case, before you take a topic for a paper, you should do some reading on that topic; otherwise, you won't know whether it is interesting, within your ability to handle, and within the scope of your assigned paper.

Once you think that you've found a topic, take great care in phrasing it. The best phrasing is a question or a series of closely related questions. Better than "The character of Brutus" is "To what extent is Brutus motivated by self-interest and to what extent by the public interest?" The latter is not only more narrow and more precise; it provides you with a criterion of relevance in selecting your sources. At the end of this volume, you will find a list of suggested topics, intended to call your attention to topics that might not occur to you. But these topics are suggestive rather than definitive or precise.

Finding Your Sources. Finding sources for a library-research paper and finding ones for a controlled-research paper, though different in several respects, are alike in certain others. Finding sources in the library requires knowledge of how to use the card catalogue, periodical indexes, special bibliographies, reserve shelves, and encyclopedias. Finding sources in this volume or a similar one does not. But, in either case, you must have a clear idea of what you are looking for; and you must be prepared to put up with a high ratio of looking to finding. In other words, you must have not only criteria of relevance but also a willingness to do a good deal of skimming and a good deal more of careful reading, some of it fruitless.

The basic criterion of relevance you provide by careful phrasing of your topic, a problem discussed in the preceding section. The other criteria you provide by making a preliminary or tentative outline —perhaps in the form of subtopics, perhaps in the form of questions. Such an outline is not to be used for your paper. The outline for your paper will probably be quite different and, in any event, cannot be made until after you find your sources and take your notes. This preliminary outline guides your research and, as we shall see, provides you with the subtopic headings necessary for your note-cards (see "Taking Your Notes," page xiii).

Making Your Working Bibliography. Once you have found a promising source ("promising" because, though it seems to be relevant, it may turn out not to be) you want to make some record of it so that, once you have completed your search for sources, you can turn back to it, read it, and, if it turns out to be relevant, take notes on it. This record of promising sources is your *working* bibliography. It is so called for two reasons: first, because you work with it as you proceed with your research and the writing of your paper, adding promising sources to it and discarding irrelevant ones; and, second, because this designation distinguishes it from your final bibliography, which appears at the very end of your research paper and contains only sources actually used in the paper. For a controlled-research paper, your working bibliography may be nothing more elaborate than a series of check marks in the table of contents of your research anthology or a list of page numbers. For a library-research paper, however, you need something quite different.

A working bibliography for a library-research paper is a collection of three-by-five cards each representing a promising source and each containing full information about that source. Once you have completed your research, written your paper, and discarded all promising but (as they turned out) irrelevant sources, this bibliography is identical with your final bibliography. Having a separate card for each source enables you to add and to discard sources easily and to sort and arrange them easily in any order you please. Eventually, when this bibliography becomes identical with your final bibliography, you will arrange sources alphabetically by au-

thors' last names. Having full information about each source on its card enables you to turn back to it easily—to locate it in the library without first looking it up again. You find this information in the card catalogue, periodical indexes, or other bibliographical aids; or, when browsing through the shelves or the stacks of the library and coming upon a promising source, you find it in or on the source itself—for example, on the spine and the title page of a book.

If the source is a *book,* you should put the following information on the three-by-five working-bibliography card:
(1) the library call number,
(2) the author's (or authors') full name (or names), last name first for the first author,
(3) the title of the book,
(4) the name of the city of publication,
(5) the name of the publisher (*not* the printer), and
(6) the year of publication (often found on the other side of the title page).
See the example of such a card on the opposite page (note the punctuation carefully).

If the source is a *periodical article,* you should put the following information on the three-by-five working-bibliography card:
(1) the author's (or authors') full name (or names),
(2) the title of the article,
(3) the name of the periodical,
(4) the volume number,
(5) the week, the month, or the season of publication, together with the year, and
(6) the page numbers covered by the article.
See the example of such a card on the opposite page (note the punctuation carefully).

These two forms take care of the two standard cases. For special cases—such things as books with editors or translators as well as authors, books published in several editions or in several volumes, and daily newspapers—see any good handbook of composition.

860.3
J23

Jones, John A., and William C. Brown. _A History of Serbia_. New York: The Rowland Press, Inc., 1934.

WORKING-BIBLIOGRAPHY CARD FOR A BOOK

Smith, Harold B. "Fishing in Serbian Waters." _Journal of Balkan Sports_, VII (May 1936), 26-32.

WORKING-BIBLIOGRAPHY CARD FOR A PERIODICAL ARTICLE

Taking Your Notes. Once you have found sources, entered them in your working bibliography, read them, and found them relevant, taking notes requires your exactly following a standard procedure if your notes are going to be useful to you when you come to write your paper. An extra five minutes given to taking a note correctly can save you a half hour in writing your paper. Here is the standard procedure:

(1) Take all notes on four-by-six cards. Never use notebooks, loose sheets of paper, or backs of old envelopes.

(2) Limit each note to information on a single subtopic of your preliminary outline *and* from a single source. It follows from this that you may have many cards on the same subtopic and many cards from the same source but that you may never have one card on more than one subtopic or from more than one source.

(3) On each card, in addition to the note itself, put

(a) the appropriate subtopic heading in the upper left-hand corner,

(b) the name of the source (usually the author's last name will do) in the upper right-hand corner, and

(c) the page number (or numbers) of that part (or those parts) of the source that you have used in taking your note. If you have used more than one page, indicate your page numbers in such a way that, when you come to write your paper, you can tell what page each part of the note comes from, for you may not use the whole note.

(If you follow these first three rules, you will be able, when you come to outline and to organize your paper, to sort your notes in any way you please—by subtopic, for example—and to arrange them in any order you please. Such flexibility is impossible if you take your notes in a notebook. If you follow the third rule, you will also be able to document your paper— write footnotes, for example—without again referring to the sources themselves.)

(4) In taking the note itself, paraphrase or quote your source or do both; but do only one at a time, and use quotation very sparingly.

Paraphrase and quotation require special care. Anything between paraphrase and quotation is not acceptable to good writers: you either paraphrase or quote, but do nothing in between. To paraphrase a source (or part of a source) is to reproduce it in words and word orders substantially different from the original. When you paraphrase well, you keep the sense of the original but change the language, retaining some key words, of course, but otherwise using your own words and your own sentence patterns. To quote a source (or part of a source) is to reproduce it exactly. When you quote well, you keep both the sense and the language of the original, retaining its punctuation, its capitalization, its type face (roman or italic), and its spelling (indeed, even its misspelling).

Omissions and additions require special care. If, when quoting, you wish to omit some of the original, you may do so only if the omission does not change the sense of the original (never leave out a "not," for example!) *and* if it is indicated by ellipses (three spaced periods: ". . ."). If you wish to add something to the original, you may do so only if the addition does not change the sense of the original (never add a "not"!) *and* it is indicated by square brackets. The most usual additions are explanations ("They [i.e., the people of Paris] were alarmed") and disclaimers of errors in the original, indicated by the Latin *"sic,"* meaning "thus" ("Colombis [*sic*] discovered America in 1592 [*sic*]"). You must, of course, carry these ellipses and square brackets from your note-cards to your paper. And, if you type your paper, brackets may be a problem, for most typewriter keyboards do not include them. If your keyboard does not, you may do one of two things—either use the slash ("/") and underlining ("__" and "——") in such a way as to produce a bracket ("⊏" and "⊐") or draw brackets in with a pen. In any event, don't substitute parentheses for brackets.

In your paper, quotations no longer than three or four lines are to be enclosed within a set of quotation marks and run into your text; longer ones are to be set off from the text, without quotation marks, by indention from the left-hand margin and, especially in typewritten copy, by single-spacing. But never use either of these devices unless the language is exactly that of the original.

Your usual treatment of a source should be paraphrase; use quotation only if the

Fly - fishing   *Smith*

   Smith says that fly-fishing is a method of fishing used chiefly by wealthy Serbians and foreign tourists, that the flies used are generally imported from Scotland, and that "Serbian trout are so snobbish that they won't glance [27/28] at a domestic fly."

   [Query: How reliable is the information in this rather facetious article ?]

NOTE-CARD

language of the original is striking (strikingly good or strikingly bad), if it is the very topic of your research (as in a paper on Shakespeare's style), or if it is so complex (as it might be in a legal document) that you don't want to risk paraphrasing it.

Let us look at the sample note-card above. The topic of research is methods of fishing in Serbia; the subtopic that the note deals with is fly-fishing in Serbia; the source is Harold B. Smith's article "Fishing in Serbian Waters," from the *Journal of Balkan Sports* (see the second of the two working-bibliography cards on page xiii).

Note the subtopic heading ("Fly-fishing") in the upper left-hand corner; the name of the source, abbreviated to the author's last name ("Smith"), in the upper right-hand corner; the page numbers ("[27/28]"), indicating that everything, both paraphrase and quotation, up through the word "glance" is from page 27 and that everything after that word is from page 28; the sparing and appropriate use of quotation; and the bracketed query, to remind the note-taker that he must use this source with caution.

Writing Your Paper. Many of the problems of writing a research paper based upon written sources—organization, the outline, the thesis paragraph, topic sentences, transitions, and the like—are problems of expository writing generally. Here we shall discuss only those problems peculiar to such a paper. Two of these problems —paraphrase and quotation—we discussed in the preceding section. Two others remain: reaching conclusions and avoiding the scissors-and-paste organization.

When you come to make the outline for your paper and to write your paper, you will have before you three things: (1) your *preliminary* outline, containing ordered subtopics of your topic; (2) your working bibliography; and (3) your note-cards. These are the *immediate* results of your research; they are not the *final* results. They are only the raw material out of which you must fashion your paper. At best, they are an intermediate stage between finding your topic and making your final outline. The preliminary outline will not do for the final outline. The working bibliography will almost certainly require further pruning. And the note-cards will require sorting, evaluation, organization, pruning, and exercise of logic and common sense. All this needs to be done, preferably before you make your final outline and begin to write your paper, though almost inevitably some of it will remain to bedevil you while you are writing it. To put the matter in another way, you are, with these things before you, a Sherlock Holmes who has gathered all his clues but who has reached no conclusions from them, who has not come to the end of his search for truth. You must discard irrelevant clues, ones that have no bearing on the questions that you want answered. You must arbitrate the claims of conflicting or contradictory clues. You must decide which one of several probable conclusions is the most probable.

Once you have reached your conclusions, you must organize your paper and set forth this organization in your final outline. Organization and the outline are, of course, problems common to all expository writing. But a problem peculiar to the research paper is avoiding the scissors-and-paste organization—avoiding a paper that looks as though you had cut paraphrases and quotations out of your note-cards, pasted them in columns on paper, and connected them only with such phrases as "Jones says" and "On the other hand, Brown says." Such an organization is the result of a failure to reach conclusions (with the consequence that there is nothing but "Jones says" to put in between paraphrases and quotations); or it is a failure to see the necessity of giving the conclusions reached *and* the reasoning by

which they were reached (with the consequence that, though there is something to put between paraphrases and quotations, nothing is put there, and the reader is left to write the paper for himself).

Documenting Your Paper. To document your paper is to give the source of each paraphrase and quotation that it contains, so that your reader can, if he wishes to, check each of your sources and judge for himself what use you have made of it. To give the source is usually to give (1) either the information that you have about that source in your working bibliography (except that the name of the publisher of a book is usually not given) or the information that accompanies each source in a research anthology *and* (2) the information about page numbers that you have in your notes. This information you may give either formally or informally, as your instructor decides.

Formal documentation is given in footnotes. For a full discussion of footnotes, see any good handbook (one cheap and widely accepted one is *The MLA Style Sheet*). The form of footnotes is similar to, but not identical with, the form of bibliographical entries. With these three sample footnotes, compare the two sample working-bibliography cards on page xiii:

[1] John A. Jones and William C. Brown, *A History of Serbia* (New York, 1934), p. 211.
[2] Harold B. Smith, "Fishing in Serbian Waters," *Journal of Balkan Sports*, VII (May 1936), 27.
[3] Smith, pp. 27-28.

Informal documentation is given in the text of the paper, usually parenthetically, as in this example:

> Fly-fishing in Serbia is chiefly a sport of wealthy Serbians and foreign tourists (Harold B. Smith, "Fishing in Serbian Waters," *Journal of Balkan Sports*, VII [May 1936], 27), though in some mountain districts it is popular among the peasants (John A. Jones and William C. Brown, *A History of Serbia* [New York, 1934], p. 211). The flies used are generally imported from Scotland; indeed, Smith facetiously adds, "Serbian trout are so snobbish that they won't glance at a domestic fly" (pp. 27-28).

As this example suggests, however, informal documentation can be an annoying distraction. It probably works out best in papers that use only a few sources. In such papers, there are few occasions for long first-references to sources: for example, "(Harold B. Smith, "Fishing in Serbian Waters," *Journal of Balkan Sports,* VII [May, 1936], 27)." But there are many occasions for short succeeding-references: for example, "(Smith, pp. 27-28)" or "(pp. 27-28)." Occasionally, informal documentation may be profitably combined with formal, as in a paper about Shakespeare's *Julius Cæsar.* In such a paper, references to the play might well be given informally —for example, "(III.ii.2-7)"—but references to critics formally.

How many footnotes (or parenthetical documentations) do you need in your paper? The answer is, of course, that you need as many footnotes as you have paraphrases or quotations of sources, unless you group several paraphrases or quotations *from the same page or consecutive pages of a given source* in such a way that one footnote will do for all. One way to do this grouping—almost the only way— is to introduce the group with such a sentence as "Smith's views on fly-fishing are quite different from Brown's" and to conclude it with the raised numeral referring to the footnote. Your reader will understand that everything between the introductory sentence and the numeral comes from the page or the successive pages of the source indicated in the footnote.

Making Your Final Bibliography. Your paper concludes with your final bibliography, which is simply a list of all the sources—and only those sources—that you actually paraphrase or quote in your paper. In other words, every source that you give in a footnote (or a parenthetical documentation) you include in your final bibliography; and you include no other sources (inclusion of others results in what is unfavorably known as "a padded bibliography"). The form for entries in your final bibliography is identical with that for ones in your working bibliography, given above. You should list these sources alphabetically by authors' last names or, if a source is anonymous, by the first word of its title, but not by "a," "an," or "the." For example:

BIBLIOGRAPHY

Jones, John A., and William C. Brown. *A History of Serbia.* New York: The Rowland Press, Inc., 1934.
"Serbian Pastimes." *Sports Gazette,* XCI (October 26, 1952), 18-19, 38, 40-42.
Smith, Harold B. "Fishing in Serbian Waters," *Journal of Balkan Sports,* VII (May 1936), 26-32.

MARTIN STEINMANN, JR.

Contents

Introduction

Cry, the Beloved Country seems an ideal starting-point for learning the possibilities, methods, and values of literary research. To begin with, it is an important twentieth-century novel and merits close analysis in its own right. Moreover, it evokes a specific time and place, South Africa in 1946, and a background of events with which we may not be familiar, thus opening up a world outside the novel for investigation. This volume offers its reader the resources to explore the novel itself, the critical issues that surround it, and the South African setting which nurtured Alan Paton and from which the novel grew.

The novel demonstrates uncommonly well the fundamental nature of literature precisely because its events are foreign to us. In these events, we discover with surprising force that, in literature, the particulars must convey some universal implications, or they will have no relevance for us nor last beyond their particular moment. This demonstration is the more forceful in *Cry, the Beloved Country* because the gap between the events of the story and the circumstances of our lives at first seems very wide. But we discover that besides acquainting us with special dilemmas—individual, social, geographic, national—rooted in its South African setting, *Cry, the Beloved Country* widens our viewpoint on current world problems: those resulting from the confrontation of different races and their distinct cultures, and those caused by the replacement of the agricultural, communal, and rural by the technological, impersonal, and urban way of life. In addition—and perhaps this is the most significant reason for the novel's strange power over us—*Cry, the Beloved Country* speaks with immediacy to analogues within our own society and our individual experience.

Cry, the Beloved Country also shows how literature springs from a deep private response to the social scene. Alan Paton began the response that culminated in this book by writing poetry and entering student affairs at the University of Natal, in Pietermaritzburg, South Africa, the city of his birth. Of English descent, Paton was brought up in the Anglican church. At twenty-one, he went to London for an Empire Students' Conference, toured England and Scotland by motorbike, and returned to Natal to teach science (his college major) for four years in a school for Zulus in the village of Ixopo. He then moved back to Pietermaritzburg, married, and continued to teach and to write poetry. He also wrote and destroyed two novels.

A severe illness from typhoid gave him time to reconsider himself and South Africa. Jan Hofmeyr, an Afrikaner and one of Paton's boyhood heroes, had just been given charge, as Minister of Education, of all institutions of juvenile correction. Paton wrote him for a job, and Hofmeyr appointed him, "somewhat to his horror," [1] as head of Diepkloof Reformatory, on the outskirts of Johannesburg. Under Hofmeyr's leadership, Paton took down the barbed-wire fences, planted geraniums, and instituted a program of progressively earned freedom.

After ten years at Diepkloof, badly needing a rest, still seeking some further answer to the questions of personal fulfillment and social responsibility, Paton sold his insurance policies, and his wife took a job, so that he could travel in Scandinavia, England, and America to study penal methods. In Sweden, he read John Steinbeck's *The Grapes of Wrath;* in Norway, he looked at the rose window

[1] Lewis Gannett, "Introduction," *Cry, the Beloved Country* (New York: Charles Scribner's Sons, 1950; Modern Standard Authors Series), p. xiii.

1

in the cathedral of Trondheim one evening by flashlight. He returned to his
hotel, and his response to South Africa
poured out as the first chapter of *Cry, the
Beloved Country*.

Paton dedicated the American edition
to friends he met in California toward the
end of his tour who helped him get the
novel published (1948). He dedicated
the British edition to Jan Hofmeyr,
the strongest voice and strongest hope for
social justice in the South African government, who died three months after *Cry,
the Beloved Country* appeared. Hofmeyr's
influence on Paton had been profound.
And Paton's respect for his friend was
never greater than when Hofmeyr, already
ill, delivered the commencement address
at the University of Witwatersrand, Johannesburg, on March 16, 1946—the year
of Paton's trip to Trondheim, the year in
which *Cry, the Beloved Country* origi-
nated, and the year in which the events in
the novel take place. Hofmeyr proclaimed
that South Africa's only hope was to
change its "*Herrenvolk* mentality," the
concept that any élite race has the right
to control the destinies of other peoples.
To Franklin D. Roosevelt's Four Freedoms,[2] he added a fifth—the freedom from
prejudice: "May you be prepared to say
with Thomas Jefferson, 'I have sworn
upon the altar of God eternal hostility
against every form of tyranny over the
mind of man'—and here in South Africa
the greatest evil of all is the tyranny of
prejudice." [3]

That speech, Paton reports, was received with thunderous applause. Two
years later, though *apartheid* had won and
Hofmeyr was dead, *Cry, the Beloved
Country* also received tremendous applause, at home and abroad, for something
very like the same message. In October
1949, Paton was brought to the United
States for the premiere of *Lost in the Stars*,

a musical play adapted from his novel by
Maxwell Anderson and Kurt Weill. In
1951, he was brought to London to consult on the film of the story, released in
1952. In 1954, *Collier's* magazine invited
him to tour the United States and write a
survey of "The Negro in America Today."
Since then, South Africa has progressively
tightened restrictions against its critics,
and Paton's passport was revoked several
years ago.

Like his Arthur Jarvis in *Cry, the Beloved Country*, Paton has devoted himself
to the service of South Africa. And his
considerable literary talents have absorbed
only a part of that devotion. "It is my
conscience that urges me to take some part
in public life," he has said, "whereas my
inclinations urge me to write." During his
years at Diepkloof, he became active in
Toc H, a Christian service-organization
that had spread throughout the British
Empire after the First World War. He
helped organize the Transvaal Association
of Non-European Boys' Clubs, of which
he became President. He served as President of the South African Liberal Party
and received a Freedom Award in 1960.
Since 1953, he and his wife have lived and
worked at Kloof, Natal, in a Toc H settle-
ment for tubercular black Africans.

The selections following the novel in
this anthology lead directly into the critical and social issues. Part Two, "The
Critics," focuses on the general question of
the uniqueness of *Cry, the Beloved Country* and its place in modern literature. On
the publication of the novel in 1948, most
reviewers were unanimous in their praise
and their lack of penetration. I have selected a review representative of the
praise, but one that also penetrates to a
significant question about the novel's ending. The four critical essays that follow
comprise almost all the notice that formal
criticism has yet given this novel, which
nevertheless continues to be read widely
throughout the world and studied in the
classroom. The essays, of course, raise
literary and critical questions and make

[2] Roosevelt's Four Freedoms, as stated in a message to
Congress on January 6, 1941, are: freedom of speech and
expression, freedom of worship, freedom from want, and
freedom from fear.
[3] Alan Paton, *South African Tragedy* (New York:
Charles Scribner's Sons, 1965), pp. 325–327.

judgments that the student may weigh against his understanding of the book and his own experience.

Part Three, "The Setting," presents the South African background. Two maps at the beginning of the section will help the student to fit the novel to the actual scene and afford a means of checking the inferences about geography in one of the critical essays. Dudley C. Lunt then provides a summary of the historical and social development of South Africa. A selection from Alan Paton's *South Africa and her People* gives a view of tribal life to be compared with that in Ndotsheni in the novel. Then follow documents by Laura Longmore and Trevor Huddleston on the young men and women who inhabit the slums of Johannesburg—the closest sociological parallels to the book available— and documents on the bus boycotts in and around Johannesburg and the discovery of gold at Odendaalsrust, which are factual antecedents to events in the novel. The last four selections by Trevor Huddleston, Alexander Steward, Francis Addington Symonds, and Alan Paton offer contrasting views of major issues to which the novel also speaks. The volume concludes with suggestions for research, designed to guide the student in his use of these materials and lead him on to further study.

PART ONE

THE NOVEL

Cry, the Beloved Country*

ALAN PATON (1903–   ) began to write Cry, the Beloved Country late in 1946 in his hotel room in Trondheim, Norway, where he was traveling on an inspection of penal institutions. He continued writing it as he traveled through Sweden, England, and the United States, finishing it in San Francisco. It was published, first in the United States then in Great Britain, in 1948, the year in which the Nationalist Party, under D. F. Malan, was elected to govern South Africa by a majority of five seats in the House of Assembly, defeating the United Party of Jan Christian Smuts and Jan Hofmeyr.

BOOK ONE [1/3]

I

There is a lovely road that runs from Ixopo into the hills. These hills are grass-covered and rolling, and they are lovely beyond any singing of it. The road climbs seven miles into them, to Carisbrooke; and from there, if there is no mist, you look down on one of the fairest valleys of Africa. About you there is grass and bracken and you may hear the forlorn crying of the titihoya, one of the birds of the veld. Below you is the valley of the Umzimkulu, on its journey from the Drakensberg to the sea; and beyond and behind the river, great hill after great hill; and beyond and behind them, the mountains of Ingeli and East Griqualand.

The grass is rich and matted, you cannot see the soil. It holds the rain and the mist, and they seep into the ground, feeding the streams in every kloof. It is well-tended, and not too many cattle feed upon it; not too many fires burn it, laying bare the soil. Stand unshod upon it, for the ground is holy, being even as it came from the Creator. Keep it, guard it, care for it, for it keeps men, guards men, cares for men. Destroy it and man is destroyed.

Where you stand the grass is rich and matted, you cannot see the soil. But the rich green hills break down. They fall to the valley below, and falling, change their nature. For they grow red and bare; they cannot hold the rain and mist, and the streams are dry in the kloofs. Too many cattle feed upon the grass, and too many fires have burned it. Stand shod upon it, for it is coarse and sharp, and the stones cut under the feet. It is not kept, or guarded, or cared for, it no longer keeps men, guards men, cares for men. The titihoya does not cry here any more. [3/4]

The great red hills stand desolate, and the earth has torn away like flesh. The lightning flashes over them, the clouds pour down upon them, the dead streams come to life, full of the red blood of the earth. Down in the valleys women scratch the soil that is left, and the maize hardly reaches the height of a man. They are valleys of old men and old women, of mothers and children. The men are away, the young men and the girls are away. The soil cannot keep them any more. [4/5]

II

The small child ran importantly to the wood-and-iron church with the letter in her hand. Next to the church was a house

* Alan Paton, Cry, the Beloved Country: A Story of Comfort in Desolation (New York: Charles Scribner's Sons, 1948).

and she knocked timidly on the door. The Reverend Stephen Kumalo looked up from the table where he was writing, and he called, Come in.

The small child opened the door, carefully like one who is afraid to open carelessly the door of so important a house, and stepped timidly in.

— I bring a letter, umfundisi.

— A letter, eh? Where did you get it, my child?

— From the store, umfundisi. The white man asked me to bring it to you.

— That was good of you. Go well, small one.

But she did not go at once. She rubbed one bare foot against the other, she rubbed one finger along the edge of the umfundisi's table.

— Perhaps you might be hungry, small one.

— Not very hungry, umfundisi.

— Perhaps a little hungry.

— Yes, a little hungry, umfundisi.

— Go to the mother then. Perhaps she has some food.

— I thank you, umfundisi.

She walked delicately, as though her feet might do harm in so great a house, a house with tables and chairs, and a clock, and a plant in a pot, and many books, more even than the books at the school.

Kumalo looked at his letter. It was dirty, especially about the stamp. It had been in many hands, no doubt. It came from [5/6] Johannesburg; now there in Johannesburg were many of his own people. His brother John, who was a carpenter, had gone there, and had a business of his own in Sophiatown, Johannesburg. His sister Gertrude, twenty-five years younger than he, and the child of his parents' age, had gone there with her small son to look for the husband who had never come back from the mines. His only child Absalom had gone there, to look for his aunt Gertrude, and he had never returned. And indeed many other relatives were there, though none so near as these. It was hard to say from whom this letter came, for it was so long since

any of these had written, that one did not well remember their writing.

He turned the letter over, but there was nothing to show from whom it came. He was reluctant to open it, for once such a thing is opened, it cannot be shut again.

He called to his wife, has the child gone?

— She is eating, Stephen.

— Let her eat then. She brought a letter. Do you know anything about a letter?

— How should I know, Stephen?

— No, that I do not know. Look at it. She took the letter and she felt it. But there was nothing in the touch of it to tell from whom it might be. She read out the address slowly and carefully—

Rev. Stephen Kumalo,
St. Mark's Church.
Ndotsheni.
Natal

She mustered up her courage, and said, it is not from our son.

— No, he said. And he sighed. It is not from our son.

— Perhaps it concerns him, she said.

— Yes, he said. That may be so.

— It is not from Gertrude, she said.

— Perhaps it is my brother John.

— It is not from John, she said. [6/7] They were silent, and she said, how we desire such a letter, and when it comes, we fear to open it.

— Who is afraid, he said. Open it.

She opened it, slowly and carefully, for she did not open so many letters. She spread it out open, and read it slowly and carefully, so that he did not hear all that she said. Read it aloud, he said.

She read it aloud, reading as a Zulu who reads English.

The Mission House,
Sophiatown,
Johannesburg.
25/9/46.

My dear brother in Christ,
I have had the experience of meet-

ing a young woman here in Johannesburg. Her name is Gertrude Kumalo,
and I understand she is the sister of
the Rev. Stephen Kumalo, St. Mark's
Church, Ndotsheni. This young woman is very sick, and therefore I ask
you to come quickly to Johannesburg.
Come to the Rev. Theophilus Msimangu, the Mission House, Sophiatown, and there I shall give you some
advices. I shall also find accommodation for you, where the expenditure
will not be very serious.

I am, dear brother in Christ,
Yours faithfully,
THEOPHILUS MSIMANGU.

They were both silent till at long last
she spoke.
— Well, my husband?
— Yes, what is it?
— This letter, Stephen. You have heard
it now.
— Yes, I have heard it. It is not an
easy letter.
— It is not an easy letter. What will
you do?
— Has the child eaten?

She went to the kitchen and came back
with the child.
— Have you eaten, my child? [7/8]
— Yes, umfundisi.
— Then go well, my child. And thank
you for bringing the letter. And will you
take my thanks to the white man at the
store?
— Yes, umfundisi.
— Then go well, my child.
— Stay well, umfundisi. Stay well,
mother.
— Go well, my child.

So the child went delicately to the door,
and shut it behind her gently, letting the
handle turn slowly like one who fears to
let it turn fast.

When the child was gone, she said to
him, what will you do, Stephen?
— About what, my wife?

She said patiently to him, about this
letter, Stephen.

He sighed. Bring me the St. Chad's
money, he said.

She went out, and came back with a tin,
of the kind in which they sell coffee or
cocoa, and this she gave to him. He held it
in his hand, studying it, as though there
might be some answer in it, till at last she
said, it must be done, Stephen.
— How can I use it, he said. This
money was to send Absalom to St. Chad's.
— Absalom will never go now to St.
Chad's.
— How can you say that, he said
sharply. How can you say such a thing?
— He is in Johannesburg, she said
wearily. When people go to Johannesburg,
they do not come back.
— You have said it, he said. It is said
now. This money which was saved for that
purpose will never be used for it. You have
opened a door, and because you have
opened it, we must go through. And *Tixo*
alone knows where we shall go.
— It was not I who opened it, she said,
hurt by his accusation. It has a long time
been open, but you would not see.
— We had a son, he said harshly. Zulus
have many children, but we had only one
son. He went to Johannesburg, and as you
said—when people go to Johannesburg,
they do not come back. They do not even
write any more. They do not go to [8/9]
St. Chad's, to learn that knowledge without which no black man can live. They go
to Johannesburg, and there they are lost,
and no one hears of them at all. And this
money. . . .

But she had no words for it, so he said,
it is here in my hand.

And again she did not speak, so he said
again, it is here in my hand.
— You are hurting yourself, she said.
— Hurting myself? hurting myself? I
do not hurt myself, it is they who are hurting me. My own son, my own sister, my
own brother. They go away and they do
not write any more. Perhaps it does not
seem to them that we suffer. Perhaps they
do not care for it.

His voice rose into loud and angry
words. Go up and ask the white man, he

said. Perhaps there are letters. Perhaps they have fallen under the counter, or been hidden amongst the food. Look there in the trees, perhaps they have been blown there by the wind.

She cried out at him. You are hurting me also.

He came to himself and said to her humbly, that I may not do.

He held out the tin to her. Open it, he said.

With trembling hands she took the tin and opened it. She emptied it out over the table, some old and dirty notes, and a flood of silver and copper.

— Count it, he said.

She counted it laboriously, turning over the notes and the coins to make sure what they were.

— Twelve pounds, five shillings, and seven pence.

— I shall take, he said, I shall take eight pounds, and the shillings and pence.

— Take it all, Stephen. There may be doctors, hospitals, other troubles. Take it all. And take the Post Office Book—there is ten pounds in it—you must take that also.

— I have been saving that for your stove, he said.

— That cannot be helped, she said. And that other money, though we saved it for St. Chad's, I had meant it for your new black clothes, and a new black hat, and new white collars.

— That cannot be helped either. Let me see, I shall go—— **[9/10]**

— Tomorrow, she said. From Carisbrooke.

— I shall write to the Bishop now, and tell him I do not know how long I shall be gone.

He rose heavily to his feet, and went and stood before her. I am sorry I hurt you, he said. I shall go and pray in the church.

He went out of the door, and she watched him through the little window, walking slowly to the door of the church. Then she sat down at his table, and put her head on it, and was silent, with the patient suffering of black women, with the suffering of oxen, with the suffering of any that are mute.

*   *   *   *   *

All roads lead to Johannesburg. Through the long nights the trains pass to Johannesburg. The lights of the swaying coach fall on the cutting-sides, on the grass and the stones of a country that sleeps. Happy the eyes that can close. **[10/11]**

III

The small toy train climbs up on its narrow gauge from the Umzimkulu valley into the hills. It climbs up to Carisbrooke, and when it stops there, you may get out for a moment and look down on the great valley from which you have come. It is not likely the train will leave you, for there are few people here, and every one will know who you are. And even if it did leave you, it would not much matter; for unless you are a cripple, or very old, you could run after it and catch it for yourself.

If there is mist here, you will see nothing of the great valley. The mist will swirl about and below you, and the train and the people make a small world of their own. Some people do not like it, and find it cold and gloomy. But others like it, and find in it mystery and fascination, and prelude to adventure, and an intimation of the unknown. The train passes through a world of fancy, and you can look through the misty panes at green shadowy banks of grass and bracken. Here in their season grow the blue agapanthus, the wild watsonia, and the red-hot poker, and now and then it happens that one may glimpse an arum in a dell. And always behind them the dim wall of the wattles, like ghosts in the mist.

It is interesting to wait for the train at Carisbrooke, while it climbs up out of the great valley. Those who know can tell you with each whistle where it is, at what road, what farm, what river. But though Stephen Kumalo has been there a full hour before he need, he does not listen to these things. This is a long way to go, and a lot of money to pay. And who knows how sick his sister may be, and what money that may cost? And if he [11/12] has to bring her back, what will that cost too? And Johannesburg is a great city, with so many streets they say that a man can spend his days going up one and down another, and never the same one twice. One must catch buses too, but not as here, where the only bus that comes is the right bus. For there there is a multitude of buses, and only one bus in ten, one bus in twenty maybe, is the right bus. If you take the wrong bus, you may travel to quite some other place. And they say it is danger to cross the street, yet one must needs cross it. For there the wife of Mpanza of Ndotsheni, who had gone there when Mpanza was dying, saw her son Michael killed in the street. Twelve years and moved by excitement, he stepped out into danger, but she was hesitant and stayed at the curb. And under her eyes the great lorry crushed the life out of her son.

And the great fear too—the greatest fear since it was so seldom spoken. Where was their son? Why did he not write any more?

There is a last whistle and the train is near at last. The parson turns to his companion.

— Friend, I thank you for your help.

— Umfundisi, I was glad to help you. You could not have done it alone. This bag is heavy.

The train is nearer, it will soon be in.

— Umfundisi.

— My friend.

— Umfundisi, I have a favour to ask.

— Ask it then.

— You know Sibeko?

— Yes.

— Well, Sibeko's daughter worked here for the white man uSmith in Ixopo. And when the daughter of uSmith married, she went to Johannesburg, and Sibeko's daughter went with them to work. The

address is here, with the new name of this married woman. But Sibeko has heard no word of his daughter this ten, twelve months. And he asks you to enquire.

Kumalo took the dirty, thumbed paper and looked at it. Springs, he said. I have heard of the place. But it is not Johan-[12/13]nesburg, though they say it is near. Friend, the train is here. I shall do what I can.

He put the paper into his wallet, and together they watched the train. As all country trains in South Africa, it was full of black travellers. On this train indeed there were not many others, for the Europeans of this district all have their cars, and hardly travel by train any more.

Kumalo climbed into the carriage for non-Europeans, already full of the humbler people of his race, some with strange assortments of European garments, some with blankets over their strange assortment, some with blankets over the semi-nudity of their primitive dress, though these were all women. Men travelled no longer in primitive dress.

The day was warm, and the smell strong in the carriage. But Kumalo was a humble man, and did not much care. They saw his clerical collar, and moved up to make room for the umfundisi. He looked around, hoping there might be someone with whom he could talk, but there was no one who appeared of that class. He turned to the window to say farewell to his friend.

— Why did Sibeko not come to me himself? he asked.

— He was afraid, umfundisi. He is not of our church.

— Is he not of our people? Can a man in trouble go only to those of his church?

— I shall tell him, umfundisi.

Kumalo's voice rose a little, as does the voice of a child, or indeed of a grown person, who wants others to hear.

— Tell him that when I am in Johannesburg I shall go to this place at Springs. He tapped the pocket where the paper was safe in his wallet. Tell him I shall make enquiries about the girl. But tell him I shall be busy. I have many things to do in Johannesburg.

He turned away from the window. It is always so, he said, as if to himself, but in truth to the people.

— I thank you for him, umfundisi.

The train whistled and jerked. Kumalo was thrown nearly off his feet. It would be safer, more dignified to take his seat.

— Stay well, my friend. [13/14]

— Go well, umfundisi.

He went to his seat, and people looked at him with interest and respect, at the man who went so often to Johannesburg. The train gathered way, to creep along the ridges of the hills, to hang over steep valleys, to pass the bracken and the flowers, to enter the darkness of the wattle plantations, past Stainton, down into Ixopo.

The journey had begun. And now the fear back again, the fear of the unknown, the fear of the great city where boys were killed crossing the street, the fear of Gertrude's sickness. Deep down the fear for his son. Deep down the fear of a man who lives in a world not made for him, whose own world is slipping away, dying, being destroyed, beyond any recall.

Already the knees are weak of the man who a moment since had shown his little vanity, told his little lie, before these respectful people.

The humble man reached in his pocket for his sacred book, and began to read. It was this world alone that was certain. [14/15]

IV

From Ixopo the toy train climbs up into other hills, the green rolling hills of Lufafa, Eastwolds, Donnybrook. From Donnybrook the broad-gauge runs to the great valley of the Umkomaas. Here the tribes live, and the soil is sick, almost beyond healing. Up out of the valley it climbs, past Hemu-hemu to Elandskop. Down the long valley of the Umsindusi, past Edendale and the black slums to Pietermaritzburg, the lovely city. Change

here to the greatest train of all, the train for Johannesburg. Here is a white man's wonder, a train that has no engine, only an iron cage on its head, taking power from iron ropes stretched out above.

Climb up to Hilton and Lion's River, to Balgowan, Rosetta, Mooi River, through hills lovely beyond any singing of it. Thunder through the night, over battlefields of long ago. Climb over the Drakensberg, on to the level plains.

Wake in the swaying coach to the half-light before the dawn. The engine is steaming again, and there are no more ropes overhead. This is a new country, a strange country, rolling and rolling away as far as the eye can see. There are new names here, hard names for a Zulu who has been schooled in English. For they are in the language that was called Afrikaans, a language that he had never yet heard spoken.

— The mines, they cry, the mines. For many of them are going to work in the mines.

Are these the mines, those white flat hills in the distance? He can ask safely, for there is no one here who heard him yesterday. [15/16]

— That is the rock out of the mines, umfundisi. The gold has been taken out of it.

— How does the rock come out?

— We go down and dig it out, umfundisi. And when it is hard to dig, we go away, and the white men blow it out with the fire-sticks. Then we come back and clear it away; we load it on to the trucks; and it goes up in a cage, up a long chimney so long that I cannot say it for you.

— How does it go up?

— It is wound up by a great wheel. Wait, and I shall show you one.

He is silent, and his heart beats a little faster, with excitement and fear.

— There is the wheel, umfundisi. There is the wheel.

A great iron structure rearing into the air, and a great wheel above it, going so fast that the spokes play tricks with the sight. Great buildings, and steam blowing out of pipes, and men hurrying about. A great white hill, and an endless procession of trucks climbing upon it, high up in the air. On the ground, motor-cars, lorries, buses, one great confusion.

— Is that Johannesburg, he asks.

But they laugh confidently. Old hands some of them are.

— That is nothing, they say. In Johannesburg there are buildings, so high—but they cannot describe them.

— My brother, says one, you know the hill that stands so, straight up, behind my father's kraal. So high as that.

The other man nods, but Kumalo does not know that hill.

And now the buildings are endless, the buildings, and the white hills, and the great wheels, the streets without number, and cars and lorries and buses.

— This surely is Johannesburg, he says.

But they laugh again. They are growing a little tired. This is nothing, they say.

Railway-lines, railway-lines, it is a wonder. To the left, to the right, so many that he cannot count. A train rushes past them, with a sudden roaring of sound that makes him jump in his seat. And on the other side of them, another races beside [16/17] them, but drops slowly behind. Stations, stations, more than he has ever imagined. People are waiting there in hundreds, but the train rushes past, leaving them disappointed.

The buildings get higher, the streets more uncountable. How does one find one's way in such a confusion? It is dusk, and the lights are coming on in the streets.

One of the men points for him.

— Johannesburg, umfundisi.

He sees great high buildings; there are red and green lights on them, almost as tall as the buildings. They go on and off. Water comes out of a bottle, till the glass is full. Then the lights go out. And when they come on again, lo the bottle is full and upright, and the glass empty. And there goes the bottle over again. Black and white, it says, black and white, though it is red and green. It is too much to understand.

He is silent, his head aches, he is afraid. There is this railway station to come, this great place with all its tunnels under the ground. The train stops, under a great roof, and there are thousands of people. Steps go down into the earth, and here is the tunnel under the ground. Black people, white people, some going, some coming, so many that the tunnel is full. He goes carefully that he may not bump anybody, holding tightly on to his bag. He comes out into a great hall, and the stream goes up the steps, and here he is out in the street. The noise is immense. Cars and buses one behind the other, more than he has ever imagined. The stream goes over the street, but remembering Mpanza's son, he is afraid to follow. Lights change from green to red, and back again to green. He has heard that. When it is green, you may go. But when he starts across, a great bus swings across the path. There is some law of it that he does not understand, and he retreats again. He finds himself a place against the wall, he will look as though he is waiting for some purpose. His heart beats like that of a child, there is nothing to do or think to stop it. *Tixo,* watch over me, he says to himself. *Tixo,* watch over me. [17/18]

*   *   *   *   *

A young man came to him and spoke to him in a language that he did not understand.

— I do not understand, he said.

— You are a Xosa, then, umfundisi?

— A Zulu, he said.

— Where do you want to go, umfundisi?

— To Sophiatown, young man.

— Come with me then and I shall show you.

He was grateful for this kindness, but half of him was afraid. He was glad the young man did not offer to carry his bag, but he spoke courteously, though in a strange Zulu.

The lights turned green, and his guide started across the street. Another car swung across the path, but the guide did not falter, and the car came to a stop. It made one feel confidence.

He could not follow the turnings that they made under the high buildings, but at last, his arm tired beyond endurance by the bag, they came to a place of many buses.

— You must stand in the line, umfundisi. Have you your money for the ticket?

Quickly, eagerly, as though he must show this young man that he appreciated his kindness, he put down his bag and took out his purse. He was nervous to ask how much it was, and took a pound from the purse.

— Shall I get your ticket for you, umfundisi? Then you need not lose your place in the line, while I go to the ticket office.

— Thank you, he said.

The young man took the pound and walked a short distance to the corner. As he turned it, Kumalo was afraid. The line moved forward and he with it, clutching his bag. And again forward, and again forward, and soon he must enter a bus, but still he had no ticket. As though he had suddenly thought of something he left the line, and walked to the corner, but there was no sign of the young man. He sought courage to speak to someone, and went to an elderly man, decently and cleanly dressed.

— Where is the ticket office, my friend?

— What ticket office, umfundisi? [18/19]

— For the ticket for the bus.

— You get your ticket on the bus. There is no ticket office.

The man looked a decent man, and the parson spoke to him humbly. I gave a pound to a young man, he said, and he told me he would get my ticket at the ticket office.

— You have been cheated, umfundisi. Can you see the young man? No, you will not see him again. Look, come with me. Where are you going, Sophiatown?

— Yes, Sophiatown. To the Mission House.

— Oh yes. I too am an Anglican. I was waiting for someone, but I shall wait no longer. I shall come with you myself. Do you know the Reverend Msimangu?

— Indeed, I have a letter from him.

They again took the last place in the line, and in due time they took their places in the bus. And it in its turn swung out into the confusion of the streets. The driver smoked carelessly, and it was impossible not to admire such courage. Street after street, light after light, as though they would never end, at times at such speed that the bus swayed from side to side, and the engine roared in the ears.

They alighted at a small street, and there were still thousands of people about. They walked a great distance, through streets crowded with people. His new friend helped to carry his bag, but he felt confidence in him. At last they stopped before a lighted house, and knocked.

The door opened and a young tall man in clerical dress opened to them.

— Mr. Msimangu, I bring a friend to you, the Reverend Kumalo from Ndotsheni.

— Come in, come in, my friends. Mr. Kumalo, I am glad to greet you. Is this your first visit to Johannesburg?

Kumalo could not boast any more. He had been safely guided and warmly welcomed. He spoke humbly. I am much confused, he said. I owe much to our friend.

— You fell into good hands. This is Mr. Mafolo, one of our big business men, and a good son of the Church.

— But not before he had been robbed, said the business man. [19/20]

So the story had to be told, and there was much sympathy and much advice.

— And you are no doubt hungry, Mr. Kumalo. Mr. Mafolo, will you stay for some food?

But Mr. Mafolo would not wait. The door shut after him, and Kumalo settled in a big chair, and accepted a cigarette though it was not his custom to smoke. The room was light, and the great bewildering town shut out. He puffed like a child at his smoke, and was thankful. The long journey to Johannesburg was over, and he had taken a liking to this young confident man. In good time no doubt they would come to discuss the reason for this pilgrimage safely at an end. For the moment it was enough to feel welcome and secure. [20/21]

V

— I have a place for you to sleep, my friend, in the house of an old woman, a Mrs. Lithebe, who is a good member of our church. She is an Msutu, but she speaks Zulu well. She will think it an honour to have a priest in the house. It is cheap, only three shillings a week, and you can have your meals there with the people of the Mission. Now there is the bell. Would you like to wash your hands?

They washed their hands in a modern place, with a white basin, and water cold and hot, and towels worn but very white, and a modern lavatory too. When you finished, you pressed a little rod, and the water rushed in as though something was broken. It would have frightened you if you had not heard of such things before.

They went into a room where a table was laid, and there he met many priests, both white and black, and they sat down after grace and ate together. He was a bit nervous of the many plates and knives and forks, but watched what others did, and used the things likewise.

He sat next to a young rosy-cheeked priest from England, who asked him where he came from, and what it was like there. And another black priest cried out—I am also from Ixopo. My father and mother are still alive there, in the valley of the Lufafa. How is it there?

And he told them all about these places, of the great hills and valleys of that far country. And the love of them must have been in his voice, for they were all silent and listened to him. He told them too of the sickness of the land, and how the grass had disappeared, and of the dongas that ran from hill to valley, [21/22] and valley to hill; how it was a land of old men and women, and mothers and children; how the maize grew barely to the height of a man; how the tribe was broken, and the house broken, and the man broken; how when they went away, many never came back, many never wrote any more. How this was true not only in Ndotsheni, but also in the Lufafa, and the Imhlavini, and the Umkomaas, and the Umzimkulu. But of Gertrude and Absalom he said nothing.

So they all talked of the sickness of the land, of the broken tribe and the broken house, of young men and young girls that went away and forgot their customs, and lived loose and idle lives. They talked of young criminal children, and older and more dangerous criminals, of how white Johannesburg was afraid of black crime. One of them went and got him a newspaper, the Johannesburg Mail, and showed him in bold black letters, OLD COUPLE ROBBED AND BEATEN IN LONELY HOUSE. FOUR NATIVES ARRESTED.

— That happens nearly every day, he said. And it is not only the Europeans who are afraid. We are also afraid, right here in Sophiatown. It was not long ago that a gang of these youths attacked one of our own African girls; they took her bag, and her money, and would have raped her too but that people came running out of the houses.

— You will learn much here in Johannesburg, said the rosy-cheeked priest. It is not only in your place that there is destruction. But we must talk again. I want to hear again about your country, but I must go now.

So they broke up, and Msimangu said he would take his visitor to his own private room.

— We have much to talk about, he said.

They went to the room, and when Msimangu had shut the door and they had sat themselves down, Kumalo said to him, you will pardon me if I am hasty, but I am anxious to hear about my sister.

— Yes, yes, said Msimangu. I am sure you are anxious. You must think I am thoughtless. But you will pardon me if I ask you first, why did she come to Johannesburg? [**22/23**]

Kumalo, though disturbed by this question, answered obediently, she came to look for her husband who was recruited for the mines. But when his time was up, he did not return, nor did he write at all. She did not know if he were dead perhaps. So she took her small child and went to look for him.

Then because Msimangu did not speak, he asked anxiously, is she very sick?

Msimangu said gravely, yes, she is very sick. But it is not that kind of sickness. It is another, a worse kind of sickness. I sent for you firstly because she is a woman that is alone, and secondly because her brother is a priest. I do not know if she ever found her husband, but she has no husband now.

He looked at Kumalo. It would be truer to say, he said, that she has many husbands.

Kumalo said, *Tixo! Tixo!*

— She lives in Claremont, not far from here. It is one of the worst places in Johannesburg. After the police have been there, you can see the liquor running in the streets. You can smell it, you can smell nothing else, wherever you go in that place.

He leant over to Kumalo. I used to drink liquor, he said, but it was good liquor, such as our fathers made. But now I have vowed to touch no liquor any more. This is bad liquor here, made strong with all manner of things that our people have never used. And that is her work, she makes and sells it. I shall hide nothing from you, though it is painful for me. These women sleep with any man for their price. A man has been killed at her place. They gamble and drink and stab. She has been in prison, more than once.

He leant back in his chair and moved a book forward and backward on the table. This is terrible news for you, he said.

Kumalo nodded dumbly, and Msimangu brought out his cigarettes. Will you smoke, he said.

Kumalo shook his head. I do not really smoke, he said.

— Sometimes it quietens one to smoke. But there should be another kind of quiet in a man, and then let him smoke to enjoy it. But in Johannesburg it is hard sometimes to find that kind of quiet. [**23/24**]

— In Johannesburg? Everywhere it is so. The peace of God escapes us.

And they were both silent, as though a word had been spoken that made it hard to speak another. At last Kumalo said, where is the child?

— The child is there. But it is no place for a child. And that too is why I sent for you. Perhaps if you cannot save the mother, you can save the child.

— Where is this place?

— It is not far from here. I shall take you tomorrow.

— I have another great sorrow.

— You may tell me.

— I should be glad to tell you.

But then he was silent, and tried to speak and could not, so Msimangu said to him, take your time, my brother.

— It is not easy. It is our greatest sorrow.

— A son, maybe. Or a daughter?

— It is a son.

— I am listening.

— Absalom was his name. He too went away, to look for my sister, but he never returned, nor after a while did he write any more. Our letters, his mother's and mine, all came back to us. And now after what you tell me, I am still more afraid.

— We shall try to find him, my brother. Perhaps your sister will know. You are tired, and I should take you to the room I have got for you.

— Yes, that would be better.

They rose, and Kumalo said, it is my habit to pray in the church. Maybe you will show me.

— It is on the way.

Kumalo said humbly, maybe you will pray for me.

— I shall do it gladly. My brother, I have of course my work to do, but so long as you are here, my hands are yours.

— You are kind.

Something in the humble voice must have touched Msimangu, for he said, I am not kind. I am a selfish and sinful man, but God put his hands on me, that is all. **[24/25]**

He picked up Kumalo's bag, but before they reached the door Kumalo stopped him.

— I have one more thing to tell you.

— Yes.

— I have a brother also, here in Johannesburg. He too does not write any more. John Kumalo, a carpenter.

— Msimangu smiled. I know him, he said. He is too busy to write. He is one of our great politicians.

— A politician? My brother?

— Yes, he is a great man in politics.

Msimangu paused. I hope I shall not hurt you further. Your brother has no use for the Church any more. He says that what God has not done for South Africa, man must do. That is what he says.

— This is a bitter journey.

— I can believe it.

— Sometimes I fear—what will the Bishop say when he hears. One of his priests?

— What can a Bishop say? Something is happening that no Bishop can stop. Who can stop these things from happening? They must go on.

— How can you say so? How can you say they must go on?

— They must go on, said Msimangu gravely. You cannot stop the world from going on. My friend, I am a Christian. It is not in my heart to hate a white man. It was a white man who brought my father out of darkness. But you will pardon me if I talk frankly to you. The tragedy is not that things are broken. The tragedy is that they are not mended again. The white man has broken the tribe. And it is my belief—and again I ask your pardon—that it cannot be mended again. But the house that is broken, and the man that falls apart when the house is broken, these are the tragic things. That is why children break the law, and old white people are robbed and beaten.

He passed his hand across his brow.

— It suited the white man to break the tribe, he continued gravely. But it has not suited him to build something in the place **[25/26]** of what is broken. I have pondered this for many hours, and I must speak it, for it is the truth for me. They are not all so. There are some white men who give their lives to build up what is broken.

— But they are not enough, he said. They are afraid, that is the truth. It is fear that rules this land.

He laughed apologetically. These things are too many to talk about now. They are things to talk over quietly and patiently. You must get Father Vincent to talk about them. He is a white man and can say what must be said. He is the one with the boy's cheeks, the one who wants to hear more about your country.

— I remember him.

— They give us too little, said Msimangu sombrely. They give us almost nothing. Come, let us go to the church.

* * * * *

— Mrs. Lithebe, I bring my friend to you. The Reverend Stephen Kumalo.

— Umfundisi, you are welcome. The room is small, but clean.

— I am sure of it.

— Goodnight, my brother. Shall I see you in the church tomorrow at seven?

— Assuredly.

— And after that I shall take you to eat. Stay well, my friend. Stay well, Mrs. Lithebe.

— Go well, my friend.

— Go well, umfundisi.

She took him to the small clean room and lit a candle for him.

— If there is anything, you will ask, umfundisi.

— I thank you.

— Sleep well, umfundisi.

— Sleep well, mother.

He stood a moment in the room. Forty-eight hours ago he and his wife had been packing his bag in far away Ndotsheni. Twenty-four hours ago the train, with the cage on its head, had been thundering through an unseen country. And now outside, [26/27] the stir and movement of people, but behind them, through them, one could hear the roar of a great city. Johannesburg. Johannesburg.

Who could believe it? [27/28]

VI

It is not far to Claremont. They lie together; Sophiatown, where any may own property, Western Native Township which belongs to the Municipality of Johannesburg, and Claremont, the garbage-heap of the proud city. These three are bounded on the West by the European district of Newlands, and on the East by the European district of Westdene.

— That is a pity, says Msimangu. I am not a man for segregation, but it is a pity that we are not apart. They run trams from the centre of the city, and part is for Europeans and part for us. But we are often thrown off the trams by young hooligans. And our hooligans are ready for trouble too.

— But the authorities, do they allow that?

— They do not. But they cannot watch every tram. And if a trouble develops, who can find how it began, and who will tell the truth? It is a pity we are not apart. Look, do you see that big building?

— I see it.

— That is the building of the Bantu Press, our newspaper. Of course there are Europeans in it too, and it is moderate and does not say all that could be said. Your brother John thinks little of the Bantu Press. He and his friends call it the Bantu Repress.

So they walked till they came to Claremont and Kumalo was shocked by its shabbiness and dirtiness, and the closeness of the houses, and the filth in the streets.

— Do you see that woman, my friend?

— I see her.

— She is one of the queens, the liquor sellers. They say she is one of the richest of our people in Johannesburg. [28/29]

— And these children? Why are they not at school?

— Some because they do not care, and some because their parents do not care, but many because the schools are full.

They walked down Lily Street, and turned off into Hyacinth Street, for the names there are very beautiful.

— It is here, brother. Number eleven. Do you go in alone?

— It would be better.

— When you are ready, you will find me next door at Number thirteen. There is a woman of our church there, and a good woman who tries with her husband to bring up good children. But it is hard. Their eldest daughter whom I prepared for confirmation has run away, and lives in Pimville, with a young loafer of the streets. Knock there, my friend. You know where to find me.

There is laughter in the house, the kind of laughter of which one is afraid. Perhaps because one is afraid already, perhaps because it is in truth bad laughter. A woman's voice, and men's voices. But he knocks, and she opens.

— It is I, my sister.

Have no doubt it is fear in her eyes. She draws back a step, and makes no move towards him. She turns and says something that he cannot hear. Chairs are moved, and other things are taken. She turns to him.

— I am making ready, my brother.

They stand and look at each other, he anxious, she afraid. She turns and looks back into the room. A door closes, and she says, Come in, my brother.

Only then does she reach her hand to him. It is cold and wet, there is no life in it.

They sit down, she is silent upon her chair.

— I have come, he said.

— It is good.

— You did not write.

— No, I did not write.

— Where is your husband?

— I have not found him, my brother.

— But you did not write. [29/30]

— That is true, indeed.

— Did you not know we were anxious?

— I had no money to write.

— Not two pennies for a stamp?

She does not answer him. She does not look at him.

— But I hear you are rich.

— I am not rich.

— I hear you have been in prison.

— That is true indeed.

— Was it for liquor?

A spark of life comes into her. She must do something, she cannot keep so silent. She tells him she was not guilty. There was some other woman.

— You stayed with this woman?

— Yes.

— Why did you stay with such a woman?

— I had no other place.

— And you helped her with her trade?

— I had to have money for the child.

— Where is the child?

She looks round vaguely. She gets up and goes to the yard. She calls, but the voice that was once so sweet has a new quality in it, the quality of the laughter that he heard in the house. She is revealing herself to him.

— I have sent for the child, she says.

— Where is it?

— It shall be fetched, she says.

There is discomfort in her eyes, and she stands fingering the wall. The anger wells up in him.

— Where shall I sleep, he asks?

The fear in her eyes is unmistakable. Now she will reveal herself, but his anger masters him, and he does not wait for it.

— You have shamed us, he says in a low voice, not wishing to make it known to the world. A liquor seller, a prostitute, with a child and you do not know where it is.

Your brother a priest. How could you do this to us?

She looks at him sullenly, like an animal that is tormented. [30/31]

— I have come to take you back. She falls on to the floor and cries; her cries become louder and louder, she has no shame.

— They will hear us, he says urgently.

She tries to control her sobs.

— Do you wish to come back?

She nods her head. I do not like Johannesburg, she says. I am sick here. The child is sick also.

— Do you wish with your heart to come back?

She nods her head again. She sobs too. I do not like Johannesburg, she says. She looks at him with eyes of distress, and his heart quickens with hope. I am a bad woman, my brother. I am no woman to go back.

His eyes fill with tears, his deep gentleness returns to him. He goes to her and lifts her from the floor to the chair. Inarticulately he strokes her face, his heart filled with pity.

— God forgives us, he says. Who am I not to forgive? Let us pray.

They knelt down, and he prayed, quietly so that the neighbors might not hear, and she punctuated his petitions with Amens. And when he had finished, she burst into a torrent of prayer, of self-denunciation, and urgent petition. And thus reconciled, they sat hand in hand.

— And now I ask you for help, he said.

— What is it, my brother?

— Our child, have you not heard of him?

— I did hear of him, brother. He was working at some big place in Johannesburg, and he lived in Sophiatown, but where I am not sure. But I know who will know. The son of our brother John and your son were often together. He will know.

— I shall go there. And now, my sister, I must see if Mrs. Lithebe has a room for you. Have you many things?

— Not many. This table and those

chairs, and a bed. And some few dishes and pots. That is all.

— I shall find someone to fetch them. You will be ready?

— My brother, here is the child.

Into the room, shepherded by an older girl, came his little nephew. His clothes were dirty and his nose running, and he [31/32] put his finger in his mouth, and gazed at his uncle out of wide saucer-like eyes.

Kumalo lifted him up, and wiped his nose clean, and kissed and fondled him.

— It will be better for the child, he said. He will go to a place where the wind blows, and where there is a school for him.

— It will be better, she agreed.

— I must go, he said. There is much to do.

He went out into the street, and curious neighbours stared at him. It was an umfundisi that was here. He found his friend, and poured out his news, and asked him where they could find a man to fetch his sister, her child and possessions.

— We shall go now, said Msimangu. I am glad for your sake, my friend.

— There is a great load off my mind, my friend. Please God the other will be as successful.

*   *   *   *   *

He fetched her with a lorry that afternoon, amidst a crowd of interested neighbours, who discussed the affair loudly and frankly, some with approval, and some with the strange laughter of the towns. He was glad when the lorry was loaded, and they left.

Mrs. Lithebe showed them their room, and gave the mother and child their food while Kumalo went down to the mission. And that night they held prayers in the dining-room, and Mrs. Lithebe and Gertrude punctuated his petitions with Amens. Kumalo himself was light-hearted and gay like a boy, more so than he had been for years. One day in Johannesburg, and already the tribe was being rebuilt the house and the soul restored. [32/33]

VII

Gertrude's dress, for all that she might once have been rich, was dirty, and the black greasy knitted cap that she wore on her head made him ashamed. Although his money was little, he brought her a red dress and a white thing that they called a turban for her head. Also a shirt, a pair of short trousers, and a jersey for the boy; and a couple of stout handkerchiefs for his mother to use on his nose. In his pocket was his Post Office Book, and there was ten pounds there that he and his wife were saving to buy the stove, for that, like any woman, she had long been wanting to have. To save ten pounds from a stipend of eight pounds a month takes much patience and time, especially for a parson, who must dress in good black clothes. His clerical collars were brown and frayed, but they must wait now a while. It was a pity about the ten pounds, that it would sooner or later have to be broken into, but the trains did not carry for nothing, and they would no doubt get a pound or two for her things. Strange that she had saved nothing from her sad employment, which brought in much money, it was said.

Gertrude was helping Mrs. Lithebe in the house, and he could hear her singing a little. The small boy was playing in the yard, with small pieces of brick and wood that a builder had left. The sun was shining, and even in this great city there were birds, small sparrows that chirped and flew about in the yard. But there was Msimangu coming up the street. He put aside the letter that he was writing to his wife, of the journey in the train, and the great city Johannesburg, and the young man who had stolen his pound, of his quick finding of Gertrude, and his [33/34] pleasure in the small boy. And above all, that this day would begin the search for their son.

— Are you ready, my friend?

— Yes, I am ready. I am writing to my wife.

— Though I do not know her, send her my greetings.

They walked up the street, and down another, and up yet another. It was true what they said, that you could go up one street and down another till the end of your days, and never walk the same one twice.

— Here is your brother's shop. You see his name.

— Yes, I see it.

— Shall I come with you?

— Yes, I think it would be right.

His brother John was sitting there on a chair, talking to two other men. He had grown fat, and sat with his hands on his knees like a chief. His brother he did not recognize, for the light from the street was on the backs of his visitors.

— Good morning, my brother.

— Good morning, sir.

— Good morning, my own brother, son of our mother.

John Kumalo looked closely at him, and stood up with a great hearty smile.

— My own brother. Well, well, who can believe? What are you doing in Johannesburg?

Kumalo looked at the visitors. I come on business, he said.

— I am sure my friends will excuse us. My own brother, the son of our mother, has come.

The two men rose, and they all said stay well and go well.

— Do you know the Reverend Msimangu, my brother?

— Well, well, he is known to everybody. Everybody knows the Reverend Msimangu. Sit down, gentlemen. I think we must have some tea.

He went to the door and called into the place behind.

— Is your wife Esther well, my brother?

John Kumalo smiled his jolly and knowing smile. My wife Esther has left me these ten years, my brother.

— And have you married again? [34/35]

— Well, well, not what the Church calls married, you know. But she is a good woman.

— You wrote nothing of this, brother.

— No, how could I write? You people in Ndotsheni do not understand the way life is in Johannesburg. I thought it better not to write.

— That is why you stopped writing.

— Well, well, that could be why I stopped. Trouble, brother, unnecessary trouble.

— But I do not understand. How is life different in Johannesburg?

— Well, that is difficult. Do you mind if I speak English? I can explain these things better in English.

— Speak in English, then, brother.

— You see I have had an experience here in Johannesburg. It is not like Ndotsheni. One must live here to understand it.

He looked at his brother. Something new is happening here, he said.

He did not sit down, but began to speak in a strange voice. He walked about, and looked through the window into the street, and up at the ceiling, and into the corners of the room as though something were there, and must be brought out.

— Down in Ndotsheni I am nobody, even as you are nobody, my brother. I am subject to the chief, who is an ignorant man. I must salute him and bow to him, but he is an uneducated man. Here in Johannesburg I am a man of some importance, of some influence. I have my own business, and when it is good, I can make ten, twelve, pounds a week.

He began to sway to and fro, he was not speaking to them, he was speaking to people who were not there.

— I do not say we are free here. I do not say we are free as men should be. But at least I am free of the chief. At least I am free of an old and ignorant man, who is nothing but a white man's dog. He is a trick, a trick to hold together something that the white man desires to hold together.

He smiled his cunning and knowing

smile and for a moment addressed himself to his visitors. [35/36]

— But it is not being held together, he said. It is breaking apart, your tribal society. It is here in Johannesburg that the new society is being built. Something is happening here, my brother.

He paused for a moment, then he said, I do not wish to offend you gentlemen, but the Church too is like the chief. You must do so and so and so. You are not free to have an experience. A man must be faithful and meek and obedient, and he must obey the laws, whatever the laws may be. It is true that the Church speaks with a fine voice, and that the Bishops speak against the laws. But this they have been doing for fifty years, and things get worse, not better.

His voice grew louder, and he was again addressing people who were not there. Here in Johannesburg it is the mines, he said, everything is the mines. These high buildings, this wonderful City Hall, this beautiful Parktown with its beautiful houses, all this is built with the gold from the mines. This wonderful hospital for Europeans, the biggest hospital south of the Equator, it is built with the gold from the mines.

There was a change in his voice, it became louder like the voice of a bull or a lion. Go to our hospital, he said, and see our people lying on the floors. They lie so close you cannot step over them. But it is they who dig the gold. For three shillings a day. We come from the Transkei, and from Basutoland, and from Bechuanaland, and from Swaziland, and from Zululand. And from Ndotsheni also. We live in the compounds, we must leave our wives and families behind. And when the new gold is found, it is not we who will get more for our labour. It is the white man's shares that will rise, you will read it in all the papers. They go mad when new gold is found. They bring more of us to live in the compounds, to dig under the ground for three shillings a day. They do not think, here is a chance to pay more for our labour. They think

only, here is a chance to build a bigger house and buy a bigger car. It is important to find gold, they say, for all South Africa is built on the mines. [36/37]

He growled, and his voice grew deep, it was like thunder that was rolling. But it is not built on the mines, he said, it is built on our backs, on our sweat, on our labour. Every factory, every theatre, every beautiful house, they are all built by us. And what does a chief know about that? But here in Johannesburg they know.

He stopped, and was silent. And his visitors were silent also, for there was something in this voice that compelled one to be silent. And Stephen Kumalo sat silent, for this was a new brother that he saw.

John Kumalo looked at him. The Bishop says it is wrong, he said, but he lives in a big house, and his white priests get four, five, six times what you get, my brother.

He sat down, and took out a large red handkerchief to wipe his face.

— That is my experience, he said. That is why I no longer go to the Church.

— And that is why you did not write any more.

— Well, well, it could be the reason.

— That, and your wife Esther?

— Yes, yes, both perhaps. It is hard to explain in a letter. Our customs are different here.

And Msimangu said, are there any customs here?

John Kumalo looked at him. There is a new thing growing here, he said. Stronger than any church or chief. You will see it one day.

— And your wife? Why did she leave?

— Well, well, said John Kumalo with his knowing smile. She did not understand my experience.

— You mean, said Msimangu coldly, that she believed in fidelity?

John looked at him suspiciously. Fidelity, he said. But Msimangu was quick to see that he did not understand.

— Perhaps we should speak Zulu again, he said.

The angry veins stood out on the great bull neck, and who knows what angry words might have been spoken, but Stephen Kumalo was quick to intervene. [37/38]

— Here is the tea, my brother. That is kind of you.

The woman was not introduced, but took round the tea humbly. When she had gone, Kumalo spoke to his brother.

— I have listened attentively to you, my brother. Much of what you say saddens me, partly because of the way you say it, and partly because much of it is true. And now I have something to ask of you. But I must tell you first that Gertrude is with me here. She is coming back to Ndotsheni.

— Well, well, I shall not say it is a bad thing. Johannesburg is not a place for a woman alone. I myself tried to persuade her, but she did not agree, so we did not meet any more.

— And now I must ask you. Where is my son?

That is something like discomfort in John's eyes. He takes out his handkerchief again.

— Well, you have heard no doubt he was friendly with my son.

— I have heard that.

— Well, you know how these young men are. I do not blame them altogether. You see, my son did not agree well with his second mother. What it was about I could never discover. Nor did he agree with his mother's children. Many times I tried to arrange matters, but I did not succeed. So he said he would leave. He had good work so I did not stop him. And your son went with him.

— Where, my brother?

— I do not rightly know. But I heard that they had a room in Alexandra. Now wait a minute. They were both working for a factory. I remember. Wait till I look in the telephone book.

He went to a table and there Kumalo saw the telephone. He felt a little pride to be the brother of a man who had such a thing.

— There it is. Doornfontein Textiles Company. 14 Krause St. I shall write it down for you, my brother.

— Can we not telephone them, asked Kumalo hesitantly.

His brother laughed. What for, he asked. To ask if Absalom Kumalo is working there? Or to ask if they will call him to the [38/39] telephone? Or to ask if they will give his address? They do not do such things for a black man, my brother.

— It does not matter, said Msimangu. My hands are yours, my friend.

They said their farewells and went out into the street.

— Huh, there you have it.

— Yes, we have it there.

— He is a big man, in this place, your brother. His shop is always full of men, talking as you have heard. But they say you must hear him at a meeting, he and Dubula and a brown man named Tomlinson. They say he speaks like a bull, and growls in his throat like a lion, and could make men mad if he would. But for that they say he has not enough courage, for he would surely be sent to prison.

— I shall tell you one thing, Msimangu continued. Many of the things that he said are true.

He stopped in the street and spoke quietly and earnestly to his companion. Because the white man has power, we too want power, he said. But when a black man gets power, when he gets money, he is a great man if he is not corrupted. I have seen it often. He seeks power and money to put right what is wrong, and when he gets them, why, he enjoys the power and the money. Now he can gratify his lusts, now he can arrange ways to get white man's liquor, he can speak to thousands and hear them clap their hands. Some of us think when we have power, we shall revenge ourselves on the white man who has had power, and because our desire is corrupt, we are corrupted, and the power has no heart in it. But most white men do not know this truth about power, and they are afraid lest we get it.

He stood as though he was testing his exposition. Yes, that is right about power, he said. But there is only one thing that has power completely, and that is love. Because when a man loves, he seeks no power, and therefore he has power. I see only one hope for our country, and that is when white men and black men, desiring neither power nor money, but desiring only the good of their country, come together to work for it.

He was grave and silent, and then he said sombrely, I have **[39/40]** one great fear in my heart, that one day when they are turned to loving, they will find we are turned to hating.

— This is not the way to get to Doornfontein, he said. Come, let us hurry.

And Kumalo followed him silently, oppressed by the grave and sombre words.

*　*　*　*　*

But they were not successful at Doornfontein, although the white men treated them with consideration. Msimangu knew how to arrange things with white men, and they went to a great deal of trouble, and found that Absalom Kumalo had left them some twelve months before. One of them remembered that Absalom had been friendly with one of their workmen, Dhlamini, and this man was sent for from his work. He told them that when he had last heard, Absalom was staying with a Mrs. Ndlela, of End St., Sophiatown, the street that separates Sophiatown from the European suburb of Westdene. He was not sure, but he thought that the number of the house was 105.

So they returned to Sophiatown, and indeed found Mrs. Ndlela at 105 End Street. She received them with a quiet kindness, and her children hid behind her skirts, and peeped out at the visitors. But Absalom was not there, she said. But wait, she had had a letter from him, asking about the things he had left behind. So while Kumalo played with her children, and Msimangu talked to her husband,

she brought out a big box full of papers and other belongings, and looked for the letter. And while she was searching, and Msimangu was watching her kind and tired face, he saw her stop in her search for a moment, and look at Kumalo for a moment, half curiously, and half with pity. At last she found the letter, and she showed them the address, c/o Mrs. Mkize, 79 Twenty-third Avenue, Alexandra.

Then they must drink a cup of tea, and it was dark before they rose to leave, and the husband stepped out with Kumalo into the street.

— Why did you look at my friend with pity, asked Msimangu of the woman. **[40/41]**

She dropped her eyes, then raised them again. He is an umfundisi, she said.

— Yes.

— I did not like his son's friends. Nor did my husband. That is why he left us.

— I understand you. Was there anything worse than that?

— No. I saw nothing. But I did not like his friends.

Her face was honest and open, and she did not drop her eyes again.

— Goodnight, mother.

— Goodnight, umfundisi.

Out in the street they said farewell to the husband, and set off back to the Mission House.

— Tomorrow, said Msimangu, we go to Alexandra.

Kumalo put his hand on his friend's arm. The things are not happy that brought me to Johannesburg, he said, but I have found much pleasure in your company.

— Huh, said Msimangu, huh, we must hurry or we shall be late for our food. **[41/42]**

VIII

The next morning, after they had eaten at the Mission House, Msimangu and Kumalo set off for the great wide road where the buses run.

— Every bus is here the right bus, said Msimangu.

Kumalo smiled at that, for it was a joke against him and his fear of catching the wrong bus.

— All these buses go to Johannesburg, said Msimangu. You need not fear to take a wrong bus here.

So they took the first bus that came, and it set them down at the place where Kumalo had lost his pound. And then they walked, through many streets full of cars and buses and people, till they reached the bus rank for Alexandra. But here they met an unexpected obstacle, for a man came up to them and said to Msimangu, are you going to Alexandra, umfundisi?

— Yes, my friend.

— We are here to stop you, umfundisi. Not by force, you see—he pointed—the police are there to prevent that. But by persuasion. If you use this bus you are weakening the cause of the black people. We have determined not to use these buses until the fare is brought back again to fourpence.

— Yes, indeed, I have heard of it.

He turned to Kumalo.

— I was very foolish, my friend. I had forgotten that there were no buses; at least I had forgotten the boycott of the buses.

— Our business is very urgent, said Kumalo humbly.

— This boycott is also urgent, said the man politely. They want us to pay sixpence, that is one shilling a day. Six shillings a week, and some of us only get thirty-five or forty shillings. [**42/43**]

— Is it far to walk, asked Kumalo.

— It is a long way, umfundisi. Eleven miles.

— That is a long way, for an old man.

— Men as old as you are doing it every day, umfundisi. And women, and some that are sick, and some crippled, and children. They start walking at four in the morning, and they do not get back till eight at night. They have a bite of food, and their eyes are hardly closed on the pillow before they must stand up again, sometimes to start off with nothing but hot water in their stomachs. I cannot stop you taking a bus, umfundisi, but this is a cause to fight for. If we lose it, then they will have to pay more in Sophiatown and Claremont and Kliptown and Pimville.

— I understand you well. We shall not use the bus.

The man thanked them and went to another would-be traveller.

— That man has a silver tongue, said Kumalo.

— That is the famous Dubula, said Msimangu quietly. A friend of your brother John. But they say—excuse me, my friend—that Tomlinson has the brains, and your brother the voice, but that this man has the heart. He is the one the Government is afraid of, because he himself is not afraid. He seeks nothing for himself. They say he has given up his own work to do this picketing of the buses, and his wife pickets the other bus rank at Alexandra.

— That is something to be proud of. Johannesburg is a place of wonders.

— They were church people, said Msimangu regretfully, but are so no longer. Like your brother, they say the church has a fine voice, but no deeds. Well, my friend, what do we do now?

— I am willing to walk.

— Eleven miles, and eleven miles back. It is a long journey.

— I am willing. You understand I am anxious, my friend. This Johannesburg— it is no place for a boy to be alone.

— Good. Let us begin then. [**43/44**]

So they walked many miles through the European city, up Twist Street to the Clarendon Circle, and down Louis Botha toward Orange Grove. And the cars and the lorries never ceased, going one way or the other. After a long time a car stopped and a white man spoke to them.

— Where are you two going, he asked.

— To Alexandra, sir, said Msimangu, taking off his hat.

— I thought you might be. Climb in.

That was a great help to them, and at

the turn-off to Alexandra they expressed their thanks.

— It is a long journey, said the white man. And I know that you have no buses.

They stood to watch him go on, but he did not go on. He swung around, and was soon on the road back to Johannesburg.

— Huh, said Msimangu, that is something to marvel at.

It was still a long way to Twenty-third Avenue, and as they passed one avenue after the other, Msimangu explained that Alexandra was outside the boundaries of Johannesburg, and was a place where a black man could buy land and own a house. But the streets were not cared for, and there were no lights, and so great was the demand for accommodation that every man if he could, built rooms in his yard and sub-let them to others. Many of these rooms were the hide-outs for thieves and robbers, and there was much prostitution and brewing of illicit liquor.

— These things are so bad, said Msimangu, that the white people of Orange Grove and Norwood and Highlands North got up a great petition to do away with the place altogether. One of our young boys snatched a bag there from an old white woman, and she fell to the ground, and died there of shock and fear. And there was a terrible case of a white woman who lived by herself in a house not far from here, and because she resisted some of our young men who broke in, they killed her. Sometimes too white men and women sit in their cars in the dark under the trees on the Pretoria Road; and some of our young men sometimes rob and assault them, sometimes even the women. It is true that they are often bad women, but that is the one crime we dare not speak of. [**44/45**]

— It reminds me, he said, of a different case on the other side of Johannesburg. One of my friends lives there in a house that stands by itself on the Potchefstroom road. It was a cold winter's night, and it was still far from morning when there was a knock on the door. It was a woman

knocking, a white woman, with scarcely a rag to cover her body. Those she had were torn, and she held them with her hands to hide her nakedness, and she was blue with the cold. A white man had done this to her, taken her in his car, and when he had satisfied himself—or not, I cannot say, I was not there—he threw her out into the cold, with these few rags, and drove back to Johannesburg. Well my friend and his wife found an old dress for her, and an old coat, and made water for tea, and wrapped her in blankets. The children were awake, and asking questions, but my friends told them to sleep, and would not let them come in to see. Then my friend went off in the dark to the house of a white farmer not very far away. The dogs were fierce and he was afraid, but he persisted, and when the white man came he told him of the trouble, and that it was the kind of thing to be settled quietly. The white man said, Huh, I will come. He brought out his car, and they went back to my friend's house. The white woman would have shown her thanks with money, but she had no money. My friend and his wife both told her it was not a matter for money. The white man said to my friend, he said it twice, *Jy is 'n goeie Kaffer,* you are a good Kaffir. Something touched him, and he said it in the words that he had.

— I am touched also.

— Well, I was telling you about this petition. Our white friends fought against this petition, for they said that the good things of Alexandra were more than the bad. That it was something to have a place of one's own, and a house to bring up children in, and a place to have a voice in, so that a man is something in the land where he was born. Professor Hoernle—he is dead, God rest his soul—he was the great fighter for us. Huh, I am sorry you cannot hear him. For he had Tomlinson's brains, and your brother's voice, and Dubula's heart, all in one [**45/46**] man. When he spoke, there was no white man that could speak against him, Huh, I remember it even now. He would say that this is here, and that is there, and that yonder is over there yonder, and there was no man that could move these things by so much as an inch from the places where he put them. Englishman or Afrikaner, they could move nothing from the places where he put them.

He took out his handkerchief and wiped his face. I have talked a great deal, he said, right up to the very house we are seeking.

A woman opened the door to them. She gave them no greeting, and when they stated their business, it was with reluctance that she let them in.

— You say the boy has gone, Mrs. Mkize?

— Yes, I do not know where he is gone.

— When did he go?

— These many months. A year it must be.

— And had he a friend?

— Yes, another Kumalo. The son of his father's brother. But they left together.

— And you do not know where they went?

— They talked of many places. But you know how these young men talk.

— How did he behave himself, this young man Absalom, Kumalo asked her.

Have no doubt it is fear in her eyes. Have no doubt it is fear now in his eyes also. It is fear, here in this house.

— I saw nothing wrong, she said.

— But you guessed there was something wrong.

— There was nothing wrong, she said.

— Then why are you afraid?

— I am not afraid, she said.

— Then why do you tremble? asked Msimangu.

— I am cold, she said.

She looked at them sullenly, watchfully.

— We thank you, said Msimangu. Stay well.

— Go well, she said. **[46/47]**

Out in the street Kumalo spoke.

— There is something wrong, he said.

— I do not deny it. My friend, two of us are too many together. Turn left at the big street and go up the hill, and you will find a place for refreshment. Wait for me there.

Heavy-hearted the old man went, and Msimangu followed him slowly till he turned at the corner. Then he turned back himself, and returned to the house.

She opened again to him, as sullen as before; now that she had recovered, there was more sullenness than fear.

— I am not from the police, he said. I have nothing to do with the police, I wish to have nothing to do with them. But there is an old man suffering because he cannot find his son.

— That is a bad thing, she said, but she spoke as one speaks who must speak so.

— It is a bad thing, he said, and I cannot leave you until you have told what you would not tell.

— I have nothing to tell, she said.

— You have nothing to tell because you are afraid. And you do not tremble because it is cold.

— And why do I tremble, she asked.

— That I do not know. But I shall not leave you till I discover it. And if it is necessary, I shall go to the police after all, because there will be no other place to go.

— It is hard for a woman who is alone, she said resentfully.

— It is hard for an old man seeking his son.

— I am afraid, she said.

— He is afraid also. Could you not see he is afraid?

— I could see it, umfundisi.

— Then tell me, what sort of life did they lead here, these two young men? But she kept silent, with the fear in her eyes, and tears near to them. He could see she would be hard to move.

— I am a priest. Would you not take my word? But she kept silent.

— Have you a Bible? **[47/48]**

— I have a Bible.

— Then I will swear to you on the Bible.

But she kept silent till he said again, I will swear to you on the Bible. So getting

no peace, she rose irresolute, and went to
a room behind, and after some time she
returned with the Bible.

— I am a priest, he said. My yea has
always been yea, and my nay nay. But
because you desire it, and because an old
man is afraid, I swear to you on this Book
that no trouble will come to you of this,
for we seek only a boy. So help me *Tixo*.

— What sort of life did they lead, he
asked.

— They brought many things here, umfundisi, in the late hours of the night.
They were clothes, and watches, and
money, and food in bottles, and many
other things.

— Was there ever blood on them?

— I never saw blood on them, umfundisi.

— That is something. Only a little, but
something.

— And why did they leave, he asked.

— I do not know, umfundisi. But I
think they were near to being discovered.

— And they left when?

— About a year since, umfundisi. Indeed as I told you.

— And here on this Book you will
swear you do not know where they are
gone?

She reached for the Book, but, it does
not matter, he said. He said farewell to
her, and hurried out after his friend. But
she called after him—

— They were friendly with the taxi-
driver Hlabeni. Near the bus rank he lives.
Everyone knows him.

— For that I give you thanks. Stay well,
Mrs. Mkize.

At the refreshment stall he found his
friend.

— Did you find anything further, asked
the old man eagerly.

— I heard of a friend of theirs, the
taxi-driver Hlabeni. Let me first eat, and
we shall find him out.

When Msimangu had eaten, he went to
ask a man where he could find Hlabeni,
the taxi-driver. There he is on the corner
[48/49] sitting in his taxi, said the man.
Msimangu walked over to the taxi, and
said to the man sitting in it, Good afternoon, my friend.

— Good afternoon, umfundisi.

— I want a taxi, my friend. What do
you charge to Johannesburg? For myself
and a friend?

— For you, umfundisi, I should charge
eleven shillings.

— It is a lot of money.

— Another taxi would charge fifteen
or twenty shillings.

— My companion is old and tired. I
shall pay you eleven shillings.

The man made to start his engine, but
Msimangu stopped him. I am told, he
said, that you can help me to find a young
man Absalom Kumalo.

Have no doubt too that this man is
afraid. But Msimangu was quick to re-
assure him. I am not here for trouble, he
said. I give you my word that I am seeking
trouble neither for you nor for myself.
But my companion, the old man who is
tired, is the father of this young man, and
he has come from Natal to find him.
Everywhere we go, we are told to go somewhere else, and the old man is anxious.

— Yes, I knew this young man.

— And where is he now, my friend?

— I heard he was gone to Orlando,
and lives there amongst the squatters of
Shanty Town. But further than that I do
not know.

— Orlando is a big place, said Msimangu.

— Where the squatters live is not so
big, umfundisi. It should not be hard to
find him. There are people from the
Municipality working amongst the squatters, and they know them all. Could you
not ask one of those people?

— There you have helped me, my
friend. I know some of those people.
Come, we shall take your taxi.

He called Kumalo, and told him they
were returning by taxi. They climbed in,
and the taxi rattled out of Alexandra on
to the broad high road that runs from
Pretoria to Johannesburg. The afternoon
was late now, and the road was crowded
with [49/50] traffic, for at this time it

pours both into and out of Johannesburg on this road.

— You see the bicycles, my friend. These are the thousands of Alexandra people returning home after their work, and just now we shall see thousands of them walking, because of the boycott of the buses.

And true, they had not gone far before the pavements were full of the walking people. There were so many that they overflowed into the streets, and the cars had to move carefully. And some were old, and some tired, and some even crippled as they had been told, but most of them walked resolutely, as indeed they had been doing now these past few weeks. Many of the white people stopped their cars, and took in the black people, to help them on their journey to Alexandra. Indeed, at one robot where they stopped, a traffic officer was talking to one of these white men, and they heard the officer asking whether the white man had a license to carry the black people. I am asking no money, said the white man. But you are carrying passengers on a bus route, said the officer. Then take me to court, said the white man. But they heard no more than that, for they had to move on because the light was green.

— I have heard of that, said Msimangu. I have heard that they are trying to prevent the white people from helping with their cars, and that they are even ready to take them to the courts.

It was getting dark now, but the road was still thick with the Alexandra people going home. And there were still cars stopping to give them lifts, especially to the old people, and the women, and the cripples. Kumalo's face wore the smile, the strange smile not known in other countries, of a black man when he sees one of his people helped in public by a white man, for such a thing is not lightly done. And so immersed was he in the watching that he was astonished when Msimangu suddenly burst out—

— It beats me, my friend, it beats me.
— What beats you, this kindness?

— No, no. To tell the truth I was not thinking of it. [50/51]

He sat up in the taxi, and hit himself a great blow across the chest.

— Take me to court, he said. He glared fiercely at Kumalo and hit himself again across the chest. Take me to court, he said.

Kumalo looked at him bewildered.

— That is what beats me, Msimangu said. [51/52]

IX

All roads lead to Johannesburg. If you are white or if you are black they lead to Johannesburg. If the crops fail, there is work in Johannesburg. If there are taxes to be paid, there is work in Johannesburg. If the farm is too small to be divided further, some must go to Johannesburg. If there is a child to be born that must be delivered in secret, it can be delivered in Johannesburg.

The black people go to Alexandra or Sophiatown or Orlando, and try to hire rooms or to buy a share of a house.

— Have you a room that you could let?
— No, I have no room.
— Have you a room that you could let?
— It is let already.
— Have you a room that you could let?

Yes, I have a room that I could let, but I do not want to let it. I have only two rooms, and there are six of us already, and the boys and girls are growing up. But school books cost money, and my husband is ailing, and when he is well it is only thirty-five shillings a week. And six shillings of that is for the rent, and three shillings for travelling, and a shilling that we may all be buried decently, and a shilling for the books, and three shillings is for the clothes and that is little enough, and a shilling for my husband's beer, and a shilling for his tobacco, and these I do not grudge for he is a decent man and does not gamble or spend his money on other women, and a shilling for the Church, and a shilling for sickness. And that leaves seventeen shillings for food for six, and we are always hungry. Yes [52/53] I have a room but I do not want to let it. How much would you pay?

— I could pay three shillings a week for the room.

— And I would not take it.

— Three shillings and sixpence?

Three shillings and sixpence. You can't fill your stomach on privacy. You need privacy when your children are growing up, but you can't fill your stomach on it. Yes, I shall take three shillings and sixpence.

The house is not broken, but it is overflowing. Ten people in two rooms, and only one door for the entrance, and people to walk over you when you go to sleep. But there is a little more food for the children, and maybe once a month a trip to the pictures.

I do not like this woman, nor the way she looks at my husband. I do not like this boy, nor the way he looks at my daughter. I do not like this man, I do not like the way he looks at me, I do not like the way he looks at my daughter.

— I am sorry, but you must go now.

— We have no place to go to.

— I am sorry, but the house is too full. It cannot hold so many.

— We have put our name down for a house. Can you not wait till we get a house?

— There are people in Orlando who have been waiting five years for a house.

— I have a friend who waited only one month for a house.

— I have heard of such. They say you can pay a bribe.

— We have no money for a bribe.

— I am sorry, but the house is full.

Yes, this house is full, and that house is full. For everyone is coming to Johannesburg. From the Transkei and the Free State, from Zululand and Sekukuniland. Zulus and Swazis, Shangaans and Bavenda, Bapedi and Basuto, Xosas and Tembus, Pondos and Fingos, they are all coming to Johannesburg.

I do not like this woman. I do not like this boy. I do not like this man. I am sorry, but you must go now. [53/54]

— Another week, that is all I ask.

— You may have one more week.

*   *   *   *   *

— Have you a room to let?

— No, I have no room to let.

— Have you a room to let?

— It is let already.

— Have you a room to let?

Yes, I have a room to let, but I do not want to let it. For I have seen husbands taken away by women, and wives taken away by men. I have seen daughters corrupted by boys, and sons corrupted by girls. But my husband gets only thirty-four shillings a week—

*   *   *   *   *

— What shall we do, those who have no houses?

— You can wait five years for a house, and be no nearer getting it than at the beginning.

— They say there are ten thousand of us in Orlando alone, living in other people's houses.

— Do you hear what Dubula says? That we must put up our own houses here in Orlando?

— And where do we put up the houses?

— On the open ground by the railway line, Dubula says.

— And of what do we build the houses?

— Anything you can find. Sacks and planks and grass from the veld and poles from the plantations.

— And when it rains?

— Siyafa. Then we die.

— No, when it rains, they will have to build us houses.

— It is foolishness. What shall we do in the Winter?

Six years waiting for a house. And full as the houses are, they grow yet fuller, for the people still come to Johannesburg. There has been a great war raging in Europe and North Africa, and no houses are being built.

— Have you a house for me yet? [54/55]

— There is no house yet.

— Are you sure my name is on the list?

— Yes, your name is on the list.

— What number am I on the list?

— I cannot say, but you must be about number six thousand on the list.

Number six thousand on the list. That means I shall never get a house, and I cannot stay where I am much longer. We have quarrelled about the stove, we have quarrelled about the children, and I do not like the way the man looks at me. There is the open ground by the railway line, but what of the rain and the winter? They say we must go there, all go together, fourteen days from today. They say we must get together the planks and the sacks and the tins and the poles, and all move together. They say we must all pay a shilling a week to the Committee, and they will move all our rubbish and put up lavatories for us, so that there is no sickness. But what of the rain and the winter?

— Have you a house for me yet?

— There is no house yet.

— But I have been two years on the list.

— You are only a child on the list.

— Is it true that if you pay money—

But the man does not hear me, he is already busy with another. But a second man comes to me from what place I do not see, and what he says bewilders me.

— I am sorry they have no house, Mrs. Seme. By the way, my wife would like to discuss with you the work of the Committee. Tonight at seven o'clock, she said. You know our house, No. 17852, near the Dutch Reformed Church. Look, I shall write down the number for you. Good morning, Mrs. Seme.

But when I make to answer him, he is already gone.

— Ho, but this man bewilders me. Who is his wife, I do not know her. And what is this committee, I know of no committee.

— Ho, but you are a simple woman. He wants to discuss with you the money you are willing to pay for a house. [55/56]

Well, I shall go there then. I hope he does not ask too much, one cannot pay too much on thirty-seven shillings a week. But a house we must have. I am afraid of the place where we are. There is too much coming and going, when all decent people

are asleep. Too many young men coming and going, that seem never to sleep, and never to work. Too much clothing, good clothing, white people's clothing. There will be trouble one day, and my husband and I have never been in trouble. A house we must have.

* * * * *

— Five pounds is too much. I have not the money.

— Five pounds is not too much for a house, Mrs. Seme.

— What, just to put my name higher on the list?

— But it is dangerous. The European manager has said that he will deal severely with any who tamper with the list.

— Well, I am sorry. But I cannot pay the money.

But before I can go, his wife comes into the room with another woman.

— There must be a mistake, my husband. I do not know this woman. She is not on the committee.

— Ho, I am sorry, my wife. I am sorry, Mrs. Seme. I thought you were on the committee. Go well, Mrs. Seme.

But I do not say stay well. I do not care if they stay well or ill. And nothing goes well with me. I am tired and lonely. Oh my husband, why did we leave the land of our people? There is not much there, but it is better than here. There is not much food there, but it is shared by all together. If all are poor, it is not so bad to be poor. And it is pleasant by the river, and while you wash your clothes the water runs over the stones, and the wind cools you. Two weeks from today, that is the day of the moving. Come my husband, let us get the planks and the tins and the sacks and the poles. I do not like the place where we are.

There are planks at the Baragwanath Hospital, left there by the builders. Let us go tonight and carry them away. There is corrugated iron at the Reformatory, they use them to cover the [56/57] bricks. Let us go tonight and carry it away. There are sacks at the Nancefield Station, lying neatly packed in bundles. Let us go tonight and carry them away. There are trees at the Crown Mines. Let us go tonight and cut a few poles quietly.

*   *   *   *   *

This night they are busy in Orlando. At one house after another the lights are burning. I shall carry the iron, and you my wife the child, and you my son two poles, and you small one, bring as many sacks as you are able, down to the land by the railway lines. Many people are moving there, you can hear the sound of digging and hammering already. It is good that the night is warm, and there is no rain. Thank you, Mr. Dubula, we are satisfied with this piece of ground. Thank you, Mr. Dubula, here is our shilling for the committee.

Shanty Town is up overnight. What a surprise for the people when they wake in the morning. Smoke comes up through the sacks, and one or two have a chimney already. There was a nice chimney-pipe lying there at the Kliptown Police Station, but I was not such a fool as to take it.

Shanty Town is up overnight. And the newspapers are full of us. Great big words and pictures. See, that is my husband, standing by the house. Alas, I was too late for the picture. Squatters, they call us. We are the squatters. This great village of sack and plank and iron, with no rent to pay, only a shilling to the Committee.

Shanty Town is up overnight. The child coughs badly, and her brow is as hot as fire. I was afraid to move her, but it was the night for the moving. The cold wind comes through the sacks. What shall we do in the rain, in the winter? Quietly my child, your mother is by you. Quietly my child, do not cough any more, your mother is by you.

*   *   *   *   *

The child coughs badly, her brow is hotter than fire. Quietly my child, your mother is by you. Outside there is laughter and jesting, digging and hammering, and calling in languages that [57/58] I do not know. Quietly my child, there is a lovely valley where you were born. The water sings over the stones, and the wind cools

you. The cattle come down to the river, they stand there under the trees. Quietly my child, oh God make her quiet. God have mercy upon us. Christ have mercy upon us. White man, have mercy upon us.

*   *   *   *   *

— Mr. Dubula, where is the doctor?

— We shall get the doctor in the morning. You need not fear, the committee will pay for him.

— But the child is like to die. Look at the blood.

— It is not long till morning.

— It is long when the child is dying, when the heart is afraid. Can we not get him now, Mr. Dubula?

— I shall try, mother. I shall go now and try.

— I am grateful, Mr. Dubula.

*   *   *   *   *

Outside there is singing, singing round a fire. It is *Nkosi sikelel' iAfrika* that they sing, God Save Africa. God save this piece of Africa that is my own, delivered in travail from my body, fed from my breast, loved by my heart, because that is the nature of women. Oh lie quietly, little one. Doctor, can you not come?

*   *   *   *   *

— I have sent for the doctor, mother. The Committee has sent a car for the doctor. A black doctor, one of our own.

— I am grateful, Mr. Dubula.

— Shall I ask them to be quiet, mother?

— It does not matter, she does not know.

Perhaps a white doctor would have been better, but any doctor if only he come. Does it matter if they are quiet, these sounds of an alien land? I am afraid, my husband. She burns my hand like fire. [58/59]

*   *   *   *   *

We do not need the doctor any more. No white doctor, no black doctor, can help her any more. Oh child of my womb and fruit of my desire, it was pleasure to hold the small cheeks in the hands, it was pleasure to feel the tiny clutching of the fingers, it was pleasure to feel the little mouth tugging at the breast. Such is the nature of woman. Such is the lot of women, to carry, to bear, to watch and to lose.

*   *   *   *   *

The white men come to Shanty Town. They take photographs of us, and moving photographs for the pictures. They come and wonder what they can do, there are so many of us. What will the poor devils do in the rain? What will the poor devils do in the winter? Men come, and machines come, and they start building rough houses for us. That Dubula is a clever man, this is what he said they would do. And no sooner do they begin to build for us, than there come in the night other black people, from Pimville and Alexandra and Sophiatown, and they too put up their houses of sack and grass and iron and poles. And the white men come again, but this time it is anger, not pity. The police come and drive the people away. And some that they drive away are from Orlando itself. They go back to the houses that they left, but of some the rooms are already taken, and some will not have them any more.

You need not be ashamed that you live in Shanty Town. It is in the papers, and that is my husband standing by the house. A man here has a paper from Durban, and my husband is there too, standing by the house. You can give your address as Shanty Town, Shanty Town alone, everyone knows where it is, and give the number that the committee has given you.

What shall we do in the rain? in the winter? Already some of them are saying, look at those houses over on the hill. They are not finished, but the roofs are on. One night we shall move there and be safe from the rain and the winter. [59/60]

X

While Kumalo was waiting for Msimangu to take him to Shanty Town, he spent the time with Gertrude and her child. But it was rather to the child, the small serious boy, that he turned for his enjoyment; for he had been a young man in the twenties when his sister was born, and there had never been great intimacy between them. After all he was a parson, sober and rather dull no doubt, and his hair was turning white, and she was a young woman still. Nor could he expect her to talk with him about the deep things that were here in Johannesburg; for it was amongst these very things that saddened and perplexed him, that she had found her life and occupation.

Here were heavy things indeed, too heavy for a woman who had not gone beyond the fifth standard of her country school. She was respectful to him, as it behooved her to be to an elder brother and a parson, and they exchanged conventional conversation; but never again did they speak of the things that had made her fall on the floor with crying and weeping.

But the good Mrs. Lithebe was there, and she and Gertrude talked long and simply about things dear to the heart of women, and they worked and sang together in the performance of the daily tasks.

Yes, it was to the small serious boy that he turned for his enjoyment. He had bought the child some cheap wooden blocks, and with these the little one played endlessly and intently, with a purpose obscure to the adult mind, but completely absorbing. Kumalo would pick the child up, and put his hand under the shirt to feel the small warm back, and tickle and poke him, till the serious face relaxed into smiles, and the smiles grew [60/61] into uncontrollable laughter. Or he would tell him of the great valley where he was born, and the names of hills and rivers, and the school that he would go to, and the mist that shrouded the tops above Ndotsheni. Of this the child understood nothing; yet something he did understand, for he would listen solemnly to the deep melodious names, and gaze at his uncle out of wide and serious eyes. And this to the uncle was pleasure indeed, for he was homesick in the great city; and something inside him was deeply satisfied by this recital. Sometimes Gertrude would hear him, and come to the door and stand shyly there, and listen to the tale of the beauties of the land where she was born. This enriched his pleasure, and sometimes he would say to her, do you remember, and she would answer, yes, I remember, and be pleased that he had asked her.

But there were times, some in the very midst of satisfaction, where the thought of his son would come to him. And then in one fraction of time the hills with the deep melodious names stood out waste and desolate beneath the pitiless sun, the streams ceased to run, the cattle moved thin and listless over the red and rootless earth. It was a place of old women and mothers and children, from each house something was gone. His voice would falter and die away, and he would fall silent and muse. Perhaps it was that, or perhaps he clutched suddenly at the small listening boy, for the little one would break from the spell, and wriggle in his arms to be put down, to play again with his blocks on the floor. As though he was searching for something that would put an end to this sudden unasked-for pain, the thought of his wife would come to him, and of many a friend that he had, and the small children coming down from the hills, dropping sometimes out of the very mist, on their way to the school. These things were so dear to him that the pain passed, and he contemplated them in quiet, and some measure of peace.

Who indeed knows the secret of the earthly pilgrimage? Who indeed knows why there can be comfort in a world of desolation? Now God be thanked that there is a beloved one who can lift up the heart in suffering, that one can play with a [**61/62**] child in the face of such misery. Now God be thanked that the name of a hill is such music, that the name of a river can heal. Aye, even the name of a river that runs no more.

Who indeed knows the secret of the earthly pilgrimage? Who knows for what we live, and struggle, and die? Who knows what keeps us living and struggling, while all things break about us? Who knows why the warm flesh of a child is such comfort, when one's own child is lost and cannot be recovered? Wise men write many books, in words too hard to understand. But this, the purpose of our lives, the end of all our struggle, is beyond all human wisdom. Oh God, my God, do not Thou forsake me. Yea though I walk through the valley of the shadow of death, I shall fear no evil, if Thou art with me. . . .

But he stood up. That was Msimangu talking at the door. It was time to continue the search.

*   *   *   *   *

— And this is Shanty Town, my friend.

Even here the children laugh in the narrow lanes that run between these tragic habitations. A sheet of iron, a few planks, hessian and grass, an old door from some forgotten house. Smoke curls from vents cunningly contrived, there is a smell of food, there is a sound of voices, not raised in anger or pain, but talking of ordinary things, of this one that is born and that one that has died, of this one that does so well at school and that one who is now in prison. There is drought over the land, and the sun shines warmly down from the cloudless sky. But what will they do when it rains, what will they do when it is winter?

— It is sad for me to see.

— Yet see them building over there. And that they have not done for many a year. Some good may come of this. And this too is Dubula's work.

— He is everywhere, it seems.

— See, there is one of our nurses. Does she not look well in her red and white, and her cap upon her head? [**62/63**]

— She looks well indeed.

— The white people are training more and more of them. It is strange how we move forward in some things, and stand still in others, and go backward in yet others. Yet in this matter of nurses we have many friends amongst the white people. There was a great outcry when it was decided to allow some of our young people to train as doctors at the European University of the Witwatersrand. But our friends stood firm, and they will train there until we have a place of our own. Good morning, nurse.

— Good morning, umfundisi.

— Nurse, have you been working here long?

— Yes, as long as the place is here.

— And did you ever know a young man, Absalom Kumalo?

— Yes, that I did. But he is not here now. And I can tell where he stayed. He stayed with the Hlatswayos, and they are still here. Do you see the place where there are many stones so that they cannot build? See, there is a small boy standing there.

— Yes, I see it.

— And beyond it the house with the pipe, where the smoke is coming out?

— Yes, I see it.

— Go down that lane, and you will find the Hlatswayos in the third or fourth house, on the side of the hand that you eat with.

— Thank you, nurse, we shall go.

Her directions were so clear that they had no difficulty in finding the house.

— Good morning, mother.

The woman was clean and nice-looking, and she smiled at them in a friendly way.

— Good morning, umfundisi.

— Mother, we are looking for a lad, Absalom Kumalo.

— He stayed with me, umfundisi. We took pity on him because he had no place to go. But I am sorry to tell you that they took him away, and I heard that the magistrate had sent him to the reformatory. [63/64]

— The reformatory?

— Yes, the big school over there, beyond the soldiers' hospital. It is not too far to walk.

— I must thank you, Mother. Stay well. Come, my friend.

They walked on in silence, for neither of them had any words. Kumalo would have stumbled, though the road was straight and even, and Msimangu took his arm.

— Have courage, my brother.

He glanced at his friend, but Kumalo's eyes were on the ground. Although Msimangu could not see his face, he could see the drop that fell on the ground, and he tightened his grip on the arm.

— Have courage, my brother.

— Sometimes it seems that I have no more courage.

— I have heard of this reformatory. Your friend the priest from England speaks well of it. I have heard him say that if any boy wishes to amend, there is help for him there. So take courage.

— I was afraid of this.

— Yes, I too was afraid of it.

— Yes, I remember when you first became afraid. The day at Alexandra, when you sent me on, and you returned to speak again to the woman.

— I see that I cannot hide from you.

— That is not because I am so wise. Only because it is my son.

They walked out of Shanty Town into Orlando, and out along the tarred street that leads to the high road to Johannesburg, to the place where the big petrol station of the white people stands at the gates of Orlando; for the black people are not allowed to have petrol stations in Orlando.

— What did the woman say to you, my friend?

— She said that these two young men were in some mischief. Many goods, white people's goods, came to the house.

— This reformatory, can they reform there?

— I do not know it well. Some people say one thing, some the other. But your friend speaks well of it. [64/65]

And after a long while, during which Msimangu's thoughts had wandered elsewhere, Kumalo said again, It is my hope that they can reform there.

— It is my hope also, my brother.

After a walk of about one hour, they came to the road that led up to the reformatory. It was midday when they arrived, and from all directions there came boys marching, into the gates of the reformatory. From every place they came, until it seemed that the marching would never end.

— There are very many here, my friend.

— Yes, I did not know there would be so many.

One of their own people, a pleasant fellow with a smiling face, came up to them and asked them what they wanted, and they told him they were searching for one Absalom Kumalo. So this man took them to an office, where a young white man enquired of them in Afrikaans what was their business.

— We are looking, sir, for the son of my friend, one Absalom Kumalo, said Msimangu in the same language.

—Absalom Kumalo. Yes, I know him well. Strange, he told me he had no people.

— Your son told him, my friend, that he had no people, said Msimangu in Zulu.

— He was no doubt ashamed, said Kumalo. I am sorry, he said to Msimangu in Zulu, that I speak no Afrikaans. For he had heard that sometimes they do not like black people who speak no Afrikaans.

— You may speak what you will, said the young man: Your son did well here, he said. He became one of our senior boys, and I have great hope for his future.

— You mean, sir, that he is gone?

— Gone, yes, only one month ago. We made an exception in his case, partly because of his good behaviour, partly because of his age, but mainly because there was a girl who was pregnant by him. She came here to see him, and he seemed fond of her, and anxious about the child that would be born. And the girl too seemed fond of him, so with all these things in mind, and with his solemn undertaking that he would work for his [65/66] child and its mother, we asked the Minister to let him go. Of course we do not succeed

in all these cases, but where there seems to be real affection between the parties, we take the chance, hoping that good will come of it. One thing is certain that if it fails, there is nothing that could have succeeded.

— And is he now married, sir?

— No, umfundisi, he is not. But everything is arranged for the marriage. This girl has no people, and your son told us he had no people, so I myself and my native assistant have arranged it.

— That is good of you, sir. I thank you for them.

— It is our work. You must not worry too much about this matter, and the fact that they were not married, the young man said kindly. The real question is whether he will care for them, and lead a decent life.

— That I can see, although it is a shock to me.

— I understand that. Now I can help you in this matter. If you will sit outside while I finish my work, I will take you to Pimville, where Absalom and this girl are living. He will not be there, because I have found work for him in the town, and they have given me good reports of him. I persuaded him to open a Post Office book, and he already has three or four pounds in it.

— Indeed, I cannot thank you, sir.

— It is our work, said the young man. Now if you will leave me, I shall finish what I have to do, and then take you to Pimville.

Outside the pleasant-faced man came and spoke to them and hearing their plans, invited them to his house, where he and his wife had a number of boys in their charge, boys who had left the big reformatory building and were living outside in these free houses. He gave them some tea and food, and he too told them that Absalom had become a head-boy, and had behaved well during his stay at the reformatory. So they talked about the reformatory, and the children that were growing up in Johannesburg without home or school or custom, and about the broken [66/67] tribe and the sickness of the land, until a messenger came from the young man to say that he was ready.

It was not long before the motorcar had reached Pimville, which is a village of half-tanks used as houses, set up many years before in emergency, and used ever since. For there have never been houses enough for all the people who came to Johannesburg. At the gate they asked permission to enter, for a white man may not go into these places without permission.

They stopped at one of these half-tank houses, and the young white man took them in, where they were greeted by a young girl, who herself seemed no more than a child.

— We have come to enquire after Absalom, said the young white man. This umfundisi is his father.

— He went on Saturday to Springs, she said, and he has not yet returned.

The young man was silent awhile, and he frowned in perplexity or anger.

— But this is Tuesday, he said. Have you heard nothing from him?

— Nothing, she said.

— When will he return, he asked.

— I do not know, she said.

— Will he ever return, he asked, indifferently, carelessly.

— I do not know, she said. She said it tonelessly, hopelessly, as one who is used to waiting, to desertion. She said it as one who expects nothing from her seventy years upon the earth. No rebellion will come out of her, no demands, no fierceness. Nothing will come out of her at all, save the children of men who will use her, leave her, forget her. And so slight was her body, and so few her years, that Kumalo for all his suffering was moved to compassion.

— What will you do, he asked.

— I do not know, she said.

— Perhaps you will find another man, said Msimangu bitterly. And before Kumalo could speak, to steal away the bitterness and hide it from her—I do not know, she said. [67/68]

And again before Kumalo could speak, Msimangu turned his back on the girl, and spoke to him privately.

— You can do nothing here, he said. Let us go.

— My friend. . . . . . .

— I tell you, you can do nothing. Have you not troubles enough of your own? I tell you there are thousands such in Johannesburg. And were your back as broad as heaven, and your purse full of gold, and did your compassion reach from here to hell itself, there is nothing you can do.

Silently they withdrew. All of them were silent, the young white man heavy with failure, the old man with grief, Msimangu still bitter with his words. Kumalo stood at the car though the others were already seated.

— You do not understand, he said. The child will be my grandchild.

— Even that you do not know, said Msimangu angrily. His bitterness mastered him again. And if he were, he said, how many more such have you? Shall we search them out, day after day, hour after hour? Will it ever end?

Kumalo stood in the dust like one who has been struck. Then without speaking any more he took his seat in the car.

Again they stopped at the gate of the village, and the young white man got out and went into the office of the European Superintendent. He came back, his face set and unhappy.

— I have telephoned the factory, he said. It is true. He has not been at work this week.

At the gates of Orlando, by the big petrol station, they stopped yet again.

— Would you like to get out here, the young man asked. They climbed out, and the young man spoke to Kumalo.

— I am sorry for this, he said.

— Yes, it is very heavy. As if his English had left him, he spoke in Zulu to Msimangu.

— I am sorry too for this end to his work, he said.

— He too is sorry for this end to your work, said Msimangu in Afrikaans.

— Yes, it is my work, but it is his son.

He turned to Kumalo [**68/69**] and spoke in English. Let us not give up all hope, he said. It has happened sometimes that a boy is arrested, or is injured and taken to hospital, and we do not know. Do not give up hope, umfundisi. I will not give up the search.

They watched him drive away. He is a good man, said Kumalo. Come, let us walk.

But Msimangu did not move. I am ashamed to walk with you, he said. His face was twisted, like that of a man much distressed.

Kumalo looked at him astonished.

— I ask your forgiveness for my ugly words, said Msimangu.

— You mean about the search?

— You understood, then?

— Yes, I understood.

— You are quick to understand.

— I am old, and have learnt something. You are forgiven.

— Sometimes I think I am not fit to be a priest. I could tell you—

— It is no matter. You have said you are a weak and selfish man, but God put his hands upon you. It is true, it seems.

— Huh, you comfort me.

— But I have something to ask of you.

Msimangu looked at him, searching his face, and then he said, it is agreed.

— What is agreed?

— That I should take you again to see this girl.

— You are clever too, it seems.

— Huh, it is not good that only one should be clever.

Yet they were not really in the mood for jesting. They walked along the hot road to Orlando, and both fell silent, each no doubt with many things in mind. [**69/70**]

XI

— I have been thinking, said Msimangu, as they were sitting in the train that would take them back to Sophiatown, that it is time for you to rest for a while.

Kumalo looked at him. How can I rest, he said.

— I know what you mean. I know you are anxious, but the young man at the reformatory will do better at this searching than you or I could do. Now this is Tuesday; the day after tomorrow I must go to Ezenzeleni, which is the place for our blind, to hold a service for them, and to attend to our own people. And that night I shall sleep there, and return the day after. I shall telephone to the superintendent, and ask if you may come with me. While I work, you can rest. It is a fine place there; there is a chapel there, and the ground falls away from one's feet to the valley below. It will lift your spirits to see what the white people are doing for our blind. Then we can return strengthened for what is still before us.

— What about your work, my friend?

— I have spoken to my superiors about the work. They are agreed that I must help you till the young man is found.

— They are indeed kind. Good, we shall go then.

*   *   *   *   *

It was a pleasant evening at the Mission House. Father Vincent, the rosy-cheeked priest, was there, and they talked about the place where Kumalo lived and worked. And the white man in his turn spoke about his own country, about the hedges and the fields, and Westminster Abbey, and the great cathedrals up and down the land. Yet even this pleasure was not to be entire, for one of the white priests came in from the city with [**70/71**] the Evening Star, and showed them the bold black lines. MURDER IN PARK-WOLD. WELL-KNOWN CITY ENGINEER SHOT DEAD. ASSAILANTS THOUGHT TO BE NATIVES.

— This is a terrible loss for South Africa, said the white priest. For this Arthur Jarvis was a courageous young man, and a great fighter for justice. And it is a terrible loss for the Church too. He was one of the finest of all our young laymen.

— Jarvis? It is indeed a terrible thing, said Msimangu. He was the President of the African Boys' Club, here in Claremont, in Gladiolus Street.

— Perhaps you might have known him, said Father Vincent to Kumalo. It says that he was the only child of Mr. James Jarvis, of High Place, Carisbrooke.

— I know the father, said Kumalo sorrowfully. I mean I know him well by sight and name, but we have never spoken. His farm is in the hills above Ndotsheni, and he sometimes rode past our church. But I did not know the son.

He was silent, then he said, yet I remember, there was a small bright boy, and he too sometimes rode on his horse past the church. A small bright boy, I remember, though I do not remember it well.

And he was silent again, for who is not silent when someone is dead, who was a small bright boy?

— Shall I read this, said Father Vincent.

At 1:30 P.M. today Mr. Arthur Jarvis, of Plantation Road, Parkwold, was shot dead in his house by an intruder, thought to be a native. It appears that Mrs. Jarvis and her two children were away for a short holiday, and that Mr. Jarvis had telephoned his partners to say that he would be staying at home with a slight cold. It would seem that a native, probably with two accomplices, entered by the kitchen, thinking no doubt that there would be no one in the house. The native servant in the kitchen was knocked unconscious, and it would appear that Mr. Jarvis heard the disturbance and came down to investigate. He was shot dead at short-range in the passageway leading from the stairs into the kitchen. There were no signs of any struggle. [71/72]

Three native youths were seen lounging in Plantation Road shortly before the tragedy occurred, and a strong force of detectives was immediately sent to the scene. Exhaustive inquiries are being made, and the plantations on Parkwold Ridge are being combed. The native servant, Richard Mpiring, is lying unconscious in the Non-European Hospital, and it is hoped that when he regains consciousness he will be able to furnish the police with important information. His condition is serious however.

The sound of the shot was heard by a neighbour, Mr. Michael Clarke, who investigated promptly and made the tragic discovery. The police were on the scene within a few minutes. On the table by the bed of the murdered man was found an unfinished manuscript on "The Truth about Native Crime," and it would appear that he was engaged in writing it when he got up to go to his death. The bowl of a pipe on the table was found still to be warm.

Mr. Jarvis leaves a widow, a nine-year-old son, and a five-year-old daughter. He was the only son of Mr. James Jarvis, of High Place Farm, Carisbrooke, Natal, and a partner in the city engineering firm of Davis, van der Walt, and Jarvis. The dead man was well known for his interest in social problems, and for his efforts for the welfare of the non-European sections of the community.

There is not much talking now. A silence falls upon them all. This is no time to talk of hedges and fields, or the beauties of any country. Sadness and fear and hate, how they swell up in the heart and mind, whenever one opens the pages of these messengers of doom. Cry for the broken tribe, for the law and the custom that is gone. Aye, and cry aloud for the man who is dead, for the woman and children bereaved. Cry, the beloved country, these things are not yet at an end. The sun pours down on the earth, on the lovely land that man cannot enjoy. He knows only the fear of his heart. [72/73]

* * * * *

Kumalo rose. I shall go to my room, he said. Good-night to you all.

— I shall walk with you, my friend.

They walked to the gate of the little house of Mrs. Lithebe. Kumalo lifted to his friend a face that was full of suffering.

— This thing, he said. This thing. Here in my heart there is nothing but fear. Fear, fear, fear.

— I understand. Yet it is nevertheless foolish to fear that one thing in this great city, with its thousands and thousands of people.

— It is not a question of wisdom and foolishness. It is just fear.

— The day after tomorrow we go to Ezenzeleni. Perhaps you will find something there.

— No doubt, no doubt. Anything but what I most desire.

— Come and pray.

— There is no prayer left in me. I am dumb here inside. I have no words at all.

— Goodnight, my brother.

— Goodnight.

Msimangu watched him go up the little path. He looked very old. He himself turned and walked back to the Mission. There are times, no doubt, when God seems no more to be about the world. [**73/74**]

XII

Have no doubt it is fear in the land. For what can men do when so many have grown lawless? Who can enjoy the lovely land, who can enjoy the seventy years, and the sun that pours down on the earth, when there is fear in the heart? Who can walk quietly in the shadow of the jacarandas, when their beauty is grown to danger? Who can lie peacefully abed, while the darkness holds some secret? What lovers can lie sweetly under the stars, when menace grows with the measure of their seclusion?

There are voices crying what must be done, a hundred, a thousand voices. But what do they help if one seeks for counsel, for one cries this, and one cries that, and another cries something that is neither this nor that.

*   *   *   *   *

It's a crying scandal, ladies and gentlemen, that we get so few police. This suburb pays more in taxes than most of the suburbs of Johannesburg, and what do we get for it? A third-class police station, with one man on the beat, and one at the telephone. This is the second outrage of its kind in six months, and we must demand more protection. *(Applause).*

Mr. McLaren, will you read us your resolution?

*   *   *   *   *

I say we shall always have native crime to fear until the native people of this country have worthy purposes to inspire them and worthy goals to work for. For it is only because they see [**74/75**] neither purpose nor goal that they turn to drink and crime and prostitution. Which do we prefer, a law-abiding, industrious, and purposeful native people, or a lawless, idle, and purposeless people? The truth is that we do not know, for we fear them both. And so long as we vacillate, so long will we pay dearly for the dubious pleasure of not having to make up our minds. And the answer does not lie, except temporarily, in more police and more protection. *(Applause).*

*   *   *   *   *

— And you think, Mr. de Villiers, that increased schooling facilities would cause a decrease in juvenile delinquency amongst native children?

— I am sure of it, Mr. Chairman.

— Have you the figures for the percentage of children at school, Mr. de Villiers?

— In Johannesburg, Mr. Chairman, not more than four out of ten are at school. But of those four not even one will reach his sixth standard. Six are being educated in the streets.

— May I ask Mr. de Villiers a question, Mr. Chairman?

— By all means, Mr. Scott.

— Who do you think should pay for this schooling, Mr. de Villiers?

— We should pay for it. If we wait till native parents can pay for it, we will pay more heavily in other ways.

— Don't you think, Mr. de Villiers,

that more schooling simply means cleverer criminals?

— I am sure that is not true.

— Let me give you a case. I had a boy working for me who had passed Standard Six. Perfect gentleman, bow-tie, hat to the side, and the latest socks. I treated him well and paid him well. Now do you know, Mr. de Villiers, that this self-same scoundrel . . . . .

*   *   *   *   *

— They should enforce the pass laws, Jackson.

— But I tell you the pass laws don't work. [**75/76**]

— They'd work if they were enforced.

— But I tell you they're unenforceable. Do you know that we send one hundred thousand natives every year to prison, where they mix with real criminals?

— That's not quite true, Jackson. I know they're trying road camps, and farm-labour, and several other things.

— Well, perhaps you know. But it doesn't alter my argument at all, that the pass laws are unenforceable. You can send 'em to road-camps or farms or anywhere else you damn well please, but you can't tell me it's a healthy thing even to convict one hundred thousand people.

— What would you do then?

— Well now you're asking. I don't know what I'd do. But I just know the pass laws don't work.

*   *   *   *   *

— We went to the Zoo Lake, my dear. But it's quite impossible. I really don't see why they can't have separate days for natives.

— I just don't go there any more on a Sunday, my dear. We take John and Penelope on some other day. But I like to be fair. Where can these poor creatures go?

— Why can't they make recreation places for them?

— When they wanted to make a recreation centre on part of the Hillside Golf Course, there was such a fuss that they had to drop it.

— But my dear, it would have been impossible. The noise would have been incredible.

— So they stay on the pavements and hang about the corners. And believe me, the noise is just as incredible there too. But that needn't worry you where you live.

— Don't be catty, my dear. Why can't they put up big recreation centres some-where, and let them all go free on the buses?

— Where for example?

— You do persist, my dear. Why not in the City?

— And how long will it take them to get there? And how [**76/77**] long to get back? How many hours do you give your servants off on a Sunday?

— Oh, it's too hot to argue. Get your racquet, my dear, they're calling us. Look, it's Mrs. Harvey and Thelma. You've got to play like a demon, do you hear?

*   *   *   *   *

And some cry for the cutting-up of South Africa without delay into separate areas, where white can live without black, and black without white, where black can farm their own land and mine their own minerals and administer their own laws. And others cry away with the compound system, that brings men to the towns without their wives and children, and breaks up the tribe and the house and the man, and they ask for the establishment of villages for the labourers in mines and industry.

And the churches cry too. The English-speaking churches cry for more education, and more opportunity, and for a removal of the restrictions on native labour and enterprise. And the Afrikaans-speaking churches want to see the native people given opportunity to develop along their own lines, and remind their own people that the decay of family religion, where the servants took part in family devotions, has contributed in part to the moral decay of the native people. But there is to be no equality in church or state.

* * * * *

Yes, there are a hundred, and a thousand voices crying. But what does one do, when one cries this thing, and one cries another? Who knows how we shall fashion a land of peace where black outnumbers white so greatly? Some say that the earth has bounty enough for all, and that more for one does not mean less for another, that the advance of one does not mean the decline of another. They say that poor-paid labour means a poor nation, and that better-paid labour means greater markets and greater scope for industry and manufacture. And others say that this is a danger, for better-paid labour will not only buy [77/78] more but will also read more, think more, ask more, and will not be content to be forever voiceless and inferior.

Who knows how we shall fashion such a land? For we fear not only the loss of our possessions, but the loss of our superiority and the loss of our whiteness. Some say it is true that crime is bad, but would this not be worse? Is it not better to hold what we have, and to pay the price of it with fear? And others say, can such fear be endured? For is it not this fear that drives men to ponder these things at all?

* * * * *

We do not know, we do not know. We shall live from day to day, and put more locks on the doors, and get a fine fierce dog when the fine fierce bitch next door has pups, and hold on to our handbags more tenaciously; and the beauty of the trees by night, and the raptures of lovers under the stars, these things we shall forego. We shall forego the coming home drunken through the midnight streets, and the evening walk over the star-lit veld. We shall be careful, and knock this off our lives, and knock that off our lives, and hedge ourselves about with safety and precaution. And our lives will shrink, but they shall be the lives of superior beings; and we shall live with fear, but at least it

will not be a fear of the unknown. And the conscience shall be thrust down; the light of life shall not be extinguished, but be put under a bushel, to be preserved for a generation that will live by it again, in some day not yet come; and how it will come, and when it will come, we shall not think about at all.

* * * * *

They are holding a meeting in Parkwold tonight, as they held one last night in Turffontein, and will hold one tomorrow night in Mayfair. And the people will ask for more police, and for heavier sentences for native housebreakers, and for the death penalty for all who carry weapons when they break in. And some will ask for a new native policy, that will show the natives who is the master, and for a curb on the activities of Kafferboeties and Communists. [78/79]

And the Left Club is holding a meeting too, on "A Long-term Policy for Native Crime," and has invited both European and non-European speakers to present a symposium. And the Cathedral Guild is holding a meeting too, and the subject is "The Real Causes of Native Crime." But there will be a gloom over it, for the speaker of the evening, Mr. Arthur Jarvis, has just been shot dead in his house at Parkwold.

* * * * *

Cry the beloved country, for the unborn child that is the inheritor of our fear. Let him not love the earth too deeply. Let him not laugh too gladly when the water runs through his fingers, nor stand too silent when the setting sun makes red the veld with fire. Let him not be too moved when the birds of his land are singing, nor give too much of his heart to a mountain or a valley. For fear will rob him of all if he gives too much.

* * * * *

— Mr. Msimangu?
— Ah, it is Mrs. Ndlela, of End St.
— Mr. Msimangu, the police have been to me.

— The police?

— Yes, they want to know about the son of the old umfundisi. They are looking for him.

— For what, mother?

— They did not say, Mr. Msimangu.

— Is it bad, mother?

— It looks as if it were bad.

— And then, mother?

— I was frightened, umfundisi. So I gave them the address. Mrs. Mkize, 79 Twenty-third Avenue, Alexandra. And one said yes, this woman was known to deal in heavy matters.

— You gave them the address?

He stood silent in the door.

— Did I do wrong, umfundisi?

— You did no wrong, mother.

— I was afraid. [**79/80**]

— It is the law, mother. We must uphold the law.

— I am glad, umfundisi.

He thanks the simple woman, and tells her to go well. He stands for a moment, then turns swiftly and goes to his room. He takes out an envelope from a drawer, and takes paper money from it. He looks at it ruefully, and then with decision puts it into his pocket, with decision takes down his hat. Then dressed, with indecision looks out of the window to the house of Mrs. Lithebe, and shakes his head. But he is too late, for as he opens his door, Kumalo stands before him.

— You are going out, my friend?

Msimangu is silent. I was going out, he says at last.

— But you said you would work in your room today.

And Msimangu would have said, can I not do as I wish, but something prevented him. Come in, he said.

— I would not disturb you, my friend.

— Come in, said Msimangu, and he shut the door. My friend, I have just had a visit from Mrs. Ndlela, at the house we visited in End Street, here in Sophiatown.

Kumalo hears the earnest tones. There is news, he asks, but there is fear, not eagerness, in his voice.

— Only this, said Msimangu, that the police came to her house, looking for the boy. She gave them the address, Mrs. Mkize, at 79 Twenty-third Avenue in Alexandra.

— Why do they want the boy, asked Kumalo in a low and trembling voice.

— That we do not know. I was ready to go there when you came.

Kumalo looked at him out of sad and grateful eyes, so that the resentment of the other died out of him. You were going alone, the old man asked.

— I was going alone, yes. But now that I have told you, you may come also.

— How were you going, my friend? There are no buses.

— I was going by taxi. I have money.

— I too have money. No one must pay but me.

— It will take a great deal of money. [**80/81**]

Kumalo opened his coat, and took out his purse eagerly. Here is my money, he said.

— We shall use it then. Come, let us look for a taxi.

*   *   *   *   *

— Mrs. Mkize!

She drew back, hostile.

— Have the police been here?

— They have been, not long since.

— And what did they want?

— They wanted the boy.

— And what did you say?

— I said it was a year since he left here.

— And where have they gone?

— To Shanty Town. She draws back again, remembering.

— To the address you did not know, he said coldly.

She looks at him sullenly. What could I do, she said. It was the police.

— No matter. What was the address?

— I did not know the address. Shanty Town, I told them.

Some fire came into her. I told you I did not know the address, she said.

*   *   *   *   *

— Mrs. Hlatswayo!

The pleasant-faced woman smiled at

them, and drew aside for them to enter the hessian house.

— We shall not come in. Have the police been here?

— They were here, umfundisi.

— And what did they want?

— They wanted the boy, umfundisi.

— For what, mother?

— I do not know, umfundisi.

— And where have they gone?

— To the school, umfundisi.

— Tell me, he said privately, did it seem heavy?

— I could not say, umfundisi. [81/82]

— Stay well, Mrs. Hlatswayo.

— Go well, umfundisi.

*   *   *   *   *

— Good morning, my friend.

— Good morning, umfundisi, said the native assistant.

— Where is the young white man?

— He is in the town. It was now, now, that he went.

— Have the police been here?

— They have been here. It was now, now, that they left.

— What did they want?

— They wanted the boy, Absalom Kumalo, the son of the old man there in the taxi.

— Why did they want him?

— I do not know. I had other work, and went out while they came in with the white man.

— And you do not know what they wanted?

— I truly do not know, umfundisi.

Msimangu was silent. Did it seem heavy, he asked at last.

— I do not know. I really could not say.

— Was the young white man—well, disturbed?

— He was disturbed.

— How did you know?

The assistant laughed. I know him, he said.

— And where did they go?

— To Pimville, umfundisi. To the home of the girl.

— Now, now, you said.

— Now, now, indeed.

— We shall go then. Stay well. And tell the white man we came.

— Go well, umfundisi. I shall tell him.

*   *   *   *   *

— My child!

— Umfundisi.

— Have the police been here?

— They have been here, now, now, they were here. [82/83]

— And what did they want?

— They wanted Absalom, umfundisi.

— And what did you tell them?

— I told them I had not seen him since Saturday, umfundisi.

— And why did they want him, cried Kumalo in torment.

She drew back frightened. I do not know, she said.

— And why did you not ask, he cried.

The tears filled her eyes. I was afraid, she said.

— Did no one ask?

— The women were about. Maybe one of them asked.

— What women, said Msimangu. Show us the women.

So she showed them the women, but they too did not know.

— They would not tell me, said a woman.

Msimangu turned privately to her. Did it seem heavy, he asked.

— It seemed heavy, umfundisi. What is the trouble, she asked.

— We do not know.

— The world is full of trouble, she said.

He went to the taxi, and Kumalo followed him. And the girl ran after them, as one runs who is with child.

— They told me I must let them know if he comes.

Her eyes were full of trouble. What shall I do, she said.

— That is what you ought to do, said Msimangu. And you will let us know also. Wait, you must go to the Superintendent's office and ask him to telephone to the Mission House in Sophiatown. I shall write the number here for you. 49-3041.

— I shall do it, umfundisi.

— Tell me, did the police say where they would go?

— They did not say, umfundisi. But I heard them say, *die spoor loop dood,* the trail runs dead.

— Stay well, my child.

— Go well, umfundisi. She turned to say go well to the other, but he was already in the taxi, bowed over his stick. [83/84]

* * * * *

— How much is your charge, my friend? asks Msimangu.

— Two pounds and ten shillings, umfundisi.

Kumalo feels with shaking hands for his purse.

— I should like to help you in this, says Msimangu. It would be my joy to help you. You are kind, says Kumalo trembling, but no one must pay but me. And he draws the notes from the dwindling store.

— You are trembling, my friend.

— I am cold, very cold.

Msimangu looks up at the cloudless sky, from which the sun of Africa is pouring down upon the earth. Come to my room, he says. We shall have a fire and make you warm again. [84/85]

XIII

It was a silent journey to Ezenzeleni, and though Msimangu tried to converse with his friend during the walk from the station to the place of the blind, the older man was little inclined for speech, and showed little interest in anything about him.

— What will you do while I am here, asked Msimangu.

— I should like to sit in one of these places that you told me of, and perhaps when you are finished you will show me round this Ezenzeleni.

— You shall do what you will.

— You must not be disappointed in me.

— I understand everything. There is no need to talk of it again.

So he introduced Kumalo to the European Superintendent, who called him Mr. Kumalo, which is not the custom. And Msimangu must have spoken privately to the Superintendent, for they did not worry him to come with them; instead the Superintendent led him to the place where the ground fell away, and told him they would call him when it was time for food.

For some hours he sat there in the sun, and whether it was the warmth of it, or the sight of the wide plain beneath stretching away to blue and distant mountains, or the mere passage of time, or the divine providence for the soul that is distressed, he could not say; but there was some rising of the spirit, some lifting of the fear.

Yes, it was true what Msimangu had said. Why fear the one thing in a great city where there were thousands upon thousands of people? His son had gone astray in the great city, where so [85/86] many others had gone astray before him, and where many others would go astray after him, until there was found some great secret that as yet no man had discovered. But that he should kill a man, a white man! There was nothing that he could remember, nothing, nothing at all, that could make it probable.

His thoughts turned to the girl, and to the unborn babe that would be his grandchild. Pity that he a priest should have a grandchild born in such a fashion. Yet that could be repaired. If they were married, then he could try to rebuild what had been broken. Perhaps his son and the girl would go back with him to Ndotsheni, perhaps he and his wife could give to the child what they had failed to give to their own. Yet where had they failed? What had they done, or left undone, that their son had become a thief, moving like a vagabond from place to place, living with a girl who was herself no more than a child, father of a child who would have had no name? Yet, he comforted himself, that was Johannesburg. And yet again, and the fear smote him as grievously as ever, his son had left the girl and the unborn child, left the work that the young white man had got for him, and was vagabond again. And what did vagabonds do? Did they not live without law or custom, without faith or purpose, might they not then lift their hand against any other, any man who stood between them and the pitiful gain that they were seeking?

What broke in a man when he could bring himself to kill another? What broke when he could bring himself to thrust down the knife into the warm flesh, to bring down the axe on the living head, to cleave down between the seeing eyes, to shoot the gun that would drive death into the beating heart?

With a shudder he turned from contemplation of so terrible a thing. Yet the contemplation of it reassured him. For there was nothing, nothing in all the years at Ndotsheni, nothing in all the years of the boyhood of his son, that could make it possible for him to do so terrible a deed. Yes, Msimangu was right. It was the suspense, the not-knowing, that made him fear this one thing, in a great city where there were thousands upon thousands of people. [86/87]

He turned with relief to the thought of rebuilding, to the home that they would fashion, he and his wife, in the evening of their lives, for Gertrude and her son, and for his son and the girl and the child. After seeing Johannesburg he would return with a deeper understanding to Ndotsheni. Yes, and with a greater humility, for had his own sister not been a prostitute? And his son a thief? And might not he himself be grandfather to a child that would have no name? This he thought without bitterness, though with pain. One could go back knowing better the things that one fought against, knowing better the kind of thing that one must build. He would go back with a new and quickened interest in the school, not as a place where children learned to read and write and count only, but as a place where they must be prepared for life in any place to which they might go. Oh for education for his people, for schools up and down

the land, where something might be built that would serve them when they went away to the towns, something that would take the place of the tribal law and custom. For a moment he was caught up in a vision, as man so often is when he sits in a place of ashes and destruction.

Yes—it was true, then. He had admitted it to himself. The tribe was broken, and would be mended no more. He bowed his head. It was as though a man borne upward into the air felt suddenly that the wings of miracle dropped away from him, so that he looked down upon the earth, sick with fear and apprehension. The tribe was broken, and would be mended no more. The tribe that had nurtured him, and his father and his father's father, was broken. For the men were away, and the young men and the girls were away, and the maize hardly reached to the height of a man.

— There is food for us, my brother.

— Already?

— You have been here a long time.

— I did not know it.

— And what have you found?

— Nothing.

— Nothing? [87/88]

— No, nothing. Only more fear and more pain. There is nothing in the world but fear and pain.

— My brother . . . . .

— What is it?

— I hesitate to speak to you.

— You have a right to speak. More right than any.

— Then I say that it is time to turn. This is madness, that is bad enough. But it is also sin, which is worse. I speak to you as a priest.

Kumalo bowed his head. You are right, father, he said. I must sit here no longer.

*   *   *   *   *

It was a wonderful place, this Ezenzeleni. For here the blind, that dragged out their days in a world they could not see, here they had eyes given to them. Here they made things that he for all his sight could never make. Baskets stout and strong, in osiers of different colours, and these osiers ran through one another by some magic that he did not understand, coming together in patterns, the red with the red, the blue with the blue, under the seeing and sightless hands. He talked with the people, and the blind eyes glowed with something that could only have been fire in the soul. It was white men who did this work of mercy, and some of them spoke English and some spoke Afrikaans. Yes, those who spoke English and those who spoke Afrikaans came together to open the eyes of black men that were blind.

His friend Msimangu would preach this afternoon, in the chapel that he had seen. But because they were not all of one church here, there was no altar with a cross upon it, but the cross was in the wall itself, two open clefts that had been left open and not filled in by the bricks. And Msimangu would not wear the vestments that he would wear at Sophiatown; those he would wear early the next morning, when he ministered to his own people. [88/89]

* * * * *

Msimangu opened the book, and read to them first from the book. And Kumalo had not known that his friend had such a voice. For the voice was of gold, and the voice had love for the words it was reading. The voice shook and beat and trembled, not as the voice of an old man shakes and beats and trembles, nor as a leaf shakes and beats and trembles, but as a deep bell when it is struck. For it was not only a voice of gold, but it was the voice of a man whose heart was golden, reading from a book of golden words. And the people were silent, and Kumalo was silent, for when are three such things found in one place together?

I the Lord have called thee in right-
　eousness
and will hold thine hand and keep
　thee
and give thee for a covenant of the
　people
for a light of the Gentiles
To open the blind eyes

to bring the prisoners from the prison
And them that sit in darkness
out of the prison house.

And the voice rose, and the Zulu tongue was lifted and transfigured, and the man too was lifted, as is one who comes to something that is greater than any of us. And the people were silent, for were they not the people of the blind eyes? And Kumalo was silent, knowing the blind man for whom Msimangu was reading these words.

And I will bring the blind by a way
　they knew not
I will lead them in paths that they
　have not known.
I will make darkness light before
　them
and crooked things straight,
these things I will do unto them
and not forsake them.

* * * * *

Yes, he speaks to me, there is no doubt of it. He says we are not forsaken. For while I wonder for what we live and struggle [89/90] and die, for while I wonder what keeps us living and struggling, men are sent to minister to the blind, white men are sent to minister to the black blind. Who gives, at this one hour, a friend to make darkness light before me? Who gives, at this one hour, wisdom to one so young, for the comfort of one so old? Who gives to me compassion for a girl my son has left?

Yes, he speaks to me, in such quiet and such simple words. We are grateful for the saints, he says, who lift up the heart in the days of our distress. Would we do less? For do we less, there are no saints to lift up any heart. If Christ be Christ he says, true Lord of Heaven, true Lord of Men, what is there that we would not do no matter what our suffering may be?

I hear you, my brother. There is no word I do not hear.

He is finishing. I can hear it in his voice. One can know that what is said, is said, is rounded, finished, it is perfection.

He opens the book and reads again. He reads to me:

Hast thou not known, hast thou not
heard
that the everlasting God, the Lord,
the Creator of the ends of the earth
fainteth not, neither is weary?

And the voice rises again, and the Zulu tongue is lifted and transfigured, and the man too is lifted . . . . .

Even the youths shall faint and be
weary
and the young men shall utterly fall
but they that wait upon the Lord
shall renew their strength
They shall mount up with wings as
eagles
they shall run and not be weary
and they shall walk and not faint.

*   *   *   *   *

The people sigh, and Kumalo sighs, as though this is a great word that has been spoken. And indeed this Msimangu is known as a preacher. It is good for the Government, they say in Johannesburg, that Msimangu preaches of a world not made by hands, [90/91] for he touches people at the hearts, and sends them marching to heaven instead of to Pretoria. And there are white people who marvel and say, what words to come from the son of a barbarian people, who not long since plundered and slaughtered, in thousands and tens of thousands, under the most terrible chief of all.

Yet he is despised by some, for this golden voice that could raise a nation, speaks always thus. For this place of suffering, from which men might escape if some such voice could bind them all together, is for him no continuing city. They say he preaches of a world not made by hands, while in the streets about him men suffer and struggle and die. They ask what folly it is that can so seize upon a man, what folly is it that seizes upon so many of their people, making the hungry patient, the suffering content, the dying at peace? And how fools listen to him, silent, enrapt, sighing when he is done, feeding their empty bellies on his empty words.

Kumalo goes to him.

— Brother, I am recovered.

Msimangu's face lights up, but he talks humbly, there is no pride or false constraint.

— I have tried every way to touch you, he says, but I could not come near. So give thanks and be satisfied. [91/92]

XIV

On the day of their return from Ezenzeleni, Kumalo ate his midday meal at the Mission, and returned to Mrs. Lithebe's to play with Gertrude's son. There was great bargaining going on, for Mrs. Lithebe had found a buyer for Gertrude's table and chairs, and for the pots and pans. Everything was sold for three pounds, which was not a bad sum for a table that was badly marked and discoloured, with what he did not ask. And the chairs too were weak, so that one had to sit carefully upon them. Indeed the price was paid for the pots and pans, which were of the stuff called aluminum. Now the black people do not buy such pots and pans, but his sister said that they were the gift of a friend, and into that too he did not enquire.

With the money she intended to buy some shoes, and a coat against the rain that was now beginning to fall; and this he approved, for her old coat and shoes went ill with the red dress and the white turban that he had bought for her.

When the last thing had been loaded, and the money paid, and the lorry had gone, he would have played with the small boy, but he saw, with the fear catching at him suddenly with a physical pain, Msimangu and the young white man walking up the street towards the house. With the habit born of experience, he forced himself to go to the gate, and noted with dread their set faces and the low tones in which they spoke.

— Good afternoon, umfundisi. Is there a place where we can talk, asked the young man.

— Come to my room, he said, hardly trusting to his voice.

In the room he shut the door, and stood not looking at them.

— I have heard what you fear, said the young man. It is true. **[92/93]**

And Kumalo stood bowed, and could not look at them. He sat down in his chair and fixed his eyes upon the floor.

Well, what does one say now? Does one put an arm about the shoulders, touch a hand maybe? As though they did not know, Msimangu and the young man talked in low voices, as one talks in a room where someone is dead.

The young man shrugged his shoulders. This will be bad for the reformatory, he said more loudly, even indifferently.

And Kumalo nodded his head, not once, nor twice, but three or four times, as though he too would say, Yes, it will be bad for the reformatory.

— Yes, said the young man, it will be bad for us. They will say we let him out too soon. Of course, he said, there is one thing. The other two were not reformatory boys. But it was he who fired the shot.

— My friend, said Msimangu, in as ordinary a voice as he could find, one of the two others is the son of your brother.

And so Kumalo nodded his head again, one, two, three, four times. And when that was finished, he began, as though he too was saying, one of the two others is the son of my brother.

Then he stood up, and looked round the room, and they watched him. He took his coat from a nail, and put it on, and he put his hat on his head, and took his stick in his hand. And so dressed he turned to them, and nodded to them again. But this time they did not know what he said.

— You are going out, my friend.

— Do you wish to come to the prison, umfundisi? I have arranged it for you.

And Kumalo nodded. He turned and looked round the room again, and found that his coat was already on him, and his

hat; he touched both coat and hat, and looked down at the stick that was in his hand.

— My brother first, he said, if you will show me the way only.

— I shall show you the way, my friend.

— And I shall wait at the Mission, said the young man.

As Msimangu put his hand to the door, Kumalo halted him. **[93/94]** I shall walk slowly up the street, he said. You must tell them—he pointed with his hand.

— I shall tell them, my friend.

So he told them, and having told them, closed the front door on the wailing of the women, for such is their custom. Slowly he followed the bent figure up the street, saw him nodding as he walked, saw the people turning. Would age now swiftly overtake him? Would this terrible nodding last now for all his days, so that men said aloud in his presence, it is nothing, he is old and does nothing but forget? And would he nod as though he too were saying, Yes, it is nothing, I am old and do nothing but forget? But who would know that he said, I do nothing but remember?

Msimangu caught him up at the top of the hill, and took his arm, and it was like walking with a child or with one that was sick. So they came to the shop. And at the shop Kumalo turned, and closed his eyes, and his lips were moving. Then he opened his eyes and turned to Msimangu.

— Do not come further, he said. It is I who must do this.

And then he went into the shop.

Yes, the bull voice was there, loud and confident. His brother John was sitting there on a chair, talking to two other men, sitting there like a chief. His brother he did not recognize, for the light from the street was on the back of the visitor.

— Good afternoon, my brother.

— Good afternoon, sir.

— Good afternoon, my own brother, son of our mother.

— Ah my brother, it is you. Well, well, I am glad to see you. Will you not come and join us?

Kumalo looked at the visitors. I am

sorry, he said, but I come again on business, urgent business.

— I am sure my friends will excuse us. Excuse us, my friends.

So they all said stay well, and go well, and the two men left them.

— Well, well, I am glad to see you, my brother. And your business, how does it progress? Have you found the prodigal? You will see I have not forgotten my early teaching altogether. [94/95]

And he laughed at that, a great bull laugh. But we must have tea, he said, and he went to the door and called into the place behind.

— It is still the same woman, he said. You see, I also have my ideas of—how do you say it in English? And he laughed his great laugh again, for he was only playing with his brother. Fidelity, that was the word. A good word, I shall not easily forget it. He is a clever man, our Mr. Msimangu. And now the prodigal, have you found him?

— He is found, my brother. But not as he was found in the early teaching. He is in prison, arrested for the murder of a white man.

— Murder? The man does not jest now. One does not jest about murder. Still less about the murder of a white man.

— Yes, murder. He broke into a house in a place that they call Parkwold, and killed the white man who would have prevented him.

— What? I remember! Only a day or two since? On Tuesday?

— Yes.

— Yes, I remember.

Yes, he remembers. He remembers too that his own son and his brother's son are companions. The veins stand out on the bull neck, and the sweat forms on the brow. Have no doubt it is fear in the eyes. He wipes his brow with a cloth. There are many questions he could ask before he need come at it. All he says is, yes, indeed, I do remember. His brother is filled with compassion for him. He will try gently to bring it to him.

— I am sorry, my brother.

What does one say? Does one say, of course you are sorry? Does one say, of course, it is your son? How can one say it, when one knows what it means? Keep silent then, but the eyes are upon one. One knows what they mean.

— You mean . . . . . he said, he asked.

— Yes. He was there also.

John Kumalo whispers *Tixo, Tixo.* And again, *Tixo, Tixo.* Kumalo comes to him and puts his hand on his shoulders.

— There are many things I could say, he said. [95/96]

— There are many things you could say.

— But I do not say them. I say only that I know what you suffer.

— Indeed, who could know better?

— Yes, that is one of the things I could say. There is a young white man at the Mission House, and he is waiting to take me now to the prison. Perhaps he would take you also.

— Let me get my coat and hat, my brother.

They do not wait for the tea, but set out along the street to the Mission House. Msimangu, watching anxiously for their return, sees them coming. The old man walks now more firmly, it is the other who seems bowed and broken.

Father Vincent, the rosy-cheeked priest from England, takes Kumalo's hand in both his own. Anything, he says, anything. You have only to ask. I shall do anything.

*   *   *   *   *

They pass through the great gate in the grim high wall. The young man talks for them, and it is arranged. John Kumalo is taken to one room, and the young man goes with Stephen Kumalo to another. There the son is brought to them.

They shake hands, indeed the old man takes his son's hand in both his own, and the hot tears fall fast upon them. The boy stands unhappy, there is no gladness in his eyes. He twists his head from side to side, as though the loose clothing is too tight for him.

— My child, my child.

— Yes, my father.

— At last I have found you.

— Yes, my father.

— And it is too late.

To this the boy makes no answer. As though he may find some hope in this silence, the father presses him. Is it not too late, he asks. But there is no answer. Persistently, almost eagerly, is it not too late, he asks. The boy turns his head from side to side, he meets the eyes of the young white man, and his own retreat swiftly. My father, it is what my father says, he answers. **[96/97]**

— I have searched in every place for you.

To that also no answer. The old man loosens his hands, and his son's hand slips from them lifelessly. There is a barrier here, a wall, something that cuts off one from the other.

— Why did you do this terrible thing, my child?

The young white man stirs watchfully, the white warder makes no sign, perhaps he does not know this tongue. There is a moisture in the boy's eyes, he turns his head from side to side, and makes no answer.

— Answer me, my child.

— I do not know, he says.

— Why did you carry a revolver?

The white warder stirs too, for the word in Zulu is like the word in English and in Afrikaans. The boy too shows a sign of life.

— For safety, he says. This Johannesburg is a dangerous place. A man never knows when he will be attacked.

— But why take it to this house?

And this again cannot be answered.

— Have they got it, my child?

— Yes, my father.

— They have no doubt it was you?

— I told them, my father.

— What did you tell them?

— I told them I was frightened when the white man came. So I shot him. I did not mean to kill him.

— And your cousin. And the other?

— Yes, I told them. They came with me, but it was I who shot the white man.

— Did you go there to steal?

And this again cannot be answered.

— You were at the reformatory, my child?

The boy looked at his boot, and pushed it forward along the ground. I was there, he said.

— Did they treat you well?

Again there is a moisture in the eyes, again he turns his head from side to side, drops his eyes again to the boot pushing for- **[97/98]** ward and backward on the ground. They treated me well, he said.

— And this is your repayment, my child?

And this again cannot be answered. The young white man comes over, for he knows that this does nothing, goes nowhere. Perhaps he does not like to see these two torturing each other.

— Well, Absalom?

— Sir?

— Why did you leave the work that I got for you?

And you too young man, can get no answer. There are no answers to these things.

— Why did you leave it, Absalom?

There are no answers to these things.

— And your girl. The one we let you go to, the girl you worried over, so that we took pity on you.

And again the tears in the eyes. Who knows if he weeps for the girl he has deserted? Who knows if he weeps for a promise broken? Who knows if he weeps for another self, that would work for a woman, pay his taxes, save his money, keep the laws, love his children, another self that has always been defeated? Or does he weep for himself alone, to be let be, to be let alone, to be free of the merciless rain of questions, why, why, why, when he knows not why. They do not speak with him, they do not jest with him, they do not sit and let him be, but they ask, ask, ask, why, why, why—his father, the white man, the prison officers, the police, the magistrates,—why, why, why.

The young white man shrugs his shoulders, smiles indifferently. But he is not indifferent, there is a mark of pain between his eyes.

— So the world goes, he says.

— Answer me one thing, my child. Will you answer me?

— I can answer, father.

— You wrote nothing, sent no message. You went with bad companions. You stole and broke in and—yes, you did these things. But why?

The boy seizes upon the word that is given him. It was bad companions, he said. [98/99]

— I need not tell you that is no answer, said Kumalo. But he knows he will get no other this way. Yes, I see, he said, bad companions. Yes, I understand. But for you, yourself, what made you yourself do it?

How they torture one another. And the boy, tortured, shows again a sign of life.

— It was the devil, he said.

Oh boy, can you not say you fought the devil, wrestled with the devil, struggled with him night and day, till the sweat poured from you and no strength was left? Can you not say that you wept for your sins, and vowed to make amends, and stood upright, and stumbled, and fell again? It would be some comfort for this tortured man, who asks you, desperately, why did you not struggle against him?

And the boy looks down at his feet again, and says, I do not know.

The old man is exhausted, the boy is exhausted, and the time is nearly over. The young white man comes to them again. Does he still wish to marry the girl, he asks Kumalo.

— Do you wish to marry this girl, my son?

— Yes, my father.

— I shall see what I can do, says the young man. I think it is time for us to go.

— May we come again?

— Yes, you may come again. We shall ask the hours at the gate.

— Stay well, my child.

— Go well, my father.

— My child, I think you may write letters here. But do not write to your mother till I see you again. I must first write to her.

— It is good, my father.

They go, and outside the gate they meet John Kumalo. He is feeling better, the big bull man. Well, well, he says, we must go at once and see a lawyer.

— A lawyer, my brother. For what should we spend such money? The story is plain, there cannot be doubt about it.

— What is the story, asks John Kumalo. [99/100]

— The story? These three lads went to a house that they thought was empty. They struck down the servant. The white man heard a noise and he came to see. And then . . . and then . . . my son . . . mine, not yours . . . shot at him. He was afraid, he says.

— Well, well, says John Kumalo, that is a story. He seems reassured. Well, well, he says, that is a story. And he told you this in front of the others?

— Why not, if it is the truth?

John Kumalo seems reassured. Perhaps you do not need a lawyer, he said. If he shot the white man, there is perhaps nothing more to be said.

— Will you have a lawyer then?

John Kumalo smiles at his brother. Perhaps I shall need a lawyer, he says. For one thing, a lawyer can talk to my son in private.

He seems to think, then he says to his brother, You see, my brother, there is no proof that my son or this other young man was there at all.

Yes, John Kumalo smiles at that, he seems quite recovered.

— Not there at all? But my son—

— Yes, yes, John Kumalo interrupts him, and smiles at him. Who will believe your son, he asks.

He says it with meaning, with cruel and pitiless meaning. Kumalo stands bereft, and the young white man climbs into the car. Kumalo looks to him for guidance, but the young man shrugs his shoulders. Do what you will, he says indifferently. It is not my work to get lawyers. But if you wish to go back to Sophiatown, I shall take you.

Kumalo, made still more nervous by this indifference, stands outside irresolute.

His irresolution seems to anger the young white man, who leans out of the window and speaks loudly.

— It is not my work to get lawyers, he says. It is my work to reform, to help, to uplift.

With his hand he makes an angry gesture of uplifting, and then draws back his head into the car and makes as if to start. But he changes his plan and leans out again. [100/101]

— It is a wonderful work, he says, a wonderful work, a noble work.

He withdraws again, then leans out again and talks to Kumalo.

— You must not think a parson's work is nobler, he says.

Perhaps he is speaking too loudly, for he lowers his voice and speaks through tight and angry lips.

— You save souls, he says, as though it is a grim jest to save souls. But I save souls also. You see people come into the world and you see them go out. And so do I. I saw this Absalom born into a new world and now I shall see him go out.

He looks at Kumalo fiercely. We shall see him go out, he says. He draws back again, and grips the wheel as though he would break it. Are you coming to Sophiatown, he asks.

But Kumalo shakes his head, for how shall he climb into the car with this stranger? The young man looks at John Kumalo and he puts out his head again and says to him, you are a clever man, he says, but thank God you are not my brother. He starts the car with a great noise, and goes off with a great sound of sliding wheels, still speaking angrily to himself.

Kumalo looks at his brother, but his brother does not look at him. Indeed he walks away. Wearily, wearily, he goes from the great gate in the wall to the street. *Tixo,* he says, *Tixo,* forsake me not. Father Vincent's words come back to him, anything, anything, he said, you have only to ask. Then to Father Vincent he will go. [101/102]

XV

Kumalo returned to Mrs. Lithebe's tired and dispirited. The two women were silent, and he had no desire to speak to them, and none to play with his small nephew. He withdrew into his room, and sat silent there, waiting till he could summon strength enough to go to the Mission House. But while he sat, there was a knock at his door, and Mrs. Lithebe stood there with the young white man. Fresh from the pain of their encounter, Kumalo shrank from him; and at that sign, the young man frowned, and spoke to Mrs. Lithebe in Sesuto, so that she withdrew.

Kumalo stood up, an old bowed man. He sought for humble and pleading words, but none came to him. And because he could not look at the young man, he fixed his eyes on the floor.

— Umfundisi.

— Sir?

The young man looked angrier than ever. I am sorry, umfundisi, that I spoke such angry words, he said. I have come to speak to you about this matter of a lawyer.

— Sir?

Indeed it was hard to speak to a man who stood thus before one. Umfundisi, do you wish me to speak to you?

Kumalo struggled within himself. For it is thus with a black man, who has learned to be humble and who yet desires to be something that is himself.

— Sir, he said again.

— Umfundisi, said the young man patiently, I know how it is. Will you not sit down?

So Kumalo sat down, and the young man, still frowning angrily, stood and talked to him. [102/103]

— I spoke like that because I was grieved and because I try to give myself to my work. And when my work goes wrong, I hurt myself and I hurt others also. But then I grow ashamed, and that is why I am here.

And then because Kumalo was still silent, he said, do you understand?

And Kumalo said, yes, I understand. He turned his face so that the young man could see that the hurt was gone out of it. I understand completely, he said.

The young man stopped frowning. About this lawyer, he said. I think you must have a lawyer. Not because the truth must not be told, but because I do not trust your brother. You can see what is in his mind. His plan is to deny that his son and the third man were with your son. Now you and I do not know whether that will make matters worse or not, but a lawyer would know. And another thing also, Absalom says that he fired the revolver because he was afraid, with no intention of killing the white man. It needs a lawyer to make the court believe that that is true.

— Yes, I see that.

— Do you know of any lawyer, of your Church maybe?

— No, sir, I do not. But it was my plan to go to see Father Vincent at the Mission House, when I had rested for a while.

— Are you rested now?

— Your visit has put a fresh heart into me, sir. I felt. . . .

— Yes, I know.

The young man frowned and said, as if to himself, it is my great fault. Shall we go then?

So they walked to the Mission House, and were shown into Father Vincent's room, and there they talked for a long time with the rosy-cheeked priest from England.

— I think I could get a good man to take the case, said Father Vincent. I think we are all agreed that it is to be the truth and nothing but the truth, and that the defense will be that the shot was fired in fear and not to kill. Our lawyer will tell us what to do about this other matter, the possibility, my friend, that your nephew and the other young man will deny [**103/104**] that they were there. For it appears that it is only your son who states that they were there. For us it is to be the truth, and nothing but the truth, and indeed, the man I am thinking of

would not otherwise take the case. I shall see him as soon as possible.

— And what about the marriage, asked the young man.

— I shall ask him about that also. I do not know if it can be arranged, but I should gladly marry them if it can be.

So they rose to separate, and Father Vincent put his hand on the old man's arm. Be of good courage, he said. Whatever happens, your son will be severely punished, but if his defense is accepted, it will not be the extreme punishment. And while there is life, there is hope for amendment of life.

— That is now always in my mind, said Kumalo. But my hope is little.

— Stay here and speak with me, said Father Vincent.

— And I must go, said the young white man. But umfundisi, I am ready to help if my help is needed.

When the young man had gone, Kumalo and the English priest sat down, and Kumalo said to the other, you can understand that this has been a sorrowful journey.

— I understand that, my friend.

— At first it was a search. I was anxious at first, but as the search went on, step by step, so did the anxiety turn to fear, and this fear grew deeper step by step. It was at Alexandra that I first grew afraid, but it was here in your House, when we heard of the murder, that my fear grew into something too great to be borne.

The old man paused and stared at the floor, remembering, indeed quite lost in remembering. He stared at it a long time and then he said, Msimangu said to me, why fear this one thing in a city where there are thousands upon thousands of people.

— That comforted me, he said.

And the way in which he said, that comforted me, was to Father Vincent so unendurable, that he sat there rigid, almost without breathing, hoping that this would soon be finished.

— That comforted me, said Kumalo, yet it did not comfort [**104/105**] me. And even now I can hardly believe that this thing, which happens one time in a thousand, has happened to me. Why, sometimes, for a moment or two, I can even believe that it has not happened, that I shall wake and find it has not happened. But it is only for a moment or two.

— To think, said Kumalo, that my wife and I lived out our lives in innocence, there in Ndotsheni, not knowing that this thing was coming, step by step.

— Why, he said, if one could only have been told, this step is taken, and this step is about to be taken. If only one could have been told that.

— But we were not told, continued Kumalo. Now we can see, but we could not see then. And yet others saw it. It was revealed to others to whom it did not matter. They saw it, step by step. They said, this is Johannesburg, this is a boy going wrong, as other boys have gone wrong in Johannesburg. But to us, for whom it was life and death, it was not revealed.

Father Vincent put his hand over his eyes, to hide them from the light, to hide them from the sight of the man who was speaking. He would himself have spoken, to break the painful spell that was being woven about him, but something told him to leave it. What was more, he had no words to say.

— There is a man sleeping in the grass, said Kumalo. And over him is gathering the greatest storm of all his days. Such lightning and thunder will come there as have never been seen before, bringing death and destruction. People hurry home past him, to places safe from danger. And whether they do not see him there in the grass, or whether they fear to halt even a moment, but they do not wake him, they let him be.

After that Kumalo seemed to have done with speaking, and they were silent a long time. Father Vincent tried a dozen sentences, but none seemed fitting. But he did say, my friend, and although he said nothing more, he hoped that Kumalo would take it as a signal that other words would follow, and himself say nothing more.

So he said again, my friend.

— Father? [**105/106**]

— My friend, your anxiety turned to fear, and your fear turned to sorrow. But sorrow is better than fear. For fear impoverishes always, while sorrow may enrich.

Kumalo looked at him, with an intensity of gaze that was strange in so humble a man, and hard to encounter.

— I do not know that I am enriched, he said.

— Sorrow is better than fear, said Father Vincent doggedly. Fear is a journey, a terrible journey, but sorrow is at least an arriving.

— And where have I arrived, asked Kumalo.

— When the storm threatens, a man is afraid for his house, said Father Vincent in that symbolic language that is like the Zulu tongue. But when the house is destroyed, there is something to do. About a storm he can do nothing, but he can rebuild a house.

— At my age? asked Kumalo. Look what has happened to the house that I built when I was young and strong. What kind of house shall I build now?

— No one can comprehend the ways of God, said Father Vincent desperately.

Kumalo looked at him, not bitterly or accusingly or reproachfully.

— It seems that God has turned from me, he said.

— That may seem to happen, said Father Vincent. But it does not happen, never, never, does it happen.

— I am glad to hear you, said Kumalo humbly.

— We spoke of amendment of life, said the white priest. Of the amendment of your son's life. And because you are a priest, this must matter to you more than all else, more even than your suffering and your wife's suffering.

— That is true. Yet I cannot see how such a life can be amended.

— You cannot doubt that. You are a

Christian. There was a thief upon the cross.

— My son was not a thief, said Kumalo harshly. There was a white man, a good man, devoted to his wife and children. And worst of all—devoted to our people. And this wife, these [106/107] children, they are bereaved because of my son. I cannot suppose it to be less than the greatest evil I have known.

— A man may repent him of any evil.

— He will repent, said Kumalo bitterly. If I say to him, do you repent, he will say, it is as my father says. If I say to him, was this not evil, he will say, it is evil. But if I speak otherwise, putting no words in his mouth, if I say, what will you do now, he will say, I do not know, or he will say, it is as my father says.

Kumalo's voice rose as though some anguish compelled him.

— He is a stranger, he said, I cannot touch him. I cannot reach him. I see no shame in him, no pity for those he has hurt. Tears come out of his eyes, but it seems that he weeps only for himself, not for his wickedness, but for his danger.

The man cried out, can a person lose all sense of evil? A boy, brought up as he was brought up? I see only his pity for himself, he who has made two children fatherless. I tell you, that whosoever offends one of these little ones, it were better. . . .

— Stop, cried Father Vincent. You are beside yourself. Go and pray, go and rest. And do not judge your son too quickly. He too is shocked into silence, maybe. That is why he says to you, it is as my father wishes, and yes that is so, and I do not know.

Kumalo stood up. I trust that is so, he said, but I have no hope any more. What did you say I must do? Yes, pray and rest.

There was no mockery in his voice, and Father Vincent knew that it was not in this man's nature to speak mockingly. But so mocking were the words that the white priest caught him by the arm, and said to him urgently, sit down, I must speak to you as a priest.

When Kumalo had sat down, Father Vincent said to him, yes, I said pray and rest. Even if it is only words that you pray, and even if your resting is only a lying on a bed. And do not pray for yourself, and do not pray to understand the ways of God. For they are secret. Who knows what life is, for life is a secret. And why you have compassion for a girl, when you yourself find no compassion, that is a secret. And why you go on, when it would seem better to die, that is a secret. Do not [107/108] pray and think about these things now, there will be other times. Pray for Gertrude, and for her child, and for the girl that is to be your son's wife, and for the child that will be your grandchild. Pray for your wife and all at Ndotsheni. Pray for the woman and the children that are bereaved. Pray for the soul of him who was killed. Pray for us at the Mission House, and for those at Ezenzeleni, who try to rebuild in a place of destruction. Pray for your own rebuilding. Pray for all white people, those who do justice, and those who would do justice if they were not afraid. And do not fear to pray for your son, and for his amendment.

— I hear you, said Kumalo humbly.

— And give thanks where you can give thanks. For nothing is better. Is there not your wife, and Mrs. Lithebe, and Msimangu, and this young white man at the reformatory? Now, for your son and his amendment, you will leave this to me and Msimangu; for you are too distraught to see God's will. And now my son, go and pray, go and rest.

He helped the old man to his feet, and gave him his hat. And when Kumalo would have thanked him, he said, we do what is in us, and why it is in us, that is also a secret. It is Christ in us, crying that men may be succoured and forgiven, even when He Himself is forsaken.

He led the old man to the door of the Mission and there parted from him.

— I shall pray for you, he said, night and day. That I shall do, and anything more that you ask. [108/109]

XVI

The next day Kumalo, who was learning to find his way about the great city, took a train to Pimville to see the girl who was with child by his son. He chose this time so that Msimangu would not be able to accompany him, not because he was offended, but because he felt he would do it better alone. He thought slowly and acted slowly, no doubt because he lived in the slow tribal rhythm; and he had seen that this could irritate those who were with him, and he had felt also that he could reach his goal more surely without them.

He found the house not without difficulty, and knocked at the door, and the girl opened to him. And she smiled at him uncertainly, with something that was fear, and something that was child-like and welcoming.

— And how are you, my child?

— I am well, umfundisi.

He sat down on the only chair in the room, sat down carefully on it, and wiped his brow.

— Have you heard of your husband, he asked. Only the word does not quite mean husband.

The smile went from her face. I have not heard, she said.

— What I have to say is heavy, he said. He is in prison.

— In prison, she said.

— He is in prison, for the most terrible deed that a man can do.

But the girl did not understand him. She waited patiently for him to continue. She was surely but a child.

— He has killed a white man.

— Au! The exclamation burst from her. She put her hands [109/110] over her face. And Kumalo himself could not continue, for the words were like knives, cutting into a wound that was still new and open. She sat down on a box, and looked at the floor, and the tears started to run slowly down her cheeks.

— I do not wish to speak of it, my child.

Can you read? The white man's newspaper?

— A little.

— Then I shall leave it with you. But do not show it to others.

— I shall not show it to others, umfundisi.

— I do not wish to speak of it any more. I have come to speak with you of another matter. Do you wish to marry my son?

— It is as the umfundisi sees it.

— I am asking you, my child.

— I can be willing.

— And why would you be willing?

She looked at him, for she could not understand such a question.

— Why do you wish to marry him, he persisted.

She picked little strips of wood from the box, smiling in her perplexedness. He is my husband, she said, with the word that does not quite mean husband.

— But you did not wish to marry him before.

The questions embarrassed her; she stood up, but there was nothing to do, and she sat down again, and fell to picking at the box.

— Speak, my child.

— I do not know what to say, umfundisi.

— Is it truly your wish to marry him?

— It is truly my wish, umfundisi.

— I must be certain. I do not wish to take you into my family if you are unwilling.

At those words she looked up at him eagerly. I am willing, she said.

— We live in a far place, he said, there are no streets and lights and buses there. There is only me and my wife, and the place is very quiet. You are a Zulu? [110/111]

— Yes, umfundisi.

— Where were you born?

— In Alexandra.

— And your parents?

— My father left my mother, umfundisi. And my second father I could not understand.

— Why did your father leave?

— They quarreled, umfundisi. Because my mother was so often drunk.

— So your father left. And he left you also?

— He left us, my two brothers and me, my younger brothers.

— And your two brothers, where are they?

— One is in the school, umfundisi, the school where Absalom was sent. And one is in Alexandra. But he is disobedient, and I have heard that he too may go to the school.

— But how could your father have left you so?

She looked at him with strange innocence. I do not know, she said.

— And you did not understand your second father? So what did you do?

— I left that place.

— And what did you do?

— I lived in Sophiatown.

— Alone?

— No, not alone.

— With your first husband? he asked coldly.

— With my first, she agreed, not noticing his coldness.

— How many have there been?

She laughed nervously, and looked down at the hand picking at the box. She looked up, and finding his eyes upon her, was confused. Only three, she said.

— And what happened to the first?

— He was caught, umfundisi.

— And the second?

— He was caught also.

— And now the third is caught also. **[111/112]**

He stood up, and a wish to hurt her came into him. Although he knew it was not seemly, he yielded to it, and he said to her, yes, your third is caught also, but now it is for murder. Have you had a murderer before?

He took a step towards her, and she shrank away on the box, crying, no, no. And he, fearing that those outside might overhear, spoke more quietly to her and told her not to be afraid, and took a step backwards. But no sooner had she recovered than he wished to hurt her again. And he said to her, will you now take a fourth husband? And desperately she said, No, no, I want no husband any more.

And a wild thought came to Kumalo in his wild and cruel mood.

— Not even, he asked, if I desired you?

— You, she said, and shrank from him again.

— Yes, I, he said.

She looked round and about her, as one that was trapped. No, no, she said, it would not be right.

— Was it right before?

— No, it was not right.

— Then would you be willing?

She laughed nervously, and looked about her, and picked strips of wood from the box. But she felt his eyes upon her, and she said in a low voice, I could be willing.

He sat down and covered his face with his hands; and she, seeing him, fell to sobbing, a creature shamed and tormented. And he, seeing her, and the frailty of her thin body, was ashamed also, but for his cruelty, not her compliance.

He went over to her and said, how old are you, my child?

— I do not know, she sobbed, but I think I am sixteen.

And the deep pity welled up in him, and he put his hand on her head. And whether it was the priestly touch, or whether the deep pity flowed into the fingers and the palm, or whether it was some other reason—but the sobbing was quietened, and he could feel the head quiet under his hand. And he lifted her hands with his other, and felt the scars of her meaningless duties about this forlorn house. **[112/113]**

— I am sorry, he said. I am ashamed that I asked you such a question.

— I did not know what to say, she said.

— I knew that you would not know. That is why I am ashamed. Tell me, do you truly wish to marry my son?

She clutched at his hands. I wish it, she said.

— And to go to a quiet and far-off place, and be our daughter?

There was no mistaking the gladness of her voice. I wish it, she said.

— Greatly?

— Greatly, she said.

— My child?

— Umfundisi?

— I must say one more hard thing to you.

— I am listening, umfundisi.

— What will you do in this quiet place when the desire is upon you? I am a parson, and live at my church, and our life is quiet and ordered. I do not wish to ask you something that you cannot do.

— I understand, umfundisi. I understand completely. She looked at him through her tears. You shall not be ashamed of me. You need not be afraid for me. You need not be afraid because it is quiet. Quietness is what I desire.

And the word, the word desire, quickened her to brilliance, that shall be my desire, she said, that is the desire that will be upon me, so that he was astonished.

— I understand you, he said. You are cleverer than I thought.

— I was clever at school, she said eagerly.

He was moved to sudden laughter, and stood wondering at the strangeness of its sound.

— What church are you?

— Church of England, umfundisi . . . this too, eagerly.

He laughed again at her simplicity, and was as suddenly solemn. I want one promise from you, he said, a heavy promise.

And she too was solemn. Yes, umfundisi?

— If you should ever repent of this plan, either here or when we are gone to my home, you must not shut it up inside you, or [113/114] run away as you did from your mother. You will promise to tell me that you have repented.

— I promise, she said gravely, and then eagerly, I shall never repent.

And so he laughed again, and let go her hands, and took up his hat. I shall come for you when everything is ready for the marriage. Have you clothes?

— I have some clothes, umfundisi. I shall prepare them.

— And you must not live here. Shall I find you a place near me?

— I would wish that, umfundisi. She clapped her hands like a child. Let it be soon, she said, and I shall give up my room at this house.

— Stay well, then, my child.

— Go well, umfundisi.

He went out of the house, and she followed him to the little gate. When he turned back to look at her, she was smiling at him. He walked on like a man from whom a pain has lifted a little, not altogether, but a little. He remembered too that he had laughed, and that it had pained him physically, as it pains a man who is ill and should not laugh. And he remembered too, with sudden and devastating shock, that Father Vincent had said, I shall pray, night and day. At the corner he turned, and looking back, saw that the girl was still watching him. [114/115]

XVII

There are few people that do not let their rooms, and Mrs. Lithebe is one. Her husband was a builder, a good and honest man, but they were not blessed with children. He built her this fine big house, it has a room to eat and live in, and three rooms to sleep in. And one she has for herself, and one for the priest that she is glad to have, for it is good to have a priest, it is good to have prayers in the house. And one she has for Gertrude and the child, for do they not belong to the priest? But strangers she will not have at all, she has money enough.

It is sad about the priest, it is sad about this Gertrude and the child, it is saddest of all about his son. But about his goodness she has no doubt at all. He is kind and gentle, and treats her with courtesy and respect, and uses the house as if it were hers. And she admires him for what he has done, for saving Gertrude and the child, for getting his sister a new dress and a clean white cloth for her head, for getting shirt and jersey and trousers for the child. According to the custom she has thanked him for these gifts.

And it is pleasant having Gertrude and the child in the house. The girl is helpful and clean, though there is a strange carelessness about her, and she talks too easily to strangers, especially if they are men. For Mrs. Lithebe knows that she is a married woman, and Gertrude knows that the old woman is strict with her house, and she understands and is obedient.

But it is saddest of all about the son, and after their custom they have wept and wailed for him. She and Gertrude talk endlessly about it, indeed it is the only thing they talk about now. [115/116] The old man is silent, and his face has fallen into a mould of suffering. But she hears it all in his prayers, and feels for him in her heart. And though he sits long hours in the chair, and stares in front of him out of tragic eyes, he will stir to life when she speaks to him, and his smile lifts his face out of the mould of its suffering, and he is never otherwise than gentle and courteous toward her. Indeed when he plays with the child, there is something that comes out of him, so that he is changed. Yet even then sometimes there is a silence, and she hears the child asking and asking unanswered, and she looks through the door, and he is sitting there silent, alone with his thoughts, his face in the mould of its suffering.

* * * * *

— Mrs. Lithebe.
— Umfundisi?
— Mrs. Lithebe, you have been so kind, and I have another kindness to ask you.
— Perhaps it can be done.
— Mrs. Lithebe, you have heard of this girl who is with child by my son.
— I have heard of her.
— She lives in Pimville, in a room in the house of other people. She wishes to marry my son, and I believe it can be arranged. Then—whatever may happen— she will go with me to Ndotsheni, and bear her child there in a clean and decent home. But I am anxious to get her away from this place, and I wondered. . . . I do not like to trouble you, mother.

— You would like to bring her here, umfundisi.
— Indeed, that would be a great kindness.
— I will take her, said Mrs. Lithebe. She can sleep in the room where we eat. But I have no bed for her.
— That would not matter. It is better for her to sleep on the floor of a decent house, than to—
— Indeed, indeed.
— Mother, I am grateful. Indeed you are a mother to me.
— Why else do we live, she said. [116/117]

And after that he was cheerful, and called to the little boy, and sat him upon his knee, and moved him up and down quickly as a man moves on a horse. But it is not a good game, for an old man gets tired and a child does not. So they brought out the blocks, and built tall buildings like the buildings in Johannesburg, and sent them toppling over to destruction with noise and laughter.

— And now I must go, said Kumalo. I have a new sister to bring to you.

He counted out his money. There were only one or two notes left. Soon he would have to break into the money in the Post Office Book. He sighed a little, and put on his coat and his hat and took up his stick. His wife would have to wait longer for her stove, and he would have to wait longer for his new black clothes, and for the collars that a parson wears.

* * * * *

The girl is not like Gertrude. She is openly glad to be in this house. Her clothes are few but clean, for she has prepared them with care, and of other belongings she has almost none at all. She opens the doors and looks into the rooms, and she is glad, not having lived before in such a house. She calls Mrs. Lithebe mother, and that pleases the good woman; and she is pleased too because the girl can speak Sesuto after a broken fashion. Gertrude too welcomes her, for it is no doubt dull for her in this house. They will talk much together.

Indeed Mrs. Lithebe comes upon them, when they have been laughing together. They fall silent, Gertrude with some amusement in her eyes, and the girl confused. But Mrs. Lithebe does not like this laughter, it is the careless laughter that she does not like. She calls the girl to the kitchen to help her, and she says she does not like it.

— You are in a decent home, my child.

— Yes, mother, says the girl with downcast eyes.

— And you are brought here by a good and kindly man, so good that there is no word for it.

The girl looked up at her eagerly. I know it, she said. [**117/118**]

— Then if you are content to be brought by him, you will not laugh so carelessly.

— Yes, mother.

— You are but a child, and laughter is good for a child. But there is one kind of laughter, and there is another.

— Yes, mother.

— You understand what I mean?

— I understand you completely.

— This old man has been hurt greatly. Do you understand what I mean?

— I understand you completely.

— And he shall not be hurt any more, not in my house.

— I understand you.

— Then go, my child. But do not speak of what we have spoken.

— I understand you.

— My child, are you content to be brought here?

The girl looks at her fully. She spread out her hands, seeking some gesture to convey her conviction. I am content, she said. I desire to be nowhere but where I am. I desire no father but the umfundisi. I desire nothing that is not here.

— I see you are content. And one thing more, my child. When the little one plays with you, do not let him press so against you. It is your time to be careful.

— I understand you.

— Go then, my child. This home is your home.

So there was no more of the careless laughter, and the girl was quiet and obedient. And Gertrude saw that she was a child, and left her alone and was indifferent and amused after her own fashion.

* * * * *

He passed again through the great gate in the grim high wall, and they brought the boy to him. Again he took the lifeless hand in his own, and was again moved to tears, this time by the dejection of his son.

— Are you in health, my son? [**118/ 119**]

The son stood and moved his head to one side, and looked for a while at the one window, and then moved and looked at the other, but not at his father.

— I am in health, my father.

— I have some business for you, my son. Are you certain that you wish to marry this girl?

— I can marry her.

— There is a friend of mine, a white priest, and he will see if it can be arranged, and he will see the Bishop to see if it can be done quickly. And he will get a lawyer for you.

There is a spark of life in the eyes, of some hope maybe.

— You would like a lawyer?

— They say one can be helped by a lawyer.

— You told the police that these other two were with you?

— I told them. And now I have told them again.

— And then?

— And then they sent for them and fetched them from their cells.

— And then?

— And then they were angry with me, and cursed me in front of the police, and said that I was trying to bring them into trouble.

— And then?

— And then they asked what proof I had. And the only proof I had was that it was true, it was these two and no other and they stood there with me in the house, I here and they yonder.

He showed his father with his hands, and the tears came into his eyes, and he said, then they cursed me again, and stood looking angrily at me, and said one to the other, how can he lie so about us?

— They were your friends?

— Yes, they were my friends.

— And they will leave you to suffer alone?

— Now I see it.

— And until this, were they friends you could trust?

— I could trust them. [**119/120**]

— I see what you mean. You mean they were the kind of friends that a good man could choose, upright, hard-working, obeying the law?

Old man, leave him alone. You lead him so far and then you spring upon him. He looks at you sullenly, soon he will not answer at all.

— Tell me, were they such friends?

But the boy made no answer.

— And now they leave you alone?

Silence, then—I see it.

— Did you not see it before?

Reluctantly the boy said, I saw it. The old man was tempted to ask, then why, why did you continue with them. But the boy's eyes were filled with tears, and the father's compassion struggled with the temptation and overcame it. He took his son's hands, and this time they were not quite lifeless, but there was some feeling in them, and he held them strongly and comfortingly.

— Be of courage, my son. Do not forget there is a lawyer. But it is only the truth you must tell him.

— I shall tell him only the truth, my father.

He opened his mouth as though there were something he would say, but he did not say it.

— Do not fear to speak, my son.

— He must come soon, my father.

He looked at the window, and his eyes filled again with tears. He tried to speak carelessly. Or it may be too late, he said.

— Have no fear of that. He will come soon. Shall I go now to see when he will come?

— Go now, soon, soon, my father.

— And Father Vincent will come to see you, so that you can make confession, and be absolved, and amend your life.

— It is good, my father.

— And the marriage, that will be arranged if we can arrange it. And the girl— I had not told you—she is living with me in Sophiatown. And she will come back with me to Ndotsheni, and the child will be born there. [**120/121**]

— It is good, my father.

— And you may write now to your mother.

— I shall write, my father.

— And wipe away your tears.

The boy stood up and wiped his eyes with the cloth that his father gave him. And they shook hands, and there was some life now in the hand of the boy. The warder said to the boy, you may stay here, there is a lawyer to see you. You, old man, you must go.

So Kumalo left him, and at the door stood a white man, ready to come in. He was tall and grave, like a man used to heavy matters, and the warder knew him and showed him much respect. He looked like a man used to great matters, much greater than the case of a black boy who has killed a man, and he went gravely into the room, even as a chief would go.

*   *   *   *   *

Kumalo returned to the Mission House, and there had tea with Father Vincent. After the tea was over there was a knock at the door, and the tall grave man was shown into the room. And Father Vincent treated him also with respect, and called him sir, and then Mr. Carmichael. He introduced Kumalo to him, and Mr. Carmichael shook hands with him, and called him Mr. Kumalo, which is not the custom. They had more tea, and fell to discussing the case.

— I shall take it for you, Mr. Kumalo, said Mr. Carmichael. I shall take it pro deo, as we say. It is a simple case, for the boy says simply that he fired because he was afraid, not meaning to kill. And it will depend entirely on the judge and his assessors, for I think we will ask for that, and not for a jury. But with regard to the other two boys, I do not know what to say. I hear, Mr. Kumalo, that your brother has found another lawyer for them, and indeed I could not defend them, for I understand that their defense will be that they were not there at all, and that your son is for reasons of his own trying to implicate them. Whether that is true or not will be for the Court to decide, but I incline to the opinion that your son is [121/122] speaking the truth, and has no motive for trying to implicate them. It is for me to persuade the Court that he is speaking the whole truth, and that he speaks the whole truth when he says that he fired because he was afraid, and therefore I obviously could not defend these two who maintain that he is not speaking the truth. Is that clear, Mr. Kumalo?

— It is clear, sir.

— Now I must have all the facts about your son, Mr. Kumalo, when and where he was born, and what sort of child he was, and whether he was obedient and truthful, and when and why he left home, and what he has done since he came to Johannesburg. You understand?

— I understand, sir.

— I want this as soon as I can, Mr. Kumalo, for the case will probably be heard at the next sessions. You must find out what he has done, not only from him, but from others. You must check the one account against the other, you understand, and if there are differences, you must give them also. And I shall do the same on my own account. Do you understand?

— I understand, sir.

— And now, Father Vincent, could you and I go into this matter of the school?

— With pleasure, sir. Mr. Kumalo, will you excuse us?

He took Kumalo to the door, and standing outside it, shut it.

— You may thank God that we have got this man, he said. He is a great man, and one of the greatest lawyers in South Africa, and one of the greatest friends of your people.

— I do thank God, and you too, father. But tell me, I have one anxiety, what will it cost? My little money is nearly exhausted.

— Did you not hear him say he would take the case pro deo? Ah yes, you have not heard of that before. It is Latin, and it means for God. So it will cost you nothing, or at least very little.

— He takes it for God?

— That is what it meant in the old days of faith, though [122/123] it has lost much of that meaning. But it still means that the case is taken for nothing.

Kumalo stammered. I have never met such kindness, he said. He turned away his face, for he wept easily in those days. Father Vincent smiled at him. Go well, he said, and went back to the lawyer who was taking the case for God. [123/125]

BOOK TWO [125/127]

XVIII

There is a lovely road that runs from Ixopo into the hills. These hills are grass-covered and rolling, and they are lovely beyond any singing of it. The road climbs seven miles into them, to Carisbrooke; and from there, if there is no mist, you look down on one of the fairest valleys of Africa. About you there is grass and bracken, and the forlorn crying of the titihoya, one of the birds of the veld. Below you is the valley of the Umzimkulu, on its journey from the Drakensberg to the sea; and beyond and behind the river, great hill after great hill; and beyond and behind them, the mountains of Ingeli and East Griqualand.

The grass is rich and matted, you cannot see the soil. It holds the rain and the mist, and they seep into the ground, feeding the streams in every kloof. It is well tended, and not too many cattle feed upon it, and not too many fires burn it, laying bare the soil.

Up here on the tops is a small and lovely valley, between two hills that shelter it. There is a house there, and flat ploughed fields; they will tell you that it is one of the finest farms of this countryside. It is called High Place, the farm and dwelling-place of James Jarvis, Esquire, and it stands high above Ndotsheni, and the great valley of the Umzimkulu.

*   *   *   *   *

Jarvis watched the ploughing with a gloomy eye. The hot afternoon sun of October poured down on the fields, and there was no cloud in the sky. Rain, rain, there was no rain. The clods turned up hard and unbroken, and here and there the [127/128] plough would ride uselessly over the iron soil. At the end of the field it stopped, and the oxen stood sweating and blowing in the heat.

— It is no use, umnumzana.

— Keep at it, Thomas. I shall go up to the tops and see what there is to see.

— You will see nothing, umnumzana. I know because I have looked already.

Jarvis grunted, and calling his dog, set out along the kaffir path that led up to the tops. There was no sign of drought there, for the grass was fed by the mists, and the breeze blew coolingly on his sweating face. But below the tops the grass was dry, and the hills of Ndotsheni were red and bare, and the farmers on the tops had begun to fear that the desolation of them would eat back, year by year, mile by mile, until they too were overtaken.

Indeed they talked about it often, for when they visited one another and sat on the long cool verandahs drinking their tea, they must needs look out over the barren valleys and the bare hills that were stretched below them. Some of their labour was drawn from Ndotsheni, and they knew how year by year there was less food grown in these reserves. There were too many cattle there, and the fields were eroded and barren; each new field extended the devastation. Something might have been done, if these people had only learned how to fight erosion, if they had built walls to save the soil from washing, if they had ploughed along the contours of the hills. But the hills were steep, and indeed some of them were never meant for ploughing. And the oxen were weak, so that it was easier to plough downwards. And the people were ignorant, and knew nothing about farming methods.

Indeed it was a problem almost beyond solution. Some people said there must be more education, but a boy with education did not want to work on the farms, and went off to the towns to look for more congenial occupation. The work was done by old men and women, and when the grown men came back from the mines and the towns, they sat in the sun and drank their [128/129] liquor and made endless conversation. Some said there was too little land anyway, and that the natives could not support themselves on it, even with the most progressive methods of agriculture. But there were many sides to such a question. For if they got more land, and treated it as they treated what they had already, the country would turn into a desert. And where was the land to come from, and who would pay for it? And indeed there was still another argument, for if they got more land, and if by some chance they could make a living from it, who would work on the white men's farms? There was a system whereby a native could live at Ndotsheni, and go to work at his will on the adjoining farms. And there was another system whereby a native could get land from the farmer, and set up his kraal and have his family there, and be given his own piece of land and work it, provided that he and his family gave so much labour each year to the white farmer. But even that was not perfect, for some of them had sons and daughters that left for the towns, and never came back to fulfil their portion of the contract; and some of them abused the land that they had; and some of them stole cattle and sheep for meat; and some of them were idle and worthless, till one had to clear them off the farm, and not be certain if their successors would be any better.

Jarvis turned these old thoughts over in his mind as he climbed to the tops, and when he reached them he sat down on a stone and took off his hat, letting the breeze cool him. This was a view that a man could look at without tiring of it, this great valley of the Umzimkulu. He could look around on the green rich hills that he had inherited from his father, and down on the rich valley where he lived and farmed. It had been his wish that his son, the only child that had been born to them, would have taken it after him. But the young man had entertained other ideas, and had gone in for engineering, and well—good luck to him. He had married a fine girl, and had presented his parents with a pair of fine grand-children. It had been a heavy blow when he decided against High Place, but his life was his own, and no other man had a right to put his hands on it. [129/130]

Down in the valley below there was a car going up to the house. He recognized it as the police-car from Ixopo, and it would probably be Binnendyk on his patrol, and a decent fellow for an Afrikaner. Indeed Ixopo was full of Afrikaners now, whereas once there had been none of them. For all the police were Afrikaners, and the post-office clerks, and the men at the railway-station, and the village people got on well with them one way and the other. Indeed, many of them had married English-speaking girls, and that was happening all over the country. His own father had sworn that he would disinherit any child of his who married an Afrikaner, but times had changed. The war had put things back a bit, for some of the

Afrikaners had joined the army, and some were for the war but didn't join the army, and some were just for neutrality and if they had any feelings they concealed them, and some were for Germany but it wasn't wise for them to say anything about it.

His wife was coming out of the house to meet the car, and there were two policemen climbing out of it. One looked like the captain himself, van Jaarsveld, one of the most popular men in the village, a great rugby-player in his day, and a soldier of the Great War. He supposed they picked their officers carefully for an English-speaking district like Ixopo. They seemed to have come to see him, for his wife was pointing up to the tops. He prepared to go down, but before he left, he looked over the great valley. There was no rain, and nothing that looked as if it would ever come. He called his dog, and set out along the path that would soon drop down steeply amongst the stones. When he reached a little plateau about half-way down to the fields, he found that van Jaarsveld and Binnendyk were already climbing the slope, and saw that they had brought their car down the rough track to the ploughing. They caught sight of him, and he waved to them, and sat down upon a stone to wait for them. Binnendyk dropped behind, and the captain came on above to meet him.

— Well, captain, have you brought some rain for us?

The captain stopped and turned to look over the valley to the mountains beyond. [130/131]

— I don't see any, Mr. Jarvis, he said.

— Neither do I. What brings you out today?

They shook hands, and the captain looked at him.

— Mr. Jarvis.

— Yes.

— I have bad news for you.

— Bad news?

Jarvis sat down, his heart beating loudly. Is it my son, he asked.

— Yes, Mr. Jarvis.

— Is he dead?

— Yes, Mr. Jarvis. The captain paused. He was shot dead at 1:30 P.M. this afternoon in Johannesburg.

Jarvis stood up, his mouth quivering. Shot dead, he asked. By whom?

— It is suspected by a native housebreaker. You know his wife was away?

— Yes, I knew that.

— And he stayed at home for the day, a slight indisposition. I suppose this native thought no one was at home. It appears that your son heard a noise, and came down to investigate. The native shot him dead. There was no sign of any struggle.

— My God!

— I'm sorry, Mr. Jarvis. I'm sorry to have to bring this news to you.

He offered his hand, but Jarvis had sat down again on the stone, and did not see it. My God, he said.

Van Jaarsveld stood silent while the older man tried to control himself.

— You didn't tell my wife, captain?

— No, Mr. Jarvis.

Jarvis knitted his brows as he thought of that task that must be performed. She isn't strong, he said. I don't know how she will stand it.

— Mr. Jarvis, I am instructed to offer you every assistance. Binnendyk can drive your car to Pietermaritzburg if you wish. You could catch the fast mail at nine o'clock. You will be in [131/132] Johannesburg at eleven tomorrow morning. There's a private compartment reserved for you and Mrs. Jarvis.

— That was kind of you.

— I'll do anything you wish, Mr. Jarvis.

— What time is it?

— Half-past three, Mr. Jarvis.

— Two hours ago.

— Yes, Mr. Jarvis.

— Three hours ago he was alive.

— Yes, Mr. Jarvis.

— My God!

— If you are to catch this train, you should leave at six. Or if you wish, you could take an aeroplane. There's one waiting at Pietermaritzburg. But we must

let them know by four o'clock. You could be in Johannesburg at midnight.

— Yes, yes. You know, I cannot think.

— Yes, I can understand that.

— Which would be better?

— I think the aeroplane, Mr. Jarvis.

— Well, we'll take it. We must let them know, you say.

— I'll do that as soon as we get to the house. Can I telephone where Mrs. Jarvis won't hear me? I must hurry, you see.

— Yes, yes, you can do that.

— I think we should go.

But Jarvis sat without moving.

— Can you stand up, Mr. Jarvis? I don't want to help you. Your wife's watching us.

— She's wondering, captain. Even at this distance, she knows something is wrong.

— It's quite likely. Something she saw in my face, perhaps, though I tried not to show it.

Jarvis stood up. My God, he said. There's still that to do.

As they walked down the steep path, Binnendyk went ahead of them. Jarvis walked like a dazed man. Out of a cloudless sky these things come.

— Shot dead, he said.

— Yes, Mr. Jarvis. [132/133]

— Did they catch the native?

— Not yet, Mr. Jarvis.

The tears filled the eyes, the teeth bit the lips. What does that matter? he said. They walked down the hill, they were near the field. Through the misted eyes he saw the plough turn over the clods, then ride high over the iron ground. Leave it, Thomas, he said. He was our only child, captain.

— I know that, Mr. Jarvis.

They climbed into the car, and in a few minutes were at the house.

— James, what's the matter?

— Some trouble, my dear. Come with me to the office. Captain, you want to use the telephone. You know where it is?

— Yes, Mr. Jarvis.

The captain went to the telephone. It

was a party-line, and two neighbors were talking.

— Please put down your receivers, said the captain. This is an urgent call from the police. Please put down your receivers.

He rang viciously, and got no answer. There should be a special police call to exchange on these country lines. He would see about it. He rang more viciously. Exchange, he said, Police Pietermaritzburg. It is very urgent.

— You will be connected immediately, said exchange.

He waited impatiently, listening to the queer inexplicable noises. Your call to Police Pietermaritzburg, said exchange.

He started to talk to them about the aeroplane. His hand felt for the second earpiece, so that he could use that also, to shut out the sound of the woman, of her crying and sobbing. [133/134]

XIX

A young man met them at the airport.
— Mr. and Mrs. Jarvis?
— Yes.
— I'm John Harrison, Mary's brother. I don't think you remember me. I was only a youngster when you saw me last. Let me carry your things. I've a car here for you.

As they walked to the control building, the young man said, I needn't tell you how grieved we are, Mr. Jarvis. Arthur was the finest man I ever knew.

In the car he spoke to them again. Mary and the children are at my mother's, and we're expecting you both to stay with us.
— How is Mary?
— She's suffering from the shock, Mr. Jarvis, but she's very brave.
— And the children?
— They've taken it very badly, Mr. Jarvis. And that has given Mary something to occupy herself.

They did not speak again. Jarvis held his wife's hand, but they all were silent with their own thoughts, until they drove through the gates of a suburban house, and came to a stop before a lighted porch. A young woman came out at the sound of the car, and embraced Mrs. Jarvis, and they wept together. Then she turned to Jarvis, and they embraced each other. This first meeting over, Mr. and Mrs. Harrison came out also, and after they had welcomed one another, and after the proper words had been spoken, they all went into the house.

Harrison turned to Jarvis. Would you like a drink, he asked.
— It would be welcome. [134/135]
— Come to my study, then.
— And now, said Harrison, you must do as you wish. If there's anything we can do, you've only to ask us. If you would wish to go to the mortuary at once, John will go with you. Or you can go tomorrow morning if you wish. The police would like to see you, but they won't worry you tonight.
— I'll ask my wife, Harrison. You know, we've hardly spoken of it yet. I'll go to her, don't you worry to come.
— I'll wait for you here.

He found his wife and his daughter-in-law hand in hand, tiptoeing out of the room where his grandchildren were sleeping. He spoke to her, and she wept again and sobbed against him. Now, she said. He went back to Harrison, and swallowed his drink, and then he and his wife and their daughter-in-law went out to the car, where John Harrison was waiting for them.

While they were driving to the Police Laboratories, John Harrison told Jarvis all that he knew about the crime, how the police were waiting for the house-boy to recover consciousness, and how they had combed the plantations on Parkwold Ridge. And he told him too of the paper that Arthur Jarvis had been writing just before he was killed, on "The Truth About Native Crime."
— I'd like to see it, said Jarvis.
— We'll get it for you tomorrow, Mr. Jarvis.

— My son and I didn't see eye to eye on the native question, John. In fact, he and I got quite heated about it on more than one occasion. But I'd like to see what he wrote.

— My father and I don't see eye to eye on the native question either, Mr. Jarvis. You know, Mr. Jarvis, there was no one in South Africa who thought so deeply about it, and no one who thought so clearly, as Arthur did. And what else is there to think deeply and clearly about in South Africa, he used to say.

So they came to the Laboratories, and John Harrison stayed in the car, while the others went to do the hard thing that had to be done. And they came out silent but for the weeping of the two women, and drove back as silently to the house, where Mary's father opened the door to them. [135/136]

— Another drink, Jarvis. Or do you want to go to bed?

— Margaret, do you want me to come up with you?

— No, my dear, stay and have your drink.

— Goodnight then, my dear.

— Goodnight, James.

He kissed her, and she clung to him for a moment. And thank you for all your help, she said. The tears came again into her eyes, and into his too for that matter. He watched her climb the stairs with their daughter-in-law, and when the door closed on them, he and Harrison turned to go to the study.

— It's always worse for the mother, Jarvis.

— Yes.

He pondered over it, and said then, I was very fond of my son, he said. I was never ashamed of having him.

They settled down to their drinks, and Harrison told him that the murder had shocked the people of Parkwold, and how the messages had poured into the house.

— Messages from every conceivable place, every kind of person, he said. By the way, Jarvis, we arranged the funeral provisionally for tomorrow afternoon,

after a service in the Parkwold Church. Three o'clock the service will be.

Jarvis nodded. Thank you, he said.

— And we kept all the messages for you. From the Bishop, and the Acting Prime Minister, and the Mayor, and from dozens of others. And from native organisations too, something called the Daughters of Africa, and a whole lot of others that I can't remember. And from coloured people, and Indians, and Jews.

Jarvis felt a sad pride rising in him. He was clever, he said, that came from his mother.

— He was that right enough—you must hear John on it. But people liked him too, all sorts of people. You know he spoke Afrikaans like an Afrikaner?

— I knew he had learnt it.

— It's a lingo I know nothing about, thank God. But he thought he ought to know it, so he took lessons in it, and went to an Afrikaner farm. He spoke Zulu as you know, but he was [136/137] talking of learning Sesuto. You know these native M.P.'s they have—well, there was talk of getting him to stand at the next election.

— I didn't know that.

— Yes, he was always speaking here and there. You know the kind of thing. Native Crime, and more Native Schools, and he kicked up a hell of a dust in the papers about the conditions at the non-European Hospital. And you know he was hot about the native compound system in the Mines, and wanted the Chamber to come out one hundred per cent for settled labour—you know, wife and family to come with the man.

Jarvis filled his pipe slowly, and listened to this tale of his son, to this tale of a stranger.

— Hathaway of the Chamber of Mines spoke to me about it, said Harrison. Asked me if I wouldn't warn the lad to pipe down a bit, because his firm did a lot of business with the Mines. So I spoke to him, told him I knew he felt deeply about these things, but asked him to go slow a bit. Told him there was Mary to consider, and the children. I didn't speak on behalf of Mary, you understand? I don't poke my nose into young people's business.

— I understand.

— I've spoken to Mary, he said to me. She and I agree that it's more important to speak the truth than to make money.

Harrison laughed at that, but cut himself short, remembering the sadness of the occasion. My son John was there, he said, looking at Arthur as though he were God Almighty. So what could I say?

They smoked in silence awhile. I asked him, said Harrison, about his partners. After all their job was to sell machinery to the Mines. I've discussed it with my partners, he said to me, and if there's any trouble, I've told them I'll get out. And what would you do, I asked him. What won't I do, he said. His face was sort of excited. Well, what could I say more?

Jarvis did not answer. For this boy of his had gone journeying in strange waters, further than his parents had known. Or perhaps his mother knew. It would not surprise him if his mother [**137/138**] knew. But he himself had never done such journeying, and there was nothing he could say.

— Am I tiring you, Jarvis? Or is there perhaps something else you'd like to talk about? Or go to bed, perhaps?

— Harrison, you're doing me more good by talking.

— Well, that's how he was. He and I didn't talk much about these things. It's not my line of country. I try to treat a native decently, but he's not my food and drink. And to tell you the truth, these crimes put me off. I tell you, Jarvis, we're scared stiff at the moment in Johannesburg.

— Of crime?

— Yes, of native crime. There are too many of these murders and robberies and brutal attacks. I tell you we don't go to bed at night without barricading the house. It was at the Phillipsons, three doors down, that a gang of these roughs broke in; they knocked old Phillipson unconscious, and beat up his wife. It was lucky the girls were out at a dance, or one

doesn't know what might have happened. I asked Arthur about that, but he reckoned we were to blame somehow. Can't say I always followed him, but he had a kind of sincerity. You sort of felt that if you had the time you could get some sort of sense out of it.

— There's one thing I don't get the sense of, said Jarvis. Why this should have happened. . . .

— You mean . . . to him, of all people?

— Yes.

— That's one of the first things that we said. Here he was, day in and day out, on a kind of mission. And it was he who was killed.

— Mind you, said Jarvis, coming to a point. Mind you, it's happened before. I mean, that missionaries were killed.

Harrison made no answer, and they smoked their pipes silently. A missionary, thought Jarvis, and thought how strange it was that he had called his son a missionary. For he had never thought much of missionaries. True, the church made a lot of it, and there were special appeals to which he had given, but one did that kind of thing without believing much in mis- [**138/139**] sionaries. There was a mission near him, at Ndotsheni. But it was a sad place as he remembered it. A dirty old wood-and-iron church, patched and forlorn, and a dirty old parson, in a barren valley where the grass hardly grew. A dirty old school where he had heard them reciting, parrot-fashion, on the one or two occasions that he had ridden past there, reciting things that could mean little to them.

— Bed, Jarvis? Or another drink?

— Bed, I think. Did you say the police were coming?

— They're coming at nine.

— And I'd like to see the house.

— I thought that you would. They'll take you there.

— Good, then I'll go to bed. Will you say good-night to your wife for me?

— I'll do that. You know your room? And breakfast? Eight-thirty?

— Eight-thirty. Goodnight, Harrison. And many thanks for your kindnesses.

— No thanks are needed. Nothing is too much trouble. Goodnight, Jarvis, and I hope you and Margaret will get some sleep.

Jarvis walked up the stairs, and went into the room. He walked in quietly, and closed the door, and did not put on the light. The moon was shining through the windows, and he stood there looking out on the world. All that he had heard went quietly through his mind. His wife turned in the bed, and said, James.

— My dear.

— What were you thinking, my dear?

He was silent, searching for an answer. Of it all, he said.

— I thought you would never come.

He went to her quickly, and she caught at his hands. We were talking of the boy, he said. All that he did, and tried to do. All the people that are grieved.

— Tell me, my dear.

And so he told her in low tones all he had heard. She marvelled a little, for her husband was a quiet silent man, not [139/140] given to much talking. But tonight he told her all that Harrison had told him.

— It makes me proud, she whispered.

— But you always knew he was like that.

— Yes, I knew.

— I knew too that he was a decent man, he said. But you were always nearer to him than I was.

— It's easier for a mother, James.

— I suppose so. But I wish now that I'd known more of him. You see, the things that he did, I've never had much to do with that sort of thing.

— Nor I either, James. His life was quite different from ours.

— It was a good life by all accounts.

He sat, she lay, in silence, with their thoughts and their memories and their grief.

— Although his life was different, he said, you understood it.

— Yes, James.

— I'm sorry I didn't understand it.

Then he said in a whisper, I didn't know it would ever be so important to understand it.

— My dear, my dear. Her arms went about him, and she wept. And he continued to whisper, there's one thing I don't understand, why it should have happened to him.

She lay there thinking of it, the pain was deep, deep and ineluctable. She tightened her arms about him. James, let's try to sleep, she said. [140/141]

XX

Jarvis sat in the chair of his son, and his wife and Mary left him to return to the Harrisons. Books, books, books, more books than he had ever seen in a house! On the table papers, letters, and more books. Mr. Jarvis, will you speak at the Parkwold Methodist Guild? Mr. Jarvis, will you speak at the Anglican Young People's Association in Sophiatown? Mr. Jarvis will you speak in a symposium at the University? No, Mr. Jarvis would be unable to speak at any of those.

Mr. Jarvis, you are invited to the Annual Meeting of the Society of Jews and Christians. Mr. Jarvis, you and your wife are invited to the wedding of Sarajini, eldest daughter of Mr. and Mrs. H. B. Singh. Mr. Jarvis, you and your wife are invited to a Toc H Guest Night in van Wyk's Valley. No, Mr. Jarvis would be unable to accept these kind invitations.

On the walls between the books there were four pictures, of Christ crucified, and Abraham Lincoln, and the white gabled house of Vergelegen, and a painting of leafless willows by a river in a wintry veld.

He rose from the chair to look at the books. Here were hundreds of books, all about Abraham Lincoln. He had not known that so many books had been written about any one man. One bookcase was full of them. And another was full of books about South Africa, Sarah Gertrude Millin's *Life of Rhodes,* and her book about Smuts, and Engelenburg's *Life of Louis Botha,* and books on South African race problems, and books on South African birds, and the Kruger Park, and innumerable others. Another bookcase was full of Afrikaans books, but the titles conveyed nothing to him. And here were books about religion, [141/142] and Soviet Russia, and crime and criminals, and books of poems. He looked for Shakespeare, and here was Shakespeare too.

He went back to the chair, and looked long at the picture of Christ crucified, and Abraham Lincoln, and Vergelegen, and the willows by the river. Then he drew some pieces of paper towards him.

The first was a letter to his son from the secretary of the Claremont African Boys' Club, Gladiolus Street, Claremont, regretting that Mr. Jarvis had not been able to attend the Annual Meeting of the Club, and informing him he had again been elected as President. And the letter concluded, with quaintness of spelling and phrase—

I am compelled by the Annual Meeting to congratulate you with this matter, and to express considerable thanks to you for all the time you have been spending with us, and for the presents you have been giving the Club. How this Club would be arranged without your participation, would be a mystery to many minds amongst us. It is on these accounts that we desire to elect you again to the President.

I am asking an apology for this writing-paper, but our Club writing-paper is lost owing to unforeseen circumstances.

I am,

Your obedient servant,

WASHINGTON LEFIFI.

The other papers were in his son's handwriting. They were obviously part of some larger whole, for the first line was the latter end of a sentence, and the last line was a sentence unfinished. He looked for the rest of it, but finding nothing, settled down to read what he had:—

was permissible. What we did when we came to South Africa was permissible. It was permissible to develop our great resources with the aid of what labour we could [142/143] find. It was permissible to use unskilled men for unskilled work. But it is not permissible to keep men unskilled for the sake of unskilled work.

It was permissible when we discovered gold to bring labour to the mines. It was permissible to build compounds and to keep women and children away from the towns. It was permissible as an experiment, in the light of what we knew. But in the light of what we know now, with certain exceptions, it is no longer permissible. It is not permissible for us to go on destroying family life when we know that we are destroying it.

It is permissible to develop any resources if the labour is forthcoming. But it is not permissible to develop any resources if they can be developed only at the cost of the labour. It is not permissible to mine any gold, or manufacture any product, or cultivate any land, if such mining and manufacture and cultivation depend for their success on a policy of keeping labour poor. It is not permissible to add to one's possessions if these things can only be done at the cost of other men. Such development has only one true name, and that is exploitation. It might have been permissible in the early days of our country, before we became aware of its cost, in the disintegration of native community life, in the deterioration of native family life, in poverty, slums, and crime. But now that the cost is known, it is no longer permissible.

It was permissible to leave native education to those who wanted to develop it. It was permissible to doubt its benefits. But it is no longer permissible in the light of what we know. Partly because it made possible industrial development, and partly because it happened in spite of us, there is now a large urbanised native population. Now society has always, for reasons of self-interest if for no other, educated its children so that they grow up law-abiding, with socialised aims and purposes. There is no other way that it can be done. Yet we continue to leave the education of our native urban society to those few Euro- [143/144] peans who feel strongly about it, and to deny opportunities and money for its expansion. That is not permissible. For reasons of self-interest alone, it is dangerous.

It was permissible to allow the destruction of a tribal system that impeded the growth of the country. It was permissible to believe that its destruction was inevitable. But it is not permissible to watch its destruction, and to replace it by nothing, or by so little, that a whole people deteriorates, physically and morally.

The old tribal system was, for all its violence and savagery, for all its superstition and witchcraft, a moral system. Our natives today produce criminals and prostitutes and drunkards, not because it is their nature to do so, but because their simple system of order and tradition and convention has been destroyed. It was destroyed by the impact of our own civilisation. Our civilisation has therefore an inescapable duty to set up another system of order and tradition and convention.

It is true that we hoped to preserve the tribal system by a policy of segregation. That was permissible. But we never did it thoroughly or honestly. We set aside one-tenth of the land for four-fifths of the people. Thus we made it inevitable, and some say we did it knowingly, that labour would come to the towns. We are caught in the toils of our own selfishness.

No one wishes to make the problem seem smaller than it is. No one wishes to make its solution seem easy. No one wishes to make light of the fears that beset us. But whether we be fearful or no, we shall never, because we are a Christian people, be able to evade the moral issues. It is time—

And there the manuscript and the page ended. Jarvis, who had become absorbed in the reading, searched again amongst the papers on the table, but he could find nothing to show that anything more than this had been written. He lit his pipe, and pulling the papers toward him, began to read them again. [144/145]

After he had finished them the second time, he sat smoking his pipe and was lost in thought. Then he got up from his chair and went and stood in front of the Lincoln bookcase, and looked up at the picture of the man who had exercised such an influence over his son. He looked at the hundreds of books, and slid aside the glass panel and took one of them out. Then he returned to his chair, and began to turn over its pages. One of the chapters was headed "The Famous Speech at Gettysburg," apparently a speech that was a failure, but that had since become one of the great speeches of the world. He turned over the preliminary pages till he came to the speech, and read it through carefully. That done, he smoked again, lost in a deep abstraction. After some time he rose and replaced the book in the case, and shut the case. Then he opened the case again, and slipped the book into his pocket, and shut the case. He looked at his watch, knocked out his pipe in the fireplace, put on his hat, took up his stick. He walked slowly down the stairs, and opened the door into the fatal passage. He took off his hat and looked down at the dark stain on the floor. Unasked, unwanted, the picture of the small boy came into his mind, the small boy at High Place, the small boy with the wooden guns. Unseeing he walked along the passage and out of the door through which death had come so suddenly. The policeman saluted him, and he answered him with words that meant nothing, that made no sense at all. He put on his hat, and walked to the gate. Undecided he looked up and down the road. Then with an effort he began to walk. With a sigh the policeman relaxed. [145/146]

XXI

The service in the Parkwold Church was over, and the church had been too small for all who wanted to come. White people, black people, coloured people, Indians— it was the first time that Jarvis and his wife had sat in a church with people who were not white. The Bishop himself had spoken, words that pained and uplifted. And the Bishop too had said that men did not understand this riddle, why a young man so full of promise was cut off in his youth, why a woman was widowed and children were orphaned, why a country was bereft of one who might have served it greatly. And the Bishop's voice rose when he spoke of South Africa, and he spoke in a language of beauty, and Jarvis listened for a while without pain, under the spell of the words. And the Bishop said that here had been a life devoted to South Africa, of intelligence and courage, of love that cast out fear, so that the pride welled up in the heart, pride in the stranger who had been his son.

*   *   *   *   *

The funeral was over. The brass doors opened soundlessly, and the coffin slid soundlessly into the furnace that would reduce it to ashes. And people that he did not know shook hands with him, some speaking their sympathy in brief conventional phrases, some speaking simply of his son. The black people—yes, the black people also—it was the first time he had ever shaken hands with black people.

They returned to the house of the Harrisons, for the night that is supposed to be the worst of all the nights that must

come. For Margaret it would no doubt be so; he would not leave her again to go to bed alone. But for him it was over; he could [146/147] sit quietly in Harrison's study, and drink his whisky and smoke his pipe, and talk about any matter that Harrison wanted to talk about, even about his son.

— How long will you stay, Jarvis? You're welcome to stay as long as you wish.

— Thank you, Harrison. I think Margaret will go back with Mary and the children, and we'll arrange for the son of one of my neighbours to stay with them. A nice lad, just out of the Army. But I'll stay to wind up Arthur's affairs, at least in the preliminary stages.

— And what did the police say, if I may ask?

— They're still waiting for the boy to recover. They have hopes that he recognised one of them. Otherwise they say it will be very difficult. The whole thing was over so quickly. They hope too that someone may have seen them getting away. They think they were frightened and excited, and wouldn't have walked away normally.

— I hope to God they get them. And string 'em all up. Pardon me, Jarvis.

— I know exactly what you mean.

— We're not safe, Jarvis. I don't even know that stringing 'em up will make us safe. Sometimes I think it's got beyond us.

— I know what you mean. But myself —perhaps it's too soon to think about it.

— I know what *you* mean. I understand —I kind of understand—that side of it isn't the side you feel about the most. I might be the same. I don't really know.

— I don't really know either. But you're right, it's not that side of it that seems important, not yet anyway. But I realize there *is* another side to it.

— We've been agitating for more police, Jarvis. There's going to be a big meeting in Parkwold tomorrow night. The place is alive with indignation. You know, Jarvis, there's hardly a householder in these suburbs who knows who lives in the servants' quarters. I won't have it. I tell my servants that I won't have a stranger near the place, let alone allow him to sleep here. Our girl's husband comes in occasionally from the [147/148] place where he works, Benoni or Springs or somewhere, and she brings him in decently, and I give permission. But I'll allow no one else. If I didn't look out, I'd have the place full of cousins and uncles and brothers, and most of 'em up to no good.

— Yes, I suppose that happens in Johannesburg.

— And these sanitary lanes that run behind the houses. We've urged them to close the damned things up now that we have proper sewerage. They're dark and dangerous, and these damned loafers use 'em as hide-outs. God knows what's coming to the country, I don't. I'm not a nigger-hater, Jarvis. I try to give 'em a square deal, decent wages, and a clean room, and reasonable time off. Our servants stay with us for years. But the natives as a whole are getting out of hand. They've even started Trade Unions, did you know that?

— I didn't know that.

— Well they have. They're threatening to strike here in the Mines for ten shillings a day. They get about three shillings a shift now, and some of the mines are on the verge of closing down. They live in decent compounds—some of the latest compounds I wouldn't mind living in myself. They get good balanced food, far better than they'd ever get at home, free medical attention, and God knows what. I tell you, Jarvis, if mining costs go up much more there won't be any mines. And where will South Africa be then? And where would the natives be themselves? They'd die by the thousands of starvation.

— Am I intruding? asked John Harrison, coming in to his father's study.

— Sit down, John, said Harrison.

So the young man sat down, and his father, who was growing warm and excited, proceeded to develop his theme.

— And where would the farmers be, Jarvis? Where would you sell your prod-

ucts, and who could afford to buy them? There wouldn't be any subsidies. There wouldn't be any industry either; industry depends on the mines to provide the money that will buy its products. And this Government of ours soaks the mines every year for a cool seventy per cent of the profits. And where would they be if there were no mines? Half the [148/149] Afrikaners in the country would be out of work. There wouldn't be any civil service, either. Half of them would be out of work, too.

He poured out some more whiskey for them both, and then resumed his subject.

— I tell you there wouldn't be any South Africa at all if it weren't for the mines. You could shut the place up, and give it back to the natives. That's what makes me so angry when people criticise the mines. Especially the Afrikaners. They have some fool notion that the mining people are foreign to the country, and are sucking the blood out of it, ready to clear out when the goose stops laying the eggs. I'm telling you that most of the mining shares are held here in the country itself, they're *our* mines. I get sick and tired of all this talk. Republic! Where would we be if we ever get a republic?

— Harrison, I'm going to bed. I don't want Margaret to go to bed alone.

— Old man, I'm sorry. I'm afraid I forgot myself.

— There's nothing to be sorry about. It's done me good to listen to you. I haven't done much talking myself, it's not because I'm not interested. I'm sure you understand.

— I'm sorry, I'm sorry, said Harrison humbly. I quite forgot myself.

— Believe me, said Jarvis, I'm sincere when I say that it's done me good to listen to you.

He looked at the two Harrisons. I'm not a man to sit and talk about death by the hour, he said.

Harrison looked at him uncomfortably. Really, really, you make it easy for me, he said.

— I could have wished that he was here

tonight, said Jarvis, that I could have heard him argue with you.

— You would have enjoyed it, Mr. Jarvis, said John Harrison eagerly, responding to this natural invitation to talk about a man not long since dead. I never heard anyone argue about these things as he could.

— I didn't agree with him, said Harrison, his discomfort passing, but I had a great respect for anything that he said. **[149/150]**

— He was a good man, Harrison. I'm not sorry that we had him. Goodnight to you.

— Goodnight, Jarvis. Did you sleep last night? Did Margaret sleep?

— We both got some sleep.

— I hope you get some more tonight. Don't forget, the house is at your service.

— Thank you, goodnight. John?

— Yes, Mr. Jarvis.

— Do you know the Boys' Club in Gladiolus Road, Claremont?

— I know it well. It was our Club. Arthur's and mine.

— I should like to see it. Any time that suits.

— I'd be glad to take you, Mr. Jarvis. And Mr. Jarvis—

— Yes, John.

— I just want to tell you that when father says Afrikaners he means Nationalists. Arthur was always telling him that. And father would agree too, but he just doesn't seem able to remember.

Jarvis smiled, first at the boy, then at his father. It's a good point, he said. Goodnight Harrison. Goodnight John.

*   *   *   *   *

The next morning Harrison waited for his guest at the foot of the stairs.

— Come in to the study, he said. They went in, and Harrison closed the door behind him.

— The police have just telephoned, Jarvis. The boy recovered consciousness this morning. He says there were three right enough. They had their mouths and noses covered, but he is sure that the one

that knocked him out was an old garden-boy of Mary's. Mary had to get rid of him for some trouble or other. He recognised him because of some twitching about the eyes. When he left Mary, he got a job at some textile factory in Doornfontein. Then he left the factory, and no one can say where he went. But they got information about some other native who had been very friendly with him. They're after him **[150/151]** now, hoping that he can tell them where to find the garden-boy. They certainly seem to be moving.

— They do seem to be.

— And here is a copy of Arthur's manuscript on native crime. Shall I leave it on the table and you can read it in peace after breakfast?

— Thank you, leave it there.

— How did you sleep? And Margaret?

— She slept heavily, Harrison. She needed it.

— I'm sure she did. Come to breakfast.

*   *   *   *   *

After breakfast, Jarvis returned to his host's study, and began to read his son's manuscript. He turned first to the last page of it, and read with pain the last unfinished paragraph. This was almost the last thing that his son had done. When this was done he had been alive. Then at this moment, at this very word that hung in the air, he had got up and gone down the stairs to his death. If one could have cried then, don't go down! If one could have cried, stop, there is danger! But there was no one to cry. No one knew then what so many knew now. But these thoughts were unprofitable; it was not his habit to dwell on what might have been but what could never be. There was no point in imagining that if one had been there, one could have prevented a thing that had happened only because it had not been prevented. It was the pain that did that, that compelled one to these unprofitable thoughts. He wanted to understand his son, not to desire what was no more accessible to desire. So he compelled himself to read the last paragraph slowly,

—with his head, not his heart, so that he could understand it.

The truth is that our Christian civilisation is riddled through and through with dilemma. We believe in the brotherhood of man, but we do not want it in South Africa. We believe that God endows men with diverse gifts, and that human life depends for its fullness on their employment and enjoyment, but we do not want it in South Africa. We believe in help for the underdog, but we want [151/152] him to stay under. And we are therefore compelled, in order to preserve our belief that we are Christian, to ascribe to Almighty God, Creator of Heaven and Earth, our own human intentions, and to say that because He created white and black, He gives the Divine Approval to any human action that is designed to keep black men from advancement. We go so far as to credit Almighty God with the intention of having created black men to hew wood and draw water for white men. We go so far as to assume that He blesses any action that is designed to prevent black men from the full employment of the gifts He gave them. Alongside of these very arguments we use others totally inconsistent, so that the accusation of repression may be refuted. We say we withhold education because the black child has not the intelligence to profit by it; we withhold opportunity to develop gifts because black people have no gifts; we justify our action by saying that it took us thousands of years to achieve our own advancement, and it would be foolish to suppose that it will take the black man any lesser time, and that therefore there is no need for hurry. We shift our ground again when a black man does achieve something remarkable, and feel deep pity for a man who is condemned to the loneliness of being

remarkable, and decide that it is a Christian kindness not to let black men become remarkable. Thus even our God becomes a confused and inconsistent creature, giving gifts and denying them employment. Is it strange then that our civilisation is riddled through and through with dilemma? The truth is that our civilisation is not Christian; it is a tragic compound of great ideal and fearful practice, of high assurance and desperate anxiety, of loving charity and fearful clutching of possessions. Allow me a minute. . . .

Jarvis sat, deeply moved. Whether because this was his son, whether because this was almost the last act of his son, he could not say. Whether because there was some quality in the words, that too he could not say, for he had given little time in his [152/153] life to the savouring and judging of words. Whether because there was some quality in the ideas, that too he could not say, for he had given little time to the study of these particular matters. He rose and went up the stairs to his room, and was glad to find his wife not there, for here was a sequence not to be interrupted. He picked up the Abraham Lincoln and went down to the study again, and there opened the book at the Second Inaugural Address of the great president. He read it through, and felt with a sudden lifting of the spirit that here was a secret unfolding, a track picked up again. There was increasing knowledge of a stranger. He began to understand why the picture of this man was in the house of his son, and the multitude of books.

He picked up the page again, but for his son, not for the words or the ideas. He looked at the words.

Allow me a minute. . . .

And nothing more. Those fingers would not write any more. Allow me a minute, I hear a sound in the kitchen. Allow a minute, while I go to my death. Allow me a thousand minutes, I am not coming back any more.

Jarvis shook it off, and put another match to his pipe, and after he had read the paper through, sat in a reverie, smoking.

— James.

He started. Yes, my dear, he said.

— You shouldn't sit by yourself, she said.

He smiled at her. It's not my nature to brood, he said.

— Then what have you been doing?

— Thinking. Not brooding, thinking. And reading. This is what I have been reading.

She took it, looked at it, and held it against her breast.

— Read it, he said quietly, it's worth reading.

So she sat down to read it, and he watching her, knew what she would do. She turned to the last page, to the last words, Allow me a minute, and sat looking at them. She looked at him, she was going to speak, he accepted that. Pain does not go away so quickly. [**153/154**]

XXII

At the head of the Court is a high seat where the Judge sits. Down below it is a table for officers of the Court, and to the left and to the right of the table are other seats. Some of these seats form a block that is enclosed, and they are for the jury if there is a jury. In front of the table are other seats, arranged in arcs of circles, with curved tables in front of the seats and it is there that the lawyers sit. And behind them is the dock, with a passage leading to some place that is underground, and from this place that is underground will be brought the men that are to be judged. At the back of the Court there are seats rising in tiers, those on the right for Europeans, those on the left for non-Europeans, according to the custom.

You may not smoke in this Court, you may not whisper or speak or laugh. You must dress decently, and if you are a man, you may not wear your hat unless such is your religion. This is in honour of the Judge and in honour of the King whose officer he is; and in honour of the Law behind the Judge, and in honour of the People behind the Law. When the Judge enters you will stand, and you will not sit till he is seated. When the Judge leaves you will stand, and you will not move till he has left you. This is in honour of the Judge, and of the things behind the Judge.

For to the Judge is entrusted a great duty, to judge and to pronounce sentence, even sentence of death. Because of their high office, Judges are called Honourable, and precede most other men on great occasions. And they are held in great honour by men both white and black. Because the land is a land of fear, a Judge must be without fear, so that justice may be [**154/ 155**] done according to the Law; therefore a Judge must be incorruptible.

The Judge does not make the Law. It is the People that make the Law. Therefore if a Law is unjust, and if the Judge judges according to the Law, that is justice, even if it is not just.

It is the duty of a Judge to do justice, but it is only the People that can be just. Therefore if justice be not just, that is not to be laid at the door of the Judge, but at the door of the People, which means at the door of the White People, for it is the White People that make the Law.

In South Africa men are proud of their Judges, because they believe they are incorruptible. Even the black men have faith in them, though they do not always have faith in the Law. In a land of fear this incorruptibility is like a lamp set upon a stand, giving light to all that are in the house.

* * * * *

They call for silence in the Court, and the people stand. Even if there were one there greater than the Judge he would stand, for behind the Judge are things greater than any man. And the Judge enters with his two assessors, and they sit, and then the people sit also. The Court is begun.

From the place under the ground come the three that are to be judged, and all the people look at them. Some people think that they look like murderers, they even whisper it, though it is dangerous to whisper. Some people think they do not look like murderers, and some think this one looks like a murderer, but that one does not.

A white man stands up and says that these three are accused of the murder of Arthur Trevelyan Jarvis, in his house at Plantation Road, Parkwold, Johannesburg, on Tuesday the eighth day of October, 1946, in the early afternoon. The first is Absalom Kumalo, the second is Matthew Kumalo, the third is Johannes Pafuri. They are called upon to plead guilty or not guilty, and the first says, I plead guilty to killing, but I did not mean to kill. The second says I am not guilty, and the third likewise. Everything is said in English and in Zulu, so [155/156] that these three may understand. For though Pafuri is not a Zulu, he understands it well, he says.

The lawyer, the white man who is taking the case for God, says that Absalom Kumalo will plead guilty to culpable homicide, but not to murder, for he had no intention to kill. But the prosecutor says there is no charge of culpable homicide; for it is murder, and nothing less than murder, with which he is charged. So Absalom Kumalo pleads, like the two others, not guilty.

Then the prosecutor speaks for a long time, and tells the Court the whole story of the crime. And Absalom Kumalo is still and silent, but the other two look grieved and shocked to think such things are said.

*   *   *   *   *

— Then after this plan was made you decided on this day, the eighth day of October?

— That is so.

— Why did you choose this day?

— Because Johannes said that no one would be in the house.

— This same Johannes Pafuri?

— This same Johannes Pafuri who is charged with me now.

— And you chose this time of half past one?

— That is so.

— Was it not a bad time to choose? White people come home to eat at this time.

But the accused makes no answer.

— Why did you choose this time?

— It was Johannes who chose this time. He said it was told to him by a voice.

— What voice?

— No, that I do not know.

— An evil voice?

And again there is no answer.

— Then you three went to the back door of the house?

— That is so.

— You and these two who are charged with you?

— I and these very two. [156/157]

— And then?

— Then we tied the handkerchiefs over our mouths.

— And then?

— Then we went into the kitchen.

— Who was there?

— The servant of the house was there.

— Richard Mpiring?

— No, I do not know his name.

— Is this the man here?

— Yes, that is the man.

— And then? Tell the Court what happened.

— This man was afraid. He saw my revolver. He stood back against the sink where he was working. He said, what do you want? Johannes said, we want money and clothes. This man said, you cannot do such a thing. Johannes said, do you want to die? This man was afraid and did not speak. Johannes said, when I speak, people must tremble. Then he said again, do you want to die? The man said nothing, but he suddenly called out, master, master. Then Johannes struck him over the head with the iron bar that he had behind his back.

— How many times did he strike him?
— Once.
— Did he call out again?
— He made no sound.
— What did you do?
— No, we were silent. Johannes said we must be silent.
— What did you do? Did you listen?
— We listened.
— Did you hear anything?
— We heard nothing.
— Where was your revolver?
— In my hand.
— And then?
— Then a white man came into the passage.
— And then?
— I was frightened. I fired the revolver.
— And then? [157/158]

The accused looked down at the floor. The white man fell, he said.

— And then?
— Johannes said quickly, we must go. So we all went quickly.
— To the back gate?
— Yes.
— And then over the road into the plantation?
— Yes.
— Did you stay together?
— No, I went alone.
— And when did you see these two again?
— At the house of Baby Mkize.

But the Judge interrupts. You may proceed shortly with your examination, Mr. Prosecutor. But I have one or two questions to ask the first accused.

— As your lordship pleases.
— But why do you carry any revolver?
— It was to frighten the servant of the house.
— Why did you carry this revolver?

The boy is silent.

— You must answer my question.
— They told me to carry it.
— Who told you?
— No, they told me Johannesburg was dangerous.
— Who told you?

The boy is silent.

— You mean you were told by the kind of man who is engaged in this business of breaking in and stealing?
— No, I do not mean that.
— Well, who told you?
— I do not remember. It was said in some place where I was.
— You mean you were all sitting there, and some man said, one needs a revolver in Johannesburg, it is dangerous?
— Yes, I mean that.
— And you knew this revolver was loaded?
— Yes, I knew it. [158/159]
— If this revolver is to frighten people, why must it be loaded?

But the boy does not answer.

— You were therefore ready to shoot with it?
— No, I would not have shot a decent person. I would have shot only if someone had shot at me.
— Would you have shot at a policeman if he had shot at you in the execution of his duty?
— No, not at a policeman.

The Judge pauses and everything is silent. Then he says gravely, and this white man you shot, was he not a decent person?

The accused looks down again at the floor. Then he answers in a low voice, I was afraid, I was afraid. I never meant to shoot him.

— Where did you get this revolver?
— I bought it from a man.
— Where?
— In Alexandra.
— Who is this man? What is his name?
— I do not know his name.
— Where does he live?
— I do not know where he lives.
— Could you find him?

— I could try to find him.

— Was this revolver loaded when you bought it?

— It had two bullets in it.

— How many bullets were in it when you went to this house?

— There was one bullet in it.

— What happened to the other?

— I took the revolver into one of the plantations in the hills beyond Alexandra, and I fired it there.

— What did you fire at?

— I fired at a tree.

— Did you hit this tree?

— Yes, I hit it. [**159/160**]

— Then you thought, now I can fire this revolver?

— Yes, that is so.

— Who carried the iron bar?

— Johannes carried it.

— Did you know he carried it?

— I knew it.

— You knew it was a dangerous weapon? That it could kill a man?

The boy's voice rises. It was not meant for killing or striking, he said. It was meant only for frightening.

— But you had a revolver for frightening?

— Yes, but Johannes said he would take the bar. It had been blessed, he said.

— It had been blessed?

— That is what he said.

— What did Johannes mean when he said the bar had been blessed?

— I do not know.

— Did he mean by a priest?

— I do not know.

— You did not ask?

— No, I did not ask.

— Your father is a priest?

The boy looks down again at the floor and in a low voice he answers, yes.

— Would he bless such a bar?

— No.

— You did not say to Johannes, you must not take this bar?

— No.

— You did not say to him, how can such a thing be blessed?

— No.

— Proceed, Mr. Prosecutor.

* * * * *

— And if these two say there was no murder discussed at the house of Baby Mkize, they are lying?

— They are lying. [**160/161**]

— And if they say that you made up this story after meeting them at the house of Mkize, they are lying?

— They are lying.

— And if Baby Mkize says that no murder was discussed in her presence, she is lying?

— She is lying. She was afraid, and said we must leave her house and never return to it.

— Did you leave together?

— No, I left first.

— And where did you go?

— I went into a plantation.

— And what did you do there?

— I buried the revolver.

— Is this the revolver before the Court?

The revolver is handed up to the accused and he examines it. This is the revolver, he says.

— How was it found?

— No, I told the Police where to find it.

— And what did you do next?

— I prayed there.

The Prosecutor seems taken aback for a moment, but the Judge says, and what did you pray there?

— I prayed for forgiveness.

— And what else did you pray?

— No, there was nothing else that I wished to pray.

* * * * *

— And on the second day you walked again to Johannesburg?

— Yes.

— And you again walked amongst the people who were boycotting the buses?

— Yes.

— Were they still talking about the murder?

— They were still talking. Some said they heard it would soon be discovered.

— And then?

— I was afraid. [161/162]

— So what did you do?

— That night I went to Germiston.

— But what did you do that day? Did you hide again?

— No, I bought a shirt, and then I walked about with the parcel.

— Why did you do that?

— No, I thought they would think I was a messenger.

— Was there anything else that you did?

— There was nothing else.

— Then you went to Germiston? To what place?

— To the house of Joseph Bhengu, at 12 Maseru Street, in the Location.

— And then?

— While I was there the Police came.

— What happened?

— They asked me if I was Absalom Kumalo. And I agreed, and I was afraid, and I had meant to go that day to confess to the Police, and now I could see I had delayed foolishly.

— Did they arrest you?

— No, they asked if I could tell them where to find Johannes. I said no, I did not know, but it was not Johannes who had killed the white man, it was I myself. But it was Johannes who had struck down the servant of the house. And I told them that Matthew was there also. And I told them I would show them where I had hidden the revolver. And I told them that I had meant that day to confess, but had delayed foolishly, because I was afraid.

— You then made a statement before Andries Coetzee, Esquire, Additional Magistrate at Johannesburg?

— I do not know his name.

— Is this the statement?

The statement is handed up to the boy. He looks at it and says, Yes, that is the statement.

— And every word is true?

— Every word is true.

— There is no lie in it?

— There is no lie in it, for I said to myself, I shall not lie [162/163] any more, all the rest of my days, nor do anything more that is evil.

— In fact you repented?

— Yes, I repented.

— Because you were in trouble?

— Yes, because I was in trouble.

— Did you have any other reason for repenting?

— No, I had no other reason.

*   *   *   *   *

The people stand when the Court is adjourned, and while the Judge and his assessors leave the Court. Then they pass out through the doors at the back of the tiers of seats, the Europeans through their door, and the non-Europeans through their door, according to the custom.

Kumalo and Msimangu, Gertrude and Mrs. Lithebe, come out together, and they hear people saying, there is the father of the white man who was killed. And Kumalo looks and sees that it is true, there is the father of the man who was murdered, the man who has the farm on the tops above Ndotsheni, the man he has seen riding past the church. And Kumalo trembles, and does not look at him any more. For how does one look at such a man? [163/164]

XXIII

There is little attention being paid to the trial of those accused of the murder of Arthur Jarvis of Parkwold. For gold has been discovered, more gold, rich gold. There is a little place called Odendaalsrust in the province of the Orange Free State. Yesterday it was quite unknown, today it is one of the famous places of the world.

This gold is as rich as any gold that has ever been discovered in South Africa, as rich as anything in Johannesburg. Men are prophesying that a new Johannesburg

will rise there, a great city of tall buildings and busy streets. Men that were
gloomy because the gold in Johannesburg could not last forever, are jubilant
and excited. A new lease of life, they say,
South Africa is to have a new lease of
life.

There is excitement in Johannesburg.
At the Stock Exchange men go mad, they
shout and scream and throw their hats in
the air, for the shares that they had
bought in hope, the shares that they had
bought in mines that did not exist, these
shares are climbing in price to heights
that are beyond expectation.

There was nothing there but the flat
rolling veld of the Orange Free State,
nothing but sheep and cattle and native
herd-boys. There was nothing but grass
and bushes, and here and there a field of
maize. There was nothing there that
looked like a mine, except the drilling
machines, and the patient engineers probing the mysteries of the earth; nobody to
watch them but a passing native, a herd-
boy, an old Afrikaans-speaking farmer
that would ride by on his horse, looking
at them with contempt or fear or hope,
according to his nature. [164/165]

Look at the wonder-share of Tweede
Vlei. For it was twenty shillings, and then
forty shillings, and then sixty shillings,
and then—believe it or not—eighty shillings. And many a man wept because he
sold at twelve o'clock instead of two
o'clock, or because he bought at two
o'clock instead of twelve o'clock. And the
man that sold will feel worse tomorrow
morning, when the shares go to a hundred
shillings.

Oh, but it is wonderful, South Africa
is wonderful. We shall hold up our heads
the higher when we go abroad, and people
say, ah, but you are rich in South Africa.

Odendaalsrust, what a name of magic.
Yet some of them are already saying at
the Stock Exchange, for their Afrikaans
is nothing to wonder at, that there must
be a simpler name. What could be easier
than Smuts or Smutsville? What could be
easier than Hofmeyr—no—but there is a

place called Hofmeyr already and apart
from that—well—perhaps it is not quite
the name after all.

That is the worst of these mines, their
names are unpronounceable. What a pity
that a great industry, controlled by such
brains, advanced by such enterprise,
should be hampered by such unpronounceable names; Blyvooruitzicht, and
Welgedacht, and Langlaagte, and now
this Odendaalsrust. But let us say these
things into our beards, let us say them in
our clubs, let us say them in private, for
most of us are members of the United
Party, that stands for co-operation and
fellowship and brotherly love and mutual
understanding. But it would save a devil
of a lot of money, if Afrikaners could only
see that bilingualism was a devil of a
waste of it.

*   *   *   *   *

Gold, gold, gold. The country is going
to be rich again. Shares are up from
twenty shillings to a hundred shillings,
think of it, thank God for it. There are
people, it is true, who are not very thankful. But it must be admitted that they do
not hold many shares, indeed it must be
admitted that some hold no shares at all.
Some of these people are speaking in public, and indeed it is interesting and ex-
asperating to some, to note at this point
that [165/166] very often people without
shares have quite a trick of words, as
though Destiny or Nature or the Life
Force or whoever controls these things,
gives some sort of compensation. Not in
any kindly way, you understand, but not
ironically either, just impersonally. But
this is a fanciful idea, and in fact it might
have been better not to have mentioned it.
Now these people, with this trick of words
but no financial standing to talk of, speak
mostly to small organisations like Left
Clubs and Church Guilds and societies
that promote love and brotherhood. And
they write too, but mostly for small pub-
lications like New Society and Mankind
is Marching; and for that extraordinary
Cross at the Crossroads, an obscure eight-

page pamphlet brought out weekly by that extraordinary Father Beresford, who looks as though he hasn't eaten for weeks. But he speaks beautiful English, the kind they speak at Oxford, I mean, not the kind they speak at Rhodes or Stellenbosch, and that makes him acceptable, for he never brushes his hair or has his trousers pressed. He looks for all the world like a converted tiger, and has burning eyes; and in fact he burns bright in the forests of the night, writing his extraordinary paper. He is a missionary and believes in God, intensely I mean, but it takes all kinds to make a world.

Well, some of these people are saying it would be nice if these shares could have stayed at twenty shillings, and the other eighty shillings had been used, for example, to erect great anti-erosion works to save the soil of the country. It would have been nice to have subsidised boys' clubs and girls' clubs, and social centres, and to have had more hospitals. It would have been nice to have paid more to the miners.

Well anyone can see that this thinking is muddled, because the price of shares has really nothing to do with the question of wages at all, for this is a matter determined solely by mining costs and the price of gold. And by the way, it is said too that there are actually some big men in the mines who hold no shares at all, and this is fine to think of, because it must really be a temptation.

In any case, we mustn't be too gloomy, as we might be disposed to be when we think that this eighty shillings has gone into [166/167] something that isn't any different from what it was before the eighty shillings went into it. Let us look at it in another way. When shares rise from twenty shillings to a hundred shillings, someone makes eighty shillings. Not necessarily one man, because that would be too good to be true, and entitle such a man to be known as a financial wizard, and as a figure behind the Government. It's more likely that several men will share this eighty shillings, because they

get nervous and sell out while the share has a lot of kick in it. It's true of course that these men don't actually work for this money, I mean, actually sweat and callous their hands. But a man must get something for his courage and foresight, and there's mental strain too, to be taken into consideration. Now these men will spend the eighty shillings, and make more work for other people, so that the country will be richer for the eighty shillings. And many of them give generously to the boys' clubs and girls' clubs, and the social centres, and the hospitals. It is wrong to say, as they do in remote places like Bloemfontein and Grahamstown and Beaufort West, that Johannesburg thinks only of money. We have as many good husbands and fathers, I think, as any town or city, and some of our big men make great collections of works of art, which means work for artists, and saves art from dying out; and some have great ranches in the North, where they shoot game and feel at one with Nature.

Now when there is more work for other people, these people will start spending part of this eighty shillings. Not all of it, of course, for the men who sell at a hundred shillings must keep some to buy back the shares when they haven't got quite so much kick in them. But the farmers will be able to produce more food, and the manufacturers will be able to make more articles, and the Civil Service will be able to offer more posts, though why we should want more Civil Servants is another question that we can hardly deal with here. And the natives need not starve in these reserves. The men can come to the mines and bigger and better compounds can be built for them, and still more vitamins be put in their food. But we shall have to be careful about that, because some fellow has discovered that labour can be over- [167/168] vitaminised. This is an example of the Law of Diminishing Returns.

And perhaps a great city will grow up, a second Johannesburg, with a second Parktown and a second Houghton, a second Parkwold and a second Kensington, a second Jeppe and a second Vrededorp, a second Pimville and a second Shanty Town, a great city that will be the pride of any Odendaalsruster. But isn't that name impossible?

* * * * *

But there are some who say that it must not be so. All the welfare workers and this Father Beresford and the other Kafferboeties say it must not be so, though it must be admitted that most of them haven't one share-certificate to rub against another. And they take heart too, for Sir Ernest Oppenheimer, one of the great men of the mines, has also said that it need not be so. For here is a chance, he says, to try out the experiment of settled mine labour, in villages, not compounds, where a man can live with his wife and children. And there is talk too that the Government will set up something like the Tennessee Valley Authority, to control the development of the Free State mining areas.

They want to hear your voice again, Sir Ernest Oppenheimer. Some of them applaud you, and some of them say thank God for you, in their hearts, even at their bedsides. For mines are for men, not for money. And money is not something to go mad about, and throw your hat into the air for. Money is for food and clothes and comfort, and a visit to the pictures. Money is to make happy the lives of children. Money is for security, and for dreams, and for hopes, and for purposes. Money is for buying the fruits of the earth, of the land where you were born.

* * * * *

No second Johannesburg is needed upon the earth. One is enough. [168/169]

XXIV

Jarvis thought he would go to the house again. It was foolish to go through the kitchen, past the stain on the floor, up the stairs that led to the bedroom. But that was the way he went. He went not to the bedroom but to the study that was so full of books. And he went round the books again, past the case full of Abraham Lincoln, and the case full of South Africa, and the case full of Afrikaans, and the case full of religion and sociology and crime and criminals, and the case full of poetry and novels and Shakespeare. He looked at the pictures of the Christ crucified, and Abraham Lincoln, and Vergelegen, and the willows in the winter. He sat down at the table, where lay the invitations to do this and that, and the invitations to come to this and that, and the paper on what was permissible and what was not permissible in South Africa.

He opened the drawers of his son's table, and here were accounts, and here were papers and envelopes, and here were pens and pencils, and here were old cheques stamped and returned by the bank. And here in a deep drawer were typewritten articles, each neatly pinned together, and placed one on top of the other. Here was an article on "The Need for Social Centres" and one on "Birds of a Parkwold Garden," and another on "India and South Africa." And here was one called "Private Essay on the Evolution of a South African," and this he took out to read:

It is hard to be born a South African. One can be born an Afrikaner, or an English-speaking South African, or a coloured man, or a Zulu. One can ride, as I rode when I was a boy, over green hills and into great valleys. One can see, [169/170] as I saw when I was a boy, the reserves of the Bantu people and see nothing of what was happening there at all. One can hear, as I heard when I was a boy, that there are more Afrikaners than English-speaking peoples in South Africa, and yet know nothing, see nothing, of them at all. One can read, as I read when I was a boy, the brochures about lovely South Africa, that land of sun and beauty sheltered from the storms of the world, and feel pride in it and love for it, and yet know nothing about it at all. It is only as one grows up that one learns that there are other things here than sun and gold and oranges. It is only then that one learns of the hates and fears of our country. It is only then that one's love grows deep and passionate, as a man may love a woman who is true, false, cold, loving, cruel, and afraid.

I was born on a farm, brought up by honourable parents, given all that a child could need or desire. They were upright and kind and law-abiding; they taught me my prayers and took me regularly to church; they had no trouble with servants and my father was never short of labour. From them I learned all that a child should learn of honour and charity and generosity. But of South Africa I learned nothing at all.

Shocked and hurt, Jarvis put down the papers. For a moment he felt something almost like anger, but he wiped his eyes with his fingers and shook it from him. But he was trembling and could read no further. He stood up and put on his hat, and went down the stairs, and as far as the stain on the floor. The policeman was ready to salute him, but he turned again, and went up the stairs, and sat down again at the table. He took up the papers and read them through to the end. Perhaps he was some judge of words after all, for the closing paragraphs moved him. Perhaps he was some judge of ideas after all.

Therefore I shall devote myself, my time, my energy, my talents, to the service of South Africa. I shall no longer ask myself if this or that is expedient, but only if it is right. I **[170/171]** shall do this, not because I am noble or unselfish, but because life slips away, and because I need for the rest of my journey a star that will not play false to me, a compass that will not lie. I shall do this, not because I am a negrophile and a hater of my own, but because I cannot find it in me to do anything else. I am lost when I balance this against that, I am lost when I ask if this is safe, I am lost when I ask if men, white men or black men, Englishmen or Afrikaners, Gentiles or Jews, will approve. Therefore I shall try to do what is right, and to speak what is true.

I do this not because I am courageous and honest, but because it is the only way to end the conflict of my deepest soul. I do it because I am no longer able to aspire to the highest with one part of myself, and to deny it with another. I do not wish to live like that, I would rather die than live like that. I understand better those who have died for their convictions, and have not thought it was wonderful or brave or noble to die. They died rather than live, that was all.

Yet it would not be honest to pretend that it is solely an inverted selfishness that moves me. I am moved by something that is not my own, that moves me to do what is right, at whatever cost it may be. In this I am fortunate that I have married a wife who thinks as I do, who has tried to conquer her own fears and hates. Aspiration is thus made easy. My children are too young to understand. It would be grievous if they grew up to hate me or fear me, or to think of me as a betrayer of those things that I call our possessions. It would be a source of unending joy if they grew up to think as we do. It would be exciting, exhilarating, a matter for thanksgiving. But it cannot be bargained for. It must be given or withheld, and whether the one or the other, it must not alter the course that is right.

Jarvis sat a long time smoking, he did not read any more. He put the papers back in the drawer and closed it. He sat there till his pipe was finished. When it was done he put on his hat and came down the stairs. At the foot of the stairs he turned [**171/172**] and walked towards the front door. He was not afraid of the passage and the stain on the floor; he was not going that way any more, that was all.

The front door was self-locking and he let himself out. He looked up at the sky from the farmer's habit, but these skies of a strange country told him nothing. He walked down the path and out of the gate. The policeman at the back door heard the door lock, and shook his head with understanding. He cannot face it any more, he said to himself, the old chap cannot face it any more. [**172/173**]

XXV

One of the favourite nieces of Margaret Jarvis, Barbara Smith by name, had married a man from Springs, and both Jarvis and his wife, on a day when the Court was not holding the case, went to spend a day with them. He had thought it would be a good thing for his wife, who had taken the death of their son even more hardly than he had feared. The two women talked of the people of Ixopo and Lufafa and Highflats and Umzimkulu, and he left them and walked in the garden, for he was a man of the soil. After a while they called to him to say they were going into the town, and asked if he wished to go with them. But he said that he would stay at the house, and read the newspaper while they were away, and this he did.

The newspaper was full of the new gold that was being found at Odendaalsrust, and of the great excitement that still prevailed on the share-market. Someone with authority was warning people against buying at higher and still higher prices, and saying that there was no proof that these shares were worth what they were fetching, and that they might come down after a while and cause much loss of money and much suffering. There was some crime

too; most of the assaults reported were by natives against Europeans, but there was nothing of the terrible nature that made some people afraid to open their newspapers.

While he was reading there was a knock at the kitchen door, and he went out to find a native parson standing on the paved stone at the foot of the three stone steps that led up to the kitchen. The parson was old, and his black clothes were green with age, and his collar was brown with age or dirt. He took off [**173/174**] his hat, showing the whiteness of his head, and he looked startled and afraid and he was trembling.

— Good morning, umfundisi, said Jarvis in Zulu, of which he was a master.

The parson answered in a trembling voice, Umnumzana, which means Sir, and to Jarvis' surprise, he sat down on the lowest step, as though he were ill or starving. Jarvis knew this was not rudeness, for the old man was humble and well-mannered, so he came down the steps, saying, Are you ill, umfundisi? But the old man did not answer. He continued to tremble, and he looked down on the ground, so that Jarvis could not see his face, and could not have seen it unless he had lifted the chin with his hand, which he did not do, for such a thing is not lightly done.

— Are you ill, umfundisi?

— I shall recover, umnumzana.

— Do you wish water? Or is it food? Are you hungry?

— No, umnumzana, I shall recover.

Jarvis stood on the paved stone below the lowest step, but the old man was not quick to recover. He continued to tremble, and to look at the ground. It is not easy for a white man to be kept waiting, but Jarvis waited, for the old man was obviously ill and weak. The old man made an effort to rise, using his stick, but the stick slipped on the paved stone, and fell clattering on the stone. Jarvis picked it up and restored it to him, but the old man put it down as a hindrance, and he put down his hat also, and tried to lift himself up by pressing his hands on the steps. But his first effort failed, and he sat down again, and continued to tremble. Jarvis would have helped him, but such a thing is not so lightly done as picking up a stick; then the old man pressed his hands again on the steps, and lifted himself up. Then he lifted his face also and looked at Jarvis, and Jarvis saw that his face was full of a suffering that was of neither illness nor hunger. And Jarvis stooped, and picked up the hat and stick, and he held the hat carefully for it was old and dirty, and he restored them to the parson.

— I thank you, umnumzana.

— Are you sure you are not ill, umfundisi? [174/175]

— I am recovered, umnumzana.

— And what are you seeking, umfundisi?

The old parson put his hat and his stick down again on the step, and with trembling hands pulled out a wallet from the inside pocket of the old green coat, and the papers fell out on the ground, because his hands would not be still.

— I am sorry, umnumzana.

He stooped to pick up the papers, and because he was old he had to kneel, and the papers were old and dirty, and some that he had picked up fell out of his hands while he was picking up others, and the wallet fell too, and the hands were trembling and shaking. Jarvis was torn between compassion and irritation, and he stood and watched uncomfortably.

— I am sorry to detain you, umnumzana.

— It is no matter, umfundisi.

At last the papers were collected, and all were restored to the wallet except one, and this one he held out to Jarvis, and on it were the name and address of this place where they were.

— This is the place, umfundisi.

— I was asked to come here, umnumzana. There is a man named Sibeko of Ndotsheni—

— Ndotsheni, I know it. I come from Ndotsheni.

— And this man had a daughter, umnumzana, who worked for a white man uSmith in Ixopo—

— Yes, yes.

— And when the daughter of uSmith married, she married the white man whose name is on the paper.

— That is so.

— And they came to live here in Springs, and the daughter of Sibeko came here also to work for them. Now Sibeko has not heard of her for these twelve months, and he asked—I am asked—to enquire about this girl.

Jarvis turned and went into the house, and returned with the boy who was working there. You may enquire from him, he said, and he turned again and went into the house. But when he was there it came suddenly to him that this was the old parson of Ndotsheni himself. So he came out again. [175/176]

— Did you find what you wanted, umfundisi?

— This boy does not know her, umnumzana. When he came she had gone already.

— The mistress of the house is out, the daughter of uSmith. But she will soon be returning, and you may wait for her if you wish.

Jarvis dismissed the boy, and waited till he was gone.

— I know you, umfundisi, he said.

The suffering in the old man's face smote him, so that he said, sit down, umfundisi. Then the old man would be able to look at the ground, and he would not need to look at Jarvis, and Jarvis would not need to look at him, for it was uncomfortable to look at him. So the old man sat down and Jarvis said to him, not looking at him, there is something between you and me, but I do not know what it is.

— Umnumzana.

— You are in fear of me, but I do not know what it is. You need not be in fear of me.

— It is true, umnumzana. You do not know what it is.

— I do not know but I desire to know.

— I doubt if I could tell it, umnumzana.

— You must tell it, umfundisi. Is it heavy?

— It is very heavy, umnumzana. It is the heaviest thing of all my years.

He lifted his face, and there was in it suffering that Jarvis had not seen before. Tell me, he said, it will lighten you.

— I am afraid, umnumzana.

— I see you are afraid, umfundisi. It is that which I do not understand. But I tell you, you need not be afraid. I shall not be angry. There will be no anger in me against you.

— Then, said the old man, this thing that is the heaviest thing of all my years, is the heaviest thing of all your years also.

Jarvis looked at him, at first bewildered, but then something came to him. You can only mean one thing, he said, you can only mean one thing. But I still do not understand.

— It was my son that killed your son, said the old man.

So they were silent. Jarvis left him and walked out into the [176/177] trees of the garden. He stood at the wall and looked out over the veld, out to the great white dumps of the mines, like hills under the sun. When he turned to come back, he saw that the old man had risen, his hat in one hand, his stick in the other, his head bowed, his eyes on the ground. He went back to him.

— I have heard you, he said. I understand what I did not understand. There is no anger in me.

— Umnumzana.

— The mistress of the house is back, the daughter of uSmith. Do you wish to see her? Are you recovered?

— It was that that I came to do, umnumzana.

— I understand. And you were shocked when you saw me. You had no thought that I would be here. How did you know me?

— I have seen you riding past Ndotsheni, past the church where I work.

Jarvis listened to the sounds in the house. Then he spoke very quietly. Perhaps you saw the boy also, he said. He too used to ride past Ndotsheni. On a red horse with a white face. And he carried wooden guns, here in his belt, as small boys do.

The old man's face was working. He continued to look on the ground, and Jarvis could see that tears fell on it. He himself was moved and unmanned, and he would have brought the thing to an end, but he could find no quick voice for it.

— I remember, umnumzana. There was a brightness in him.

— Yes, yes, said Jarvis, there was a brightness in him.

— Umnumzana, it is a hard word to say. But my heart holds a deep sorrow for you, and for the inkosikazi, and for the young inkosikazi, and for the children.

— Yes, yes, said Jarvis. Yes, yes, he said fiercely. I shall call the mistress of the house.

He went in and brought her out with him. This old man, he said in English, has come to enquire about the daughter of a native named Sibeko, who used to work for you in Ixopo. They have heard nothing of her for months.

— I had to send her away, said Smith's daughter. She was good when she started, and I promised her father to look after [177/178] her. But she went to the bad and started to brew liquor in her room. She was arrested and sent to gaol for a month, and after that of course I could not take her back again.

— You do not know where she is, asked Jarvis.

— I'm sure I do not know, said Smith's daughter in English. And I do not care.

— She does not know, said Jarvis in Zulu. But he did not add that Smith's daughter did not care.

— I thank you, said the old man in Zulu. Stay well, umnumzana. And he bowed to Smith's daughter and she nodded her acknowledgement.

He put on his hat and started to walk down the path to the back gate, according to the custom. Smith's daughter went into the house, and Jarvis followed the old man slowly, as though he were not following him. The old man opened the gate and went out through it and closed it behind him. As he turned to close it he saw that Jarvis had followed him, and he bowed to him.

— Go well, umfundisi, said Jarvis.

— Stay well, umnumzana. The old man raised his hat and put it back again on his head. Then he started to walk slowly down the road to the station, Jarvis watching him until he was out of sight. As he turned to come back, he saw that his wife was coming to join him, and he saw with a pang that she too walked as if she were old.

He walked to join her, and she put her arm in his.

— Why are you so disturbed, James, she asked. Why were you so disturbed when you came into the house?

— Something that came out of the past, he said. You know how it comes suddenly?

She was satisfied, and said, I know.

She held his arm more closely. Barbara wants us for lunch, she said. [**178/179**]

XXVI

The great bull voice is speaking there in the square. There are many policemen there, both white and black; it gives one no doubt a sense of power to see them there, and to be speaking to so many people, for the great bull voice growls and rises and falls.

There are those who can be moved by the sound of the voice alone. There are those who remember the first day they heard it as if it were today, who remember their excitement, and the queer sensations of their bodies as though electricity were passing through them. For the voice has magic in it, and it has threatening in it, and it is as though Africa itself were in it. A lion growls in it, and thunder echoes in it over black mountains.

Dubula and Tomlinson listen to it, with contempt, and with envy. For here is a voice to move thousands, with no brain behind it to tell it what to say, with no courage to say it if it knew.

The policemen hear it, and one says to the other, this man is dangerous. And the other says, it is not my job to think about such things.

We do not ask for what cannot be given, says John Kumalo. We ask only for our share of what is produced by our labour. New gold has been found, and South Africa is rich again. We ask only for our share of it. This gold will stay in the bowels of the earth if we do not dig it out. I do not say it is our gold, I say only that we should get our share in it. It is the gold of the whole people, the white, and the black, and the coloured, and the Indian. But who will get the most of this gold? [**179/180**]

And here the great voice growls in the bull throat. A wave of excitement passes through the crowd. The policemen stand more alert, except those who have heard this before. For they know that this Kumalo goes so far and no further. What if this voice should say words that it speaks already in private, should rise and not fall again, should rise and rise and rise, and the people rise with it, should madden them with thoughts of rebellion and dominion, with thoughts of power and possession? Should paint for them pictures of Africa awakening from sleep, of Africa resurgent, of Africa dark and savage? It would not be hard to do, it does not need a brain to think such words. But the man is afraid, and the deep thundering growl dies down, and the people shiver and come to themselves.

Is it wrong to ask more money, John Kumalo asks. We get little enough. It is only our share that we ask, enough to keep our wives and our families from starvation. For we do

not get enough. The Lansdown Commission said that we do not get
enough. The Smit Commission said
that we do not get enough.

And here the voice growls again, and
the people stir.

We know that we do not get
enough, Kumalo says. We ask only
for those things that labouring men
fight for in every country in the
world, the right to sell our labour for
what it is worth, the right to bring up
our families as decent men should.
They say that higher wages will
cause the mines to close down. Then
what is it worth, this mining industry? And why should it be kept alive,
if it is only our poverty that keeps it
alive? They say it makes the country
rich, but what do we see of these
riches? Is it we that must be kept poor
so that others may stay rich?

The crowd stirs as though a great wind
were blowing through it. Here is the moment, John Kumalo, for the great voice to
reach even to the gates of Heaven. Here is
the moment for [**180/181**] words of passion, for wild indiscriminate words that
can waken and madden and unleash. But
he knows. He knows the great power that
he has, the power of which he is afraid.
And the voice dies away, as thunder dies
away over mountains, and echoes and
re-echoes more and more faintly.
— I tell you, the man is dangerous,
said the one policeman.
— I believe you now that I have heard
him, said the other. Why don't they put
the bastard inside?
— Why don't they shoot him, asked
the first.
— Or shoot him, agreed the other.
— The Government is playing with
fire, said the first.
— I believe you, said the second.

All we ask is justice, says Kumalo.
We are not asking here for equality

and the franchise and the removal of
the colour-bar. We are asking only for
more money from the richest industry
in the world. This industry is power-
less without our labour. Let us cease
to work and this industry will die.
And I say, it is better to cease to work
than to work for such wages.

The native policemen are smart and
alert. They stand at their posts like soldiers. Who knows what they think of this
talk, who knows if they think at all? The
meeting is quiet and orderly. So long as
it stays quiet and orderly, there is nothing
to be done. But at the first sign of disorder,
John Kumalo will be brought down and
put in the van, and taken to some other
place. And what will happen to the carpenter's shop, that brings in eight, ten,
twelve pounds a week? What will happen
to the talks in the carpenter's shop, where
men come from every part of the country
to listen to him?
There are some men who long for
martyrdom, there are those who know that
to go to prison would bring greatness to
them, there are those who would go to
prison not caring if it brought greatness
or not. But John Kumalo is not one of
them. There is no applause in prison.
Who knows why a man has a gift and
buries it in a hole in [**181/182**] the
ground? Who knows why a man has a gift
and is afraid of it? Perhaps it is the time,
the country where he was born? Perhaps
it is the spirit that is too craven to contain
the gift.
Perhaps Dubula knows, or Tomlinson.
Perhaps Dubula, whose voice is only of
silver, who knows the art of persuasion,
perhaps he knows. Perhaps Tomlinson,
who has the brain amongst all these people, whose voice carries so little that most
people never hear him, perhaps he knows.
Perhaps they sit there groaning in spirit,
perhaps they sit there and see a vision that
can never become reality.

I shall not keep you any longer,
says John Kumalo. It is getting late,

and there is another speaker, and many of you will be in trouble with the police if you do not get home. It does not matter to me, but it matters to those of you who must carry a pass. And we do not wish to trouble the police. I tell you we have labour to sell, and it is a man's freedom to sell his labour for what it is worth. It is for that freedom that this war has just been fought. It is for that freedom that many of our own African soldiers have been fighting.

The voice growls again, something is coming.

Not only here, he says, but in all Africa, in all the great continent where we Africans live.

The people growl also. The one meaning of this is safe, but the other meaning is dangerous. And John Kumalo speaks the one meaning, and means the other meaning.

Therefore let us sell our labour for what it is worth, he says. And if an industry cannot buy our labour, let that industry die. But let us not sell our labour cheap to keep any industry alive.

John Kumalo sits down, and the people applaud him, a great wave of shouting and clapping. They are simple people, and [182/183] they do not know that this is one of the country's greatest orators, with one thing lacking. They have heard only the great bull voice, they have been lifted up, and let fall again, but by a man who can lift up again after he has let fall.

— Now you have heard him, said Msimangu.

Stephen Kumalo nodded his head. I have never heard its like, he said. Even I —his brother—he played with me as though I were a child.

— Power, said Msimangu, power. Why God should give such power is not for us to understand. If this man were a preacher, why, the whole world would follow him.

— I have never heard its like, said Kumalo.

— Perhaps we should thank God he is corrupt, said Msimangu solemnly. For if he were not corrupt, he could plunge this country into bloodshed. He is corrupted by his possessions, and he fears their loss, and the loss of the power he already has. We shall never understand it. Shall we go, or shall we listen to this man Tomlinson?

— I could listen to him.

— Then let us go nearer. He is difficult to hear.

* * * * *

— Shall we go, Mr. Jarvis?

— Yes, John, let's go.

— What did you think of it, Mr. Jarvis?

— I don't care for that sort of thing, said Jarvis briefly.

— I don't quite mean that. I mean, it's happening, isn't it?

Jarvis grunted. I don't care for it, John. Let's go on to your Club.

— He's too old to face it, thought John Harrison to himself. I don't blame him, nor my father.

He climbed into the car and started up the engine.

— But we have to face it, he reflected soberly.

* * * * *

The captain saluted the high officer.

— The report, sir. [183/184]

— How did it go, captain?

— No trouble, sir. But this man Kumalo is dangerous. He works the crowd up to a point, and then he pulls back. But I could imagine what he would be like if we weren't there.

— Well, we shall have to be there, that's all. It's strange, the reports always say that; he goes so far and no further. What do you mean, he's dangerous?

— It's the voice, sir. I've never heard anything like it. It's like the grand stop of an organ. You can see the whole crowd swaying. I felt it myself. It's almost as though he sees what's happening, and pulls himself in.

— Yellow, said the high officer briefly. I've heard that about the voice too. I must go to hear it myself one day.

— Will there be a strike, sir?

— Wish to God I knew. It may be a nasty business. As though we hadn't enough to do. It's time you went home.

— Goodnight, sir.

— Goodnight, Harry. Harry!

— Sir.

— I hear there may be a promotion for you.

— Thank you, sir.

— That puts you in line for my job one day. Good salary, high rank, prestige. And all the worry in the world. Like sitting on the top of a volcano. God knows if it's worth it. Goodnight, Harry.

— Goodnight, sir.

The high officer sighed, and pulled the papers toward him. Lines of worry puckered his brow.

— Good pay, high rank, prestige, he said. Then he settled down to work.

*　　*　　*　　*　　*

It will be a serious matter if there is a strike. For there are three hundred thousand black miners here on the Witwatersrand. They come from the Transkei, from Basutoland and Zululand and Bechuanaland and Sekukuniland, and from countries outside South Africa. They are simple people, illiterate, tribal [184/185] people, an easy tool in the hand. And when they strike they go mad; they imprison mine officials in their offices, and throw bottles and stones, and set places on fire. It is true they are in compounds in a hundred mines, and that makes control of them easier. But they can do great damage, and endanger human life, and bring the great industry of South Africa to a standstill, the industry on which South Africa was built up, and on which it depends.

There are worrying rumours about, that the strike will not be limited to the mines, but will spread to every kind of industry, to the railways and the ships.

There are even rumours that every black man, every black woman, will stop working; that every school, every church, will close. They will stand idle and sullen about the streets, in every city and town and village, on every road and every farm, eight millions of them. But such a thing is fantastic. They are not organized for it, they would suffer untold hardships, they would die of starvation. Yet the thought of so fantastic a thing is terrifying, and white people realise how dependent they are on the labour of the black people.

The times are anxious, there can be no doubt about that. Strange things are happening in the world, and the world has never let South Africa alone.

*　　*　　*　　*　　*

The strike has come and gone. It never went beyond the mines. The worst trouble was at the Driefontein, where the police were called in to drive the black miners into the mines. There was fighting, and three of the black miners were killed. But all is quiet, they report, all is quiet.

The Annual Synod of the Diocese of Johannesburg cannot be supposed to know too much about the mines. The days seem over when Synods confined themselves to religion, and one of the clergymen made a speech about the matter. He urged that it was time to recognise the African Mine Workers' Union, and prophesied a bloodbath if it were not. It is supposed that he meant that the Union should be treated as a responsible body, competent to negotiate with its employers about conditions of [185/186] work and pay. But a man called a spokesman has pointed out that the African Miners are simple souls, hardly qualified in the art of negotiation, and an easy tool for unscrupulous agitators. And in any event, everyone knows that rising costs would threaten the very existence of the mines, and the very existence of South Africa.

There are many sides to this difficult problem. And people persist in discussing soil-erosion, and tribal decay, and lack of schools, and crime, as though they were all parts of the matter. If you think long enough about it, you will be brought to consider republics, and bilingualism, and immigration, and Palestine, and God knows what. So in a way it is best not to think about it at all.

In the meantime the strike is over, with a remarkably low loss of life. All is quiet, they report, all is quiet.

*   *   *   *   *

In the deserted harbour there is yet water that laps against the quays. In the dark and silent forest there is a leaf that falls. Behind the polished panelling the white ant eats away the wood. Nothing is ever quiet, except for fools. [186/187]

XXVII

Mrs. Lithebe and Gertrude entered the house, and Mrs. Lithebe shut the door behind them.

— I have done my best to understand you, my daughter. But I do not succeed in it.

— I did no wrong.

— I do not say you did wrong. But you do not understand this house, you do not understand the people that live in it.

Gertrude stood sullenly. I do understand it, she said.

— Then why do you speak with such people, my daughter?

— I did not know they were not decent people.

— Do you not hear the way they speak, the way they laugh? Do you not hear them laugh idly and carelessly?

— I did not know it was wrong.

— I did not say it was wrong. It is idle and careless, the way they speak and laugh. Are you not trying to be a good woman?

— I am trying.

— Then such people will not help you.

— I hear you.

— I do not like to reproach you. But your brother the umfundisi has surely suffered enough.

— He has suffered.

— Then do not make him suffer further, my daughter.

— I shall be glad to leave this place, Gertrude said. The tears came into her eyes. I do not know what to do in this place.

— It is not this place only, said Mrs. Lithebe. Even in Ndotsheni you will find those who are ready to laugh and speak carelessly. [187/188]

— It is the place, said Gertrude. I have known nothing but trouble in this Johannesburg. I shall be glad to be gone.

— It will not be long before you go, for the case will finish tomorrow. But I am afraid for you, and for the umfundisi also.

— There is no need to be afraid.

— I am glad to hear it, my daughter. I am not afraid for the child, she is willing and obedient. She desires to please the umfundisi. And indeed it should be so, for she receives from him what her own father denied her.

— She can also talk carelessly.

— I am not blind, my child. But she learns otherwise, and she learns quickly. Let us finish with the matter. Someone is coming.

There was a knock at the door, and a great stout woman stood there, breathing heavily from her walk to the house. There is a bad thing in the paper, she said, I have brought it to show you. She put the paper down on the table, and showed the other women the headlines. ANOTHER MURDER TRAGEDY IN CITY. EUROPEAN HOUSEHOLDER SHOT DEAD BY NATIVE HOUSEBREAKER.

They were shocked. These were the headlines that men feared in these days. Householders feared them, and their wives feared them. All those who worked for South Africa feared them. All law-abiding black men feared them. Some people were urging the newspapers to drop the word native from their headlines, others found it hard to know what the hiding of the painful truth would do.

— It is a hard thing that this should

happen at this moment, said the stout woman, just when the case is to finish.

For she knew all about the case, and had gone each time with Mrs. Lithebe to the trial.

— That is a true thing that you say, said Mrs. Lithebe.

She heard the click of the gate, and threw the paper under a chair. It was Kumalo and the girl. The girl was holding his arm, for he was frail in these days. She guided him to his room, and they were hardly gone before the gate clicked again, and [188/189] Msimangu entered. His eyes fell on the paper at once, and he picked it up from under the chair.

— Has he seen it, he asked.

— No, umfundisi, said the stout woman. Is it not a hard thing that this should happen at this moment?

— This judge is a great judge, said Msimangu. But it is a hard thing, as you say. He likes to read the paper. What shall we do?

— There is no paper here but the one that she has brought, said Mrs. Lithebe. But when he goes to eat at the Mission House he will see it.

— That is why I came, said Msimangu. Mother, could we not eat here tonight?

— That is a small thing to ask. There is food enough, though it is simple.

— Indeed, mother, you are always our helper.

— For what else are we born, she said.

— And after the meal we can go straight to the meeting, said Msimangu. Tomorrow will be easy, he does not read the paper on the days we go to the case. And after that it will not matter.

So they hid the newspaper. They all ate at Mrs. Lithebe's, and after the meal they went to the meeting at the church, where a black woman spoke to them about her call to become a nun and to renounce the world, and how God had taken from her that desire which is in the nature of women.

After the meeting, when Msimangu had left, and Kumalo had gone to his room, and while the girl was making up the bed in the place where they ate and lived, Gertrude followed Mrs. Lithebe to her room.

— May I speak to you, mother?

— That is nothing to ask, my child.

She shut the door, and waited for Gertrude to speak.

— I was listening to the black sister, mother, and it came to me that perhaps I should become a nun.

Mrs. Lithebe clapped her hands, she was happy, and then solemn. [189/190]

— I clap my hands not because you should do it, she said, but because you should think of it. But there is the boy.

Gertrude's eyes filled with tears.

— Perhaps the wife of my brother would care better for him, she said. I am a weak woman, you know it. I laugh and speak carelessly. Perhaps it would help me to become a nun.

— You mean, the desire?

Gertrude hung her head. It is that I mean, she said.

Mrs. Lithebe took Gertrude's hands in hers.

— It would be a great thing, she said. But they say it is not to be done lightly or quickly. Did she not say so?

— She said so, mother.

— Let us keep it unspoken except between us. I shall pray for you, and you shall pray also. And after a time we shall speak again. Do you think that is wise?

— That is very wise, mother.

— Then sleep well, my daughter. I do not know if this will happen. But if it happens, it will comfort the old man.

— Sleep well, mother.

Gertrude closed the door of Mrs. Lithebe's room, and on the way to her own, moved by sudden impulse, she dropped on the floor by the bed of the girl.

— I have a feeling to become a nun, she said.

The girl sat up in her blankets.

— Au! she said, that is a hard thing.

— It is a hard thing, said Gertrude, I am not yet decided. But if it should be so, would you care for the boy?

— Indeed, the girl answered, and her

face was eager. Indeed I should care for him.

— As though he were your own?

— Indeed so. As though he were my own.

— And you will not talk carelessly before him?

The girl was solemn. I do not talk carelessly any more, she said.

— I too shall not talk carelessly any more, said Gertrude. Remember, it is not yet decided.

— I shall remember. **[190/191]**

— And you must not speak of it yet. My brother would be grieved if we talked of it and decided otherwise.

— I understand you.

— Sleep well, small one.

— Sleep well. **[191/192]**

XXVIII

The people stand when the great Judge comes into the Court, they stand more solemnly today, for this is the day of the judgement. The Judge sits, and then his two assessors, and then the people; and the three accused are brought from the place under the Court.

I have given long thought and consideration to this case, says the Judge, and so have my assessors. We have listened carefully to all the evidence that has been brought forward, and have discussed it and tested it piece by piece.

And the interpreter interprets into Zulu what the Judge has said:

The accused Absalom Kumalo has not sought to deny his guilt. The defence has chosen to put the accused in the witness-box, where he has told straightforwardly and simply the story of how he shot the late Arthur Jarvis in his house at Park-wold. He has maintained further that it was not his intention to kill or even to shoot, that the weapon was brought to intimidate the servant Richard Mpiring,

that he supposed the murdered man to have been elsewhere. With this evidence we must later deal, but part of it is of the gravest importance in determining the guilt of the second and third accused. The first accused states that the plan was put forward by the third accused Johannes Pafuri, and that Pafuri struck the blow that rendered unconscious the servant Mpiring. In this he is supported by Mpiring himself, who says that he recognised Pafuri by the twitching of the eyes above the mask. It is further true that he picked out **[192/193]** Pafuri from among ten men similarly disguised, more than one of whom suffered from a tic similar to that suffered by Pafuri. But the defence has pointed out that these tics were similar and not identical, that it was difficult to find even a few men of similar build with any tic at all, and that Pafuri was well-known to Mpiring. The defence has argued that the identification would have been valid only if all ten men had been of similar build and had suffered from identical tics. We cannot accept this argument in its entirety, because it would seem to lead to the conclusion that identification is only valid when all the subjects are identical. But the partial validity of the argument is clear; a marked characteristic like a tic can lead as easily to wrong identification as to correct identification, especially when the lower half of the face is concealed. It must be accepted that identification depends on the recognition of a pattern, of a whole, and that it becomes uncertain when the pattern is partially concealed. In fact it becomes dangerous, because it would obviously be possible to conceal the unlike features, and to reveal only the like. Two people with similar scars, shall we say, are more easily confused one with the other when the area surrounding the scar is revealed, and the rest concealed. It would appear therefore that Mpiring's identification of his assailant is not of itself sufficient proof that Pafuri was that man.

It must further be borne in mind that, although the first accused, Absalom Kumalo, stated that Pafuri was present, and that he had assaulted Mpiring, he made this statement only after the Police had questioned him as to the whereabouts of Pafuri. Did it then first occur to him to implicate Pafuri? Or was there a pre-existing connection between Pafuri and the murder? Counsel for the first accused has argued that Absalom Kumalo had been in a continuous state of fear for some days, and that once he had been arrested, no matter what name or names had been submitted to him, he would have confessed what was so heavily burdening his mind, and that it was this state of mind that led to the confession, and not the mention of Pafuri's name. Indeed his own account of his fearful state lends colour to that supposition. But one cannot exclude the [193/194] possibility that he seized upon Pafuri's name, and said that Pafuri was one of the three, not wishing to be alone on so grave a charge. Why however should he not give the name of his real confederates, for there seems no reason to doubt Mpiring's evidence that three men came into the kitchen? He has given a straightforward account of his own actions. Why should he then implicate two innocent men and conceal the names of two guilty men?

One must also bear in mind the strange coincidence that what is argued to be a wrong identification led to the apprehension of an associate who immediately confessed.

There is a further difficulty in this perplexing case. Neither of the other accused, nor the woman Baby Mkize, denies that all four were present at 79 Twenty-third Avenue, Alexandra, on the night following the murder. Was this again a chance meeting that caused the first accused to name both the second and third accused as his confederates? Or was it indeed the kind of meeting that he claims it to be? Was the murder discussed at this meeting? The woman Baby Mkize is a most unsatisfactory witness, and while the prosecution, and the Counsel for the defence of the first accused, demonstrated

this most clearly, neither was able to produce that conclusive proof that the murder had been discussed. This woman at first lied to the Police, telling them that she had not seen the first accused for a year. She was a confused, contradictory, and frightened witness, but was this fear and its resulting confusion caused by mere presence in a Court, or by knowledge of other crimes to which she had been a party, or by the guilty knowledge that the murder was in fact discussed? That does not seem to us to have been clearly established.

The prosecution has made much of the previous association of the three accused, and indeed has made out so strong a case that further investigation is called for into the nature of that association. But previous association, even of a criminal nature, is not in itself a proof of association in the grave crime of which these three persons stand accused.

After long and thoughtful consideration, my assessors and I [194/195] have come to the conclusion that the guilt of the second and third accused is not established, and they will be accordingly discharged. But I have no doubt that their previous criminal association will be exhaustively investigated.

There is a sigh in the Court. One act of this drama is over. The accused Absalom Kumalo makes no sign. He does not even look at the two who are now free. But Pafuri looks about as though he would say, this is right, this is just, what has been done.

There remains the case against the first accused. His confession has been thoroughly investigated, and where it could be tested, it has been found to be true. There seems no reason to suppose that an innocent person is confessing the commission of a crime that he did not in fact commit. His learned Counsel pleads that he should not suffer the extreme penalty, argues that he is shocked and overwhelmed and stricken by his act, commends him for his truthful and straightforward confession, draws attention to his youth and to the disastrous effect of a great and wicked city on the character of a simple tribal boy. He has dealt profoundly with the disaster that has overwhelmed our native tribal society, and has argued cogently the case of our own complicity in this disaster. But even if it be true that we have, out of fear and selfishness and thoughtlessness, wrought a destruction that we have done little to repair, even if it be true that we should be ashamed of it and do something more courageous and forthright than we are doing, there is nevertheless a law, and it is one of the most monumental achievements of this defective society that it has made a law, and has set judges to administer it, and has freed those judges from any obligation whatsoever but to administer the law. But a Judge may not trifle with the Law because the society is defective. If the law is the law of a society that some feel to be unjust, it is the law and the society that must be changed. In the meantime there is an existing law that must be administered, and it is the sacred duty of a Judge to administer it. And [**195/196**] the fact that he is left free to administer it must be counted as righteousness in a society that may in other respects not be righteous. I am not suggesting of course that the learned Counsel for the defence for a moment contemplated that the law should not be administered. I am only pointing out that a Judge cannot, must not, dare not allow the existing defects of society to influence him to do anything but administer the law.

Under the law a man is held responsible for his deeds, except under certain circumstances which no one has suggested here to obtain. It is not for a judge otherwise to decide in how far human beings are in truth responsible; under the law they are fully responsible. Nor is it for a judge to show mercy. A higher authority, in this case the Governor-General-in-Council, may be merciful, but that is a matter for that authority. What are the facts of this case? This young man goes to a house with the intention to break in and steal. He takes with him a loaded revolver. He maintains that this was for the purpose of intimidation. Why then must it be loaded? He maintains that it was not his intention to kill. Yet one of his accomplices cruelly struck down the native servant, and one must suppose that the servant might easily have been killed. He states himself that the weapon was an iron bar, and there is surely no more cruel, no more dangerous way to do such a deed. In this plan he concurred, and when the Court questioned him, he said that he had made no protest against the taking of this murderous and dangerous weapon. It is true that the victim was a black man, and there is a school of thought which would regard such an offence as less serious when the victim is black. But no Court of Justice could countenance such a view.

The most important point to consider here is the accused's repeated assertion that he had no intention to kill, that the coming of the white man was unexpected, and that he fired the revolver out of panic and fear. If the Court could accept this as truth, then the Court must find that the accused did not commit murder.

What again are the facts of the case? How can one suppose otherwise than that here were three murderous and dangerous [**196/197**] young men? It is true that they did not go to the house with the express intention of killing a man. But it is true that they took with them weapons the use of which might well result in the death of any man who interfered with the carrying out of their unlawful purpose.

The law on this point has been stated by a great South African judge. "An intention to kill," he says, "is an essential element in murder; but its existence may be inferred from the relevant circumstances. And the question is whether on the facts here proved an inference of that nature was rightly drawn. Such an intent is not confined to cases where there is a definite purpose to kill; it is also present in cases where the object is to inflict grievous bodily harm, calculated to cause death regardless of whether death results or not."

Are we to suppose that in this small room, where in this short and tragic space of time an innocent black man is cruelly struck down and an innocent white man is shot dead, that there was no intention to inflict grievous bodily harm of this kind should the terrible need for it arise? I cannot bring myself to entertain such a supposition.

They are silent in the Court. And the Judge too is silent. There is no sound there. No one coughs or moves or sighs. The Judge speaks:

This Court finds you guilty, Absalom Kumalo, of the murder of Arthur Trevelyan Jarvis at his residence in Parkwold, on the afternoon of the eighth day of October, 1946. And this Court finds you, Matthew Kumalo, and Johannes Pafuri, not guilty, and you are accordingly discharged.

So these two go down the stairs into the place that is under the ground, and leave the other alone. He looks at them going, perhaps he is thinking, now it is I alone.

The Judge speaks again. On what grounds, he asks, can this Court make any recommendation to mercy? I have given this [197/198] long and serious thought, and I cannot find any extenuating circumstances. This is a young man, but he has reached the age of manhood. He goes to a house with two companions, and they take with them two dangerous weapons, either of which can encompass the death of a man. These two weapons are used, one with serious, the other with fatal results. This Court has a solemn duty to protect society against the murderous attacks of dangerous men, whether they be old or young, and to show clearly that it will punish fitly such offenders. Therefore I can make no recommendation to mercy.

The Judge speaks to the boy.

— Have you anything to say, he asks, before I pronounce sentence?

— I have only this to say, that I killed this man, but I did not mean to kill him, only I was afraid.

They are silent in the Court, but for all that a white man calls out in a loud voice for silence. Kumalo puts his face in his hands, he has heard what it means. Jarvis sits stern and erect. The young white man looks before him and frowns fiercely. The girl sits like the girl she is, her eyes are fixed on the Judge, not on her lover.

I sentence you, Absalom Kumalo, to be returned to custody, and to be hanged by the neck until you are dead. And may the Lord have mercy upon your soul.

The Judge rises, and the people rise. But not all is silent. The guilty one falls to the floor, crying and sobbing. And there is a woman wailing, and an old man crying, *Tixo, Tixo*. No one calls for silence, though the Judge is not quite gone. For who can stop the heart from breaking?

*   *   *   *   *

They come out of the Court, the white on one side, the black on the other, according to the custom. But the young [198/199] white man breaks the custom, and he and Msimangu help the old and broken man, one on each side of him. It is not often that such a custom is broken. It is only when there is a deep experience that such a custom is broken. The young man's brow is set, and he looks fiercely before him. That is partly because it is a deep experience, and partly because of the custom that is being broken. For such a thing is not lightly done. [199/200]

XXIX

They passed again through the great gate in the grim high wall, Father Vincent and Kumalo and the girl and Msimangu.

The boy was brought to them, and for a moment some great hope showed in his eyes, and he stood there trembling and shaking. But Kumalo said to him gently, we are come for the marriage, and the hope died out.

— My son, here is your wife that is to be.

The boy and the girl greeted each other like strangers, each giving hands without life, not to be shaken, but to be held loosely, so that the hands fell apart easily. They did not kiss after the European fashion, but stood looking at each other without words, bound in a great constraint. But at last she asked, Are you in health, and he answered, I am greatly. And he asked, are you in health, and she answered, I am greatly also. But beyond that there was nothing spoken between them.

Father Vincent left them, and they all stood in the same constraint. Msimangu saw that Gertrude would soon break out into wailing and moaning, and he turned his back on the others and said to her gravely and privately, heavy things have happened, but this is a marriage, and it were better to go at once than to wail or moan in this place. When she did not answer he said sternly and coldly, do you understand me? And she said resentfully, I understand you. He left her and went to a window in the great grim wall, and she stood sullenly silent, but he knew she would not do what it was in her mind to have done.

And Kumalo said desperately to his son, are you in health? And the boy answered, I am greatly. Are you in health, my father? So Kumalo said, I am greatly. He longed for other [**200/201**] things to say, but he could not find them. And indeed it was a mercy for them all, when a white man came to take them to the prison chapel.

Father Vincent was waiting there in his vestments, and he read to them from his book. Then he asked the boy if he took this woman, and he asked the girl if she took this man. And when they had answered as it is laid down in that book, for better for worse, for richer for poorer, in sickness and in health, till death did them part, he married them. Then he preached a few words to them, that they were to remain faithful, and to bring up what children there might be in the fear of God. So were they married and signed their names in the book.

After it was done, the two priests and the wife left father and son, and Kumalo said to him, I am glad you are married.

— I also am glad, my father.

— I shall care for your child, my son, even as if it were my own.

But when he realised what it was he had said, his mouth quivered and he would indeed have done that which he was determined not to do, had not the boy said out of his own suffering, when does my father return to Ndotsheni?

— Tomorrow, my son.

— Tomorrow?

— Yes, tomorrow.

— And you will tell my mother that I remember her.

Yes, indeed I shall tell her. Yes, indeed, I shall take her that message. Why yes indeed. But he did not speak those words, he only nodded his head.

— And my father.

— Yes, my son.

— I have money in a Post Office Book. Nearly four pounds is there. It is for the child. They will give it to my father at the office. I have arranged for it.

Yes, indeed I shall get it. Yes, indeed, even as you have arranged. Why yes indeed.

— And my father.

— Yes, my son. [**201/202**]

— If the child is a son, I should like his name to be Peter.

— And Kumalo said in a strangled voice, Peter.

— And if it is a daughter.

— No, if it is a daughter, I have not thought of any name. And my father.

— Yes, my son.

— I have a parcel at Germiston, at the home of Joseph Bhengu, at Number 12,

Maseru Street. I should be glad if it could be sold for my son.

— Yes, I hear you.

— There are other things that Pafuri had. But I think he will deny that they are mine.

— Pafuri? This same Pafuri?

— Yes, my father.

— It is better to forget them.

— It is as my father sees.

— And these things at Germiston, my son. I do not know how I could get them, for we leave tomorrow.

— Then it does not matter.

But because Kumalo could see that it did matter, he said, I shall speak to the Reverend Msimangu.

— That would be better.

— And this Pafuri, said Kumalo bitterly. And your cousin. I find it hard to forgive them.

The boy shrugged his shoulders hopelessly.

— They lied, my father. They were there, even as I said.

— Indeed they were there. But they are not here now.

— They are here, my father. There is another case against them.

— I did not mean that, my son. I mean they are not . . . they are not. . . .

But he could not bring himself to say what he meant.

— They are here, said the boy not understanding. Here in this very place. Indeed, my father, it is I who must go.

— Go? [**202/203**]

— Yes, I must go . . . to . . .

Kumalo whispered, to Pretoria?

At those dread words the boy fell on the floor, he was crouched in the way that some of the Indians pray, and he began to sob, with great tearing sounds that convulsed him. Aye, but a boy is afraid of death. The old man, moved to it by that deep compassion which was there within him, knelt by his son, and ran his hand over his head. And the boy was moved by this compassion to more terrible sobbing.

— Be of courage, my son.

— I am afraid, he cried. I am afraid.

— Be of courage, my son.

The boy reared up on to his haunches. He hid nothing, his face was distorted by his cries. Au! au! I am afraid of the hanging, he sobbed, I am afraid of the hanging.

Still kneeling, the father took his son's hands, and they were not lifeless any more, but clung to his, seeking some comfort, some assurance. And the old man held them more strongly, and said again, be of good courage, my son.

The white warder, hearing these cries, came in and said, but not with unkindness, old man, you must go now.

— I am going, sir. I am going, sir. But give us a little time longer.

So the warder said, well, only a little time longer, and he withdrew.

— My son, dry your tears.

So the boy took the cloth that was offered him and dried his tears. He kneeled on his knees, and though the sobbing was ended, the eyes were far-seeing and troubled.

— My son, I must go now. Stay well, my son. I shall care for your wife and your child.

— It is good, he says. Yes, he says it is good, but his thoughts are not on any wife or child. Where his thoughts are there is no wife or child, where his eyes are there is no marriage.

— My son, I must go now.

He stood up, but the boy caught his father by the knees, and [**203/204**] cried out to him, you must not leave me, you must not leave me. He broke out again into the terrible sobbing, and cried, No, no, you must not leave me.

The white warder came in again and said sternly, old man, you must go now. And Kumalo would have gone, but the boy held him by the knees, crying out and sobbing. The warder tried to pull his arms away, but he could not, and he called another man to help him. Together they pulled the boy away, and Kumalo said desperately to him, stay well, my son, but the boy did not hear him.

And so they parted.

Heavy with grief Kumalo left him, and

went out to the gate in the wall where the others were waiting. And the girl came to him, and said shyly, but with a smile, umfundisi.

— Yes, my child.

— I am now your daughter.

He forced himself to smile at her. It is true, he said. And she was eager to talk of it, but when she looked at him she could see that his thoughts were not of such matters. So she did not speak of it further.

* * * * *

After he had returned from the prison, Kumalo walked up the hill that led to the street where his brother had the carpenter's shop. For a wonder there was no one in the shop except the big bull man, who greeted him with a certain constraint.

— I am come to say farewell to you, my brother.

— Well, well, you are returning to Ndotsheni. You have been a long time away, my brother, and your wife will be glad to see you. When are you leaving?

— We leave tomorrow by the train that goes at nine o'clock.

— So Gertrude is going with you. And her child. You are doing a good thing, my brother. Johannesburg is not a place for a woman alone. But we must drink some tea.

He stood up to go and call to the woman at the back of the house, but Kumalo said, I do not wish for any tea, my brother. [204/205]

— You must do as you wish, my brother, said John Kumalo. It is my custom to offer tea to my visitors.

He sat down and made much show of lighting a big bull pipe, holding it between his teeth, and searching amongst some papers for matches, but not looking at his brother.

— It is a good thing you are doing, my brother, he said with the pipe between his teeth. Johannesburg is not a place for a woman alone. And the child will be better in the country.

— I am taking another child also, said Kumalo. The wife of my son. And she too is with child.

— Well, well, I have heard of it, said John Kumalo, giving attention to the match above his pipe. That is another good thing you are doing.

His pipe was lit, and he thumbed the tobacco down giving it much attention. But at last there was nothing left to do, and he looked at his brother through the smoke.

— Not one, but more than one person has said to me, these are good things that your brother is doing. Well, well, you must give my remembrances to your wife, and to our other friends. You will get to Pietermaritzburg early in the morning, and you will catch the train to Donnybrooke. And that evening you will be at Ndotsheni. Well, well, it is a long journey.

— My brother, there is a matter that must be spoken between us.

— It is as you wish, my brother.

— I have considered it very deeply. I have not come here to reproach you.

And John Kumalo said quickly—as though he had been expecting it,

— Reproach me? why should you reproach me? There is a case and a judge. That is not for you or me or any other person.

The veins stood out on the bull neck, but Kumalo was quick to speak.

— I do not say that I should reproach you. As you say there is a case and a judge. There is also a great Judge, but of Him you and I do not speak. But there is quite another matter that must be spoken. [205/206]

— Well, well, I understand. What is this matter?

— One thing is to greet you before I go. But I could not greet you and say nothing. You have seen how it is with my son. He left his home and he was eaten up. Therefore I thought that this must be spoken, what of your own son? He also has left his home.

— I am thinking about this matter, said John Kumalo. When this trouble is finished, I shall bring him back here.

— Are you determined?

— I am determined. I promise you that. He laughed his bull laugh. I cannot leave all the good deeds to you, my brother. The fatted calf will be killed here.

— That is a story to remember.

— Well, well, it is a story to remember. I do not throw away good teaching because—well—you understand me.

— And there is one last thing, said Kumalo.

— You are my older brother. Speak what you wish.

— Your politics, my brother. Where are they taking you?

The bull veins stood out again on the bull throat. My politics, my brother, are my own. I do not speak to you about your religion.

— You said, speak what you wish.

— Well, well, I did say it. Well—yes—I am listening.

— Where are they taking you?

— I know what I am fighting for. You will pardon me—he laughed his great laugh—the Reverend Msimangu is not here, so you will pardon me if I talk English.

— Speak what you will.

— You have read history, my brother. You know that history teaches that the men who do the work cannot be kept down for ever. If they will stand together, who will stand against them? More and more our people understand that. If they so decide, there will be no more work done in South Africa.

— You mean if they strike?

— Yes, I mean that.

— But this last strike was not successful. **[206/207]**

John Kumalo stood on his feet, and his voice growled in his throat.

— Look what they did to us, he said. They forced us into the mines as though we were slaves. Have we no right to keep back our labour?

— Do you hate the white man, my brother?

John Kumalo looked at him with suspicion. I hate no man, he said. I hate only injustice.

— But I have heard some of the things you have said.

— What things?

— I have heard that some of them are dangerous things. I have heard that they are watching you, that they will arrest you when they think it is time. It is this matter that I must bring to you, because you are my brother.

Have no doubt it is fear in the eyes. The big man looks like a boy that is caught. I do not know what these things are, he says.

— I hear it is some of the things that are said in this shop, said Kumalo.

— In this shop? Who would know what is said in this shop?

For all his prayers for the power to forgive, Kumalo desired to hurt his brother. Do you know every man who comes to this shop, he asked. Could a man not be sent to this shop to deceive you?

The big bull man wiped the sweat from his brow. He was wondering, Kumalo knew, if such a thing might not be. And for all the prayers, the desire to hurt was stronger, so strong that he was tempted to lie, yielded, and lied. I have heard, he said, that a man might have been sent to this shop to deceive you. As a friend.

— You heard that?

And Kumalo, ashamed, had to say, I heard it.

— What a friend, said the big bull man. What a friend.

And Kumalo cried at him out of his suffering, my son had two such friends.

The big man looked at him. Your son? he said. Then the meaning of it came to him, and anger overwhelmed him. Out of my shop, he roared, out of my shop. **[207/208]**

He kicked over the table in front of him, and came at Kumalo, so that the old man had to step out of the door into the street, and the door shut against him, and he could hear the key turned and the bolt shot home in his brother's anger.

Out there in the street, he was humiliated and ashamed. Humiliated because the people passing looked in astonishment, ashamed because he had not come for this purpose at all. He had come to tell his brother that power corrupts, that a man who fights for justice must himself be cleansed and purified, that love is greater than force. And none of these things had he done. God have mercy on me, Christ have mercy on me. He turned to the door, but it was locked and bolted. Brother had shut out brother, from the same womb had they come.

The people were watching, so he walked away in his distress.

*   *   *   *   *

— I cannot thank you enough, said Jarvis.

— We would have done more if we could, Jarvis.

John Harrison drove up, and Jarvis and Harrison stood for a moment outside the car.

— Our love to Margaret, and to Mary and the children, Jarvis. We'll come down and see you one of these days.

— You'll be welcome, Harrison, very welcome.

— One thing I wanted to say, Jarvis, said Harrison, dropping his voice. About the sentence. It can't bring the dead back, but it was right, absolutely right. It couldn't have been any other way so far as I'm concerned. If it had been any other way, I'd have felt there was no justice in the world. I'm only sorry the other two got off. The Crown made a mess of the case. They should have hammered at that woman Mkize.

— Yes, I felt that way too. Well, goodbye to you, and thank you again.

— I'm glad to do it.

At the station Jarvis gave John Harrison an envelope.

— Open it when we're gone, he said.

So when the train had gone, young Harrison opened it. For your club, it said. Do all the things you and Arthur wanted to [208/209] do. If you like to call it the "Arthur Jarvis Club," I'll be pleased. But that is not a condition.

Young Harrison turned it over to look at the cheque underneath. He looked at the train as though he might have run after it. One thousand pounds, he said. Helen of Troy, one thousand pounds!

*   *   *   *   *

They had a party at Mrs. Lithebe's at which Msimangu was the host. It was not a gay party, that was hardly to be thought of. But the food was plentiful, and there was some sad pleasure in it. Msimangu presided after the European fashion, and made a speech commending the virtues of his brother priest, and the motherly care that Mrs. Lithebe had given to all under her roof. Kumalo made a speech too, but it was stumbling and uncertain, for the lie and the quarrel were uppermost in his mind. But he thanked Msimangu and Mrs. Lithebe for all their kindnesses. Mrs. Lithebe would not speak, but giggled like a girl, and said that people were born to do such kindness. But her friend the stout woman spoke for her, a long speech that seemed as if it would never end, about the goodness of both priests, and the goodness of Mrs. Lithebe; and she spoke plainly about the duty of Gertrude and the girl to lead good lives, and to repay all the kindnesses shown to them. And that led her on to talk about Johannesburg, and the evils of that great city, and the sinfulness of the people in Sophiatown and Claremont and Alexandra and Pimville. Indeed Msimangu was compelled to rise and say to her, Mother, we must rise early in the morning, otherwise we could listen to you for ever, so that happy and smiling she sat down. Then Msimangu told them that he had news for them, news that had been private until now, and that this was the first place where it would be told. He was retiring into a community, and would forswear the world and all possessions, and this was the first time that a black man had done such a thing in South Africa. There was clapping of hands, and all gave thanks for it. And Gertrude sat listening with enjoyment to the speeches at this great dinner, her small son asleep [**209/210**] against her breast. And the girl listened also, with eager and smiling face, for in all her years she had never seen anything the like of this.

Then Msimangu said, We must all rise early to catch the train, my friends, and it is time we went to our beds, for the man with the taxi will be here at seven.

So they closed with a hymn and prayers, and the stout woman went off with yet more thanks to Mrs. Lithebe for her kindness to these people. Kumalo went with his friend to the gate, and Msimangu said, I am forsaking the world and all possessions, but I have saved a little money. I have no father or mother to depend on me, and I have the permission of the Church to give this to you, my friend, to help you with all the money you have spent in Johannesburg, and all the new duties you have taken up. This book is in your name.

He put the book into Kumalo's hand, and Kumalo knew by the feeling of it that it was a Post Office Book. And Kumalo put his hands with the book on the top of the gate, and he put his head on his hands, and he wept bitterly. And Msimangu said to him, do not spoil my pleasure, for I have never had a pleasure like this one. Which words of his made the old man break from weeping into sobbing, so that Msimangu said, there is a man coming, be silent, my brother.

They were silent till the man passed, and then Kumalo said, in all my days I have known no one as you are. And Msimangu said sharply, I am a weak and sinful man, but God put His hands on me, that is all. And as for the boy, he said, it is the Governor-General-in-Council who must decide if there will be mercy. As soon as Father Vincent hears, he will let you know.

— And if they decide against him?

— If they decide against him, said Msi-

mangu soberly, one of us will go to Pretoria on that day, and let you know —when it is finished. And now I must go, my friend. We must be up early in the morning. But of you too I ask a kindness.

— Ask all that I have, my friend.

— I ask that you will pray for me in this new thing I am about to do. [**210/211**]

— I shall pray for you, morning and evening, all the days that are left.

— Goodnight, brother.

— Goodnight, Msimangu, friend of friends. And may God watch over you always.

— And you also.

Kumalo watched him go down the street and turn into the Mission House. Then he went into the room and lit his candle and opened the book. There was thirty-three pounds four shillings and fivepence in the book. He fell on his knees and groaned and repented of the lie and the quarrel. He would have gone there and then to his brother, even as it is commanded, but the hour was late. But he would write his brother a letter. He thanked God for all the kindnesses of men, and was comforted and uplifted. And these things done, he prayed for his son. Tomorrow they would all go home, all except his son. And he would stay in the place where they would put him, in the great prison in Pretoria, in the barred and solitary cell; and mercy failing, would stay there till he was hanged. Aye, but the hand that had murdered had once pressed the mother's breast into the thirsting mouth, had stolen into the father's hand when they went out into the dark. Aye, but the murderer afraid of death had once been a child afraid of the night.

In the morning he rose early, it was yet dark. He lit his candle, and suddenly remembering, went on his knees and prayed his prayer for Msimangu. He opened the door quietly, and shook the girl gently. It is time for us to rise, he said. She was eager at once, she started up from the blankets, I shall not be long, she said. He smiled at the eagerness. Ndotsheni, he said, tomorrow it is Ndotsheni. He opened Gertrude's door, and held up his candle. But Gertrude was gone. The little boy was there, the red dress and the white turban were there. But Gertrude was gone. [211/213]

BOOK THREE [213/215]

XXX

The engine steams and whistles over the veld of the Transvaal. The white flat hills of the mines drop behind, and the country rolls away as far as the eye can see. They sit all together, Kumalo, and the little boy on his knees, and the girl with her worldly possessions in one of those paper carriers that you find in the shops. The little boy has asked for his mother, but Kumalo tells him she has gone away, and he does not ask any more.

At Volksrust the steam engine leaves them, and they change it for one that has the cage, taking power from the iron ropes stretched overhead. Then they wind down the escarpment, into the hills of Natal, and Kumalo tells the girl this is Natal. And she is eager and excited, never having seen it before.

Darkness falls, and they thunder through the night, over battlefields of long ago. They pass without seeing them the hills of Mooi River, Rosetta, Balgowan, lovely beyond any singing of it. As the sun rises they wind down the greatest hills of all, to Pietermaritzburg, the lovely city.

Here they enter another train, and the train runs along the valley of the Umsindusi, past the black slums, past Edendale, past Elandskop, and down into the great valley of the Umkomaas, where the tribes live, and the soil is sick almost beyond healing. And the people tell Kumalo that the rains will not fall; they cannot plough or plant, and there will be hunger in this valley.

At Donnybrook they enter still another train, the small toy train that runs to Ixopo through the green rolling hills of Eastwolds and Lufafa. And at Ixopo they alight, and people greet him and say, au! but you have been a long time away. [215/216]

There they enter the last train, that runs beside the lovely road that goes into the hills. Many people know him, and he is afraid of their questions. They talk like children, these people, and it is nothing to ask, who is this person, who is this girl, who is this child, where do they come from, where do they go. They will ask how is your sister, how is your son, so he takes his sacred book and reads in it, and they turn to another who has taste for conversation.

The sun is setting over the great valley of the Umzimkulu, behind the mountains of East Griqualand. His wife is there, and the friend to help the umfundisi with his bags. He goes to his wife quickly, and embraces her in the European fashion. He is glad to be home.

She looks her question, and he says to her, our son is to die, perhaps there may be mercy, but let us not talk of it now.

— I understand you, she says.

— And Gertrude. All was ready for her to come. There we were all in the same house. But when I went to wake her, she was gone. Let us not talk of it now.

She bows her head.

— And this is the small boy, and this is our new daughter.

Kumalo's wife lifts the small boy and kisses him after the European fashion. You are my child, she says. She puts him down and goes to the girl who stands there humbly with her paper bag. She takes her in her arms after the European fashion, and says to her, you are my daughter. And the girl bursts suddenly into weeping, so that the woman must say to her, Hush, hush, do not cry. She says to her further, our home is simple and quiet, there are no great things there. The girl looks up through her tears and says, mother, that is all that I desire.

Something deep is touched here, something that is good and deep. Although it comes with tears, it is like a comfort in such desolation.

Kumalo shakes hands with his friend, and they all set out on the narrow path that leads into the setting sun, into the valley of Ndotsheni. But here a man calls, umfundisi, you are back, it is a good thing that you have returned. And here a [216/217] woman says to another, look, it is the umfundisi that has returned. One woman dressed in European fashion throws her apron over her head, and runs to the hut, calling and crying more like a child than a woman, it is the umfundisi that has returned. She brings her children to the door · and they peep out behind her dresses to see the umfundisi that has returned.

A child comes into the path and she stands before Kumalo so that he must stop. We are glad that the umfundisi is here again, she says.

— But you have had an umfundisi here, he says, speaking of the young man that the Bishop had sent to take his place.

— We did not understand him, she says. It is only our umfundisi that we understand. We are glad that he is back.

The path is dropping now, from the green hills where the mist feeds the grass and the bracken. It runs between the stones, and one must walk carefully for it is steep. A woman with child must walk carefully, so Kumalo's wife goes before the girl, and tells her, here is a stone, be careful that you do not slip. Night is falling, and the hills of East Griqualand are blue and dark against the sky.

The path is dropping into the red land of Ndotsheni. It is a wasted land, a land of old men and women and children, but it is home. The maize hardly grows to the height of a man, but it is home.

— It is dry here, umfundisi. We cry for rain.

— I have heard it, my friend.

— Our mealies are nearly finished, umfundisi. It is known to *Tixo* alone what we shall eat.

The path grows more level, it goes by the little stream that runs by the church. Kumalo stops to listen to it, but there is nothing to hear.

— The stream does not run, my friend.

— It has been dry for a month, umfundisi.

— Where do you get water, then?

— The women must go to the river, umfundisi, that comes from the place of uJarvis. [217/218]

At the sound of the name of Jarvis, Kumalo feels fear and pain, but he makes himself say, how is uJarvis?

— He returned yesterday, umfundisi. I do not know how he is. But the inkosikazi returned some weeks ago, and they say she is sick and thin. I work there now, umfundisi.

Kumalo is silent, and cannot speak. But his friend says to him, it is known here, he says.

— Ah, it is known.

— It is known, umfundisi.

They do not speak again, and the path levels out, running past the huts, and the red empty fields. There is calling here, and in the dusk one voice calls to another in some far distant place. If you are a Zulu you can hear what they say, but if you are not, even if you know the language, you would find it hard to know what is being called. Some white men call it magic, but it is no magic, only an art perfected. It is Africa, the beloved country.

— They call that you are returned, umfundisi.

— I hear it, my friend.

— They are satisfied, umfundisi.

Indeed they are satisfied. They come from the huts along the road, they come running down from the hills in the dark. The boys are calling and crying, with the queer tremulous call that is known in this country.

— Umfundisi, you have returned.

— Umfundisi, we give thanks for your return.

— Umfundisi, you have been too long away.

A child calls to him, there is a new teacher at the school. A second child says to her, foolish one, it is a long time since she came. A boy salutes as he has learned in the school, and cries umfundisi. He waits for no response, but turns away and gives the queer tremulous call, to no person at all, but to the air. He turns away and makes the first slow steps of a dance, for no person at all, but for himself.

There is a lamp outside the church, the lamp they light for the services. There are women of the church sitting on the red earth under the lamp; they are dressed in white dresses, each [218/219] with a green cloth about her neck. They rise when the party approaches, and one breaks into a hymn, with a high note that cannot be sustained; but others come in underneath it, and support and sustain it, and some men come in too, with the deep notes and the true. Kumalo takes off his hat and he and his wife and his friend join in also, while the girl stands and watches in wonder. It is a hymn of thanksgiving, and man remembers God in it, and prostrates himself and gives thanks for the Everlasting Mercy. And it echoes in the bare red hills and over the bare red fields of the broken tribe. And it is sung in love and humility and gratitude, and the humble simple people pour their lives into the song.

And Kumalo must pray. He prays, *Tixo,* we give thanks to Thee for Thy unending mercy. We give thanks to Thee for this safe return. We give thanks to Thee for the love of our friends and our families. We give thanks to Thee for all Thy mercies.

Tixo, give us rain, we beseech Thee—

And here they say Amen, so many of them that he must wait till they are finished.

Tixo, give us rain, we beseech Thee, that we may plough and sow our seed. And if there is no rain, protect us against hunger and starvation, we pray Thee.

And here they say Amen, so that he must wait again till they are finished. His heart is warmed that they have so welcomed him, so warmed that he casts out his fear, and prays that which is deep within him.

Tixo, let this small boy be welcome in Ndotsheni, let him grow tall in this place. And his mother—

His voice stops as though he cannot say it, but he humbles himself, and lowers his voice.

And his mother—forgive her her trespasses. [219/220]

A woman moans, and Kumalo knows her, she is one of the great gossips of this place. So he adds quickly—

Forgive us all, for we all have trespasses. And *Tixo,* let this girl be welcome in Ndotsheni, and deliver her child safely in this place.

He pauses, then says gently—

Let her find what she seeks, and have what she desires.

And this is the hardest that must be prayed, but he humbles himself.

And *Tixo,* my son—

They do not moan, they are silent. Even the woman who gossips does not moan. His voice drops to a whisper—

Forgive him his trespasses.

It is done, it is out, the hard thing that was so feared. He knows it is not he, it is these people who have done it. Kneel, he says. So they kneel on the bare red earth, and he raises his hand, and his voice also, and strength comes into the old and broken man, for is he not a priest?

The Lord bless you and keep you, and make His face to shine upon you, and give you peace, now and for ever. And the grace of our Lord Jesus Christ, and the love of God, and the fellowship of the Holy Spirit, be with you and abide with you, and with all those that are dear to you, now and forever more. Amen.

They rise, and the new teacher says, can we not sing *Nkosi Sikelel' iAfrika,* God Save Africa? And the old teacher says, they do not know it here, it has not come here yet. The new [220/221] teacher says, we have it in Pietermaritzburg, it is known there. Could we not have it here? The old teacher says, we are not in Pietermaritzburg here. We have much to do in our school. For she is cold with this new teacher, and she is ashamed too, because she does not know *Nkosi Sikelel' iAfrika,* God Save Africa.

* * * * *

Yes, God save Africa, the beloved country. God save us from the deep depths of our sins. God save us from the fear that is afraid of justice. God save us from the fear that is afraid of men. God save us all.

Call oh small boy, with the long tremulous cry that echoes over the hills. Dance oh small boy, with the first slow steps of the dance that is for yourself. Call and dance, Innocence, call and dance while you may. For this is a prelude, it is only a beginning. Strange things will be woven into it, by men you have never heard of, in places you have never seen. It is life you are going into, you are not afraid because you do not know. Call and dance, call and dance. Now, while you may.

* * * * *

The people have all gone now, and Kumalo turns to his friend.

— There are things I must tell you. Some day I shall tell you others, but some I must tell you now. My sister Gertrude was to come with us. We were all together, all ready in the house. But when I went to wake her, she was gone.

— Au! umfundisi.

— And my son, he is condemned to be hanged. He may be given mercy. They will let me know as soon as they hear.

— Au! umfundisi.

— You may tell your friends. And they will tell their friends. It is not a thing that can be hidden. Therefore you may tell them.

— I shall tell them, umfundisi.

— I do not know if I should stay here, my friend. [**221/222**]

— Why, umfundisi?

— What, said Kumalo bitterly. With a sister who has left her child, and a son who has killed a man? Who am I to stay here?

— Umfundisi, it must be what you desire. But I tell you that there is not one man or woman that would desire it. There is not one man or woman here that has not grieved for you, that is not satisfied that you are returned. Why, could you not see? Could it not touch you?

— I have seen and it has touched me. It is something, after all that has been suffered. My friend, I do not desire to go. This is my home here. I have lived so long here, I could not desire to leave it.

— That is good, umfundisi. And I for my part have no desire to live without you. For I was in darkness—

— You touch me, my friend.

— Umfundisi, did you find out about Sibeko's daughter? You remember?

— Yes, I remember. And she too is gone. Where, there is not one that knows. They do not know, they said.

Some bitterness came suddenly into him and he added, they said also, they do not care.

— Au! umfundisi.

— I am sorry, my friend.

— This world is full of trouble, umfundisi.

— Who knows it better?

— Yet you believe?

Kumalo looked at him under the light of the lamp. I believe, he said, but I have learned that it is a secret. Pain and suffering, they are a secret. Kindness and love, they are a secret. But I have learned that kindness and love can pay for pain and suffering. There is my wife, and you, my friend, and these people who welcomed me, and the child who is so eager to be with us here in Ndotsheni—so in my suffering I can believe.

— I have never thought that a Christian would be free of suffering, umfundisi. For our Lord suffered. And I come to believe that he suffered, not to save us from suffering, but to [**222/223**] teach us how to bear suffering. For he knew that there is no life without suffering.

Kumalo looked at his friend with joy. You are a preacher, he said.

His friend held out his rough calloused hands. Do I look like a preacher, he asked.

Kumalo laughed. I look at your heart, not your hands, he said. Thank you for your help, my friend.

— It is yours whenever you ask, um-fundisi. Stay well.

— Go well, my friend. But what road are you going?

The man sighed. I go past Sibeko's, he said. I promised him as soon as I knew.

Kumalo walked soberly to the little house. Then he turned suddenly and called after his friend.

— I must explain to you, he said. It was the daughter of uSmith who said, she did not know, she did not care. She said it in English. And when uJarvis said it to me in Zulu, he said, she does not know. But uJarvis did not tell me that she said, she did not care. He kept it for himself.

— I understand you, umfundisi.

— Go well, my friend.

— Stay well, umfundisi.

Kumalo turned again and entered the house, and his wife and the girl were eating.

— Where is the boy, he asked.

— Sleeping, Stephen. You have been a long time talking.

— Yes, there were many things to say.

— Did you put out the lamp?

— Let it burn a little longer.

— Has the church so much money, then?

He smiled at her. This is a special night, he said.

Her brow contracted with pain, he knew what she was thinking.

— I shall put it out, he said.

— Let it burn a little longer. Put it out when you have had your food.

— That will be right, he said soberly. Let it burn for what [**223/224**] has happened here, let it be put out for what has happened otherwise.

He put his hand on the girl's head. Have you eaten, my child?

She looked up at him, smiling. I am satisfied, she said.

— To bed then, my child.

— Yes, father.

She got up from her chair. Sleep well, father, she said. Sleep well, mother.

— I shall take you to your room, my child.

When she came back, Kumalo was looking at the Post Office Book. He gave it to her and said, there is money there, more than you and I have ever had.

She opened it and cried out when she saw how much there was. Is it ours, she asked.

— It is ours, he said. It is a gift, from the best man of all my days.

— You will buy new clothes, she said. New black clothes, and new collars, and a new hat.

— And you will buy new clothes, also, he said. And a stove. Sit down, and I shall tell you about Msimangu, he said, and about other matters.

She sat down trembling. I am listening, she said. [**224/225**]

XXXI

Kumalo began to pray regularly in his church for the restoration of Ndotsheni. But he knew that was not enough. Somewhere down here upon the earth men must come together, think something, do something. And looking round the hills of his country he could find only two men, the chief and the headmaster. Now the chief was a great stout man in riding breeches, and he wore a fur cap such as they wear in cold countries, and he rode about with counsellors, though what they counselled him to, it was hard to understand. The headmaster was a small smiling man in great round spectacles, and his office was filled with notices in blue and red and green. For reasons of diplomacy Kumalo decided first to go to the chief.

The morning was already hot beyond endurance, but the skies were cloudless and held no sign of rain. There had never been such a drought in this country. The oldest men of the tribe could not remember such a time as this, when the leaves fell from the trees till they stood as though it were winter, and the small tough-footed boys ran from shade to shade because of the heat of the ground. If one walked on the grass, it crackled underfoot as it did after a fire, and in the whole valley there was not one stream that was running. Even on the tops the grass was yellow, and neither below nor above was there any ploughing. The sun poured down out of the pitiless sky, and the cattle moved thin and listless over the veld to the dried-up streams, to pluck the cropped grass from the edges of the beds.

Kumalo climbed the hill to the place of the chief and was told to wait. This was no strange thing, for if he wished a chief could tell a man to wait simply because he was a chief. If he [225/226] wished he could tell a man to wait while he idly picked his teeth, or stared out day-dreaming over a valley. But Kumalo was glad of the chance to rest. He took off his coat and sat in the shade of a hut, and pondered over the ways of a chief. For who would be chief over this desolation? It was a thing the white man had done, knocked these chiefs down, and put them up again, to hold the pieces together. But the white men had taken most of the pieces away. And some chiefs sat with arrogant and blood-shot eyes, rulers of pitiful kingdoms that had no meaning at all. They were not all like that; there were some who had tried to help their people, and who had sent their sons to schools. And the Government had tried to help them too. But they were feeding an old man with milk, and pretending that he would one day grow into a boy.

Kumalo came to himself with a start and realized how far he had travelled since that journey to Johannesburg. The great city had opened his eyes to something that had begun and must now be continued. For there in Johannesburg things were happening that had nothing to do with any chief. But he got to his feet, for they had summoned him to the presence of the ruler of the tribe.

He made his greetings, and put as deep a respect into them as he could find, for he knew that a chief had a sharp ear for such things.

— And what is it you want, umfundisi?

— Inkosi, I have been to Johannesburg.

— Yes, that is known to me.

— Many of our people are there, inkosi.

— Yes.

— And I have thought, inkosi, that we should try to keep some of them in this valley.

— Ho! And how would we do it?

— By caring for our land before it is too late. By teaching them in the school how to care for the land. Then some at least would stay in Ndotsheni.

Then the chief was silent and alone with his thoughts, and it is not the custom to interrupt a chief who is thus occupied [226/227] with his thoughts. But Kumalo could see that he did not know what to say. He commenced to speak more than once, but whether he checked himself, or whether he could not see to the end of the words that he had in his mind, Kumalo could not say. Indeed a man is always so when another brings heavy matters to him, matters that he himself has many times considered, finding no answers to them.

But at last he spoke, and he said, I have thought many times over these heavy matters.

— Yes, inkosi.

— And I have thought on what must be done.

— Yes, inkosi.

— Therefore I am pleased to find that you too have thought about them.

And with that there was more silence, and Kumalo could see that the chief was struggling with his words.

— You know, umfundisi, that we have been teaching these things for many years in the schools. The white inspector and I have many times spoken about these things.

— I know that, inkosi.

— The inspector will be coming again soon, and we shall take these things yet further.

The chief ended his words in a tone of hope and encouragement, and he spoke as though between them they had brought the matter to a successful end. Kumalo knew that the interview would now be quickly finished, and although it was not altogether proper to do so, he summoned up courage and said in a way that meant he had other words to follow, Inkosi?

— Yes.

— It is true, inkosi, that they have been teaching these things for many years. Yet it is sad to look upon the place where they are teaching it. There is neither grass nor water there. And when the rain comes, the maize will not reach to the height of a man. The cattle are dying there, and there is no milk. Malusi's child is dead, Kuluse's child is dying. And what others must die, *Tixo* alone knows.

And Kumalo knew he had said a hard and bitter thing, and **[227/228]** had destroyed the hope and encouragement, so that the matter was no longer at a successful end. Indeed the chief might have been angered, not because these things were not true, but because Kumalo had prevented him from bringing the matter to an end.

— It is dry, umfundisi. You must not forget that it is dry.

— I do not forget it, said Kumalo respectfully. But dry or not, for many years it has been the same.

So the chief was silent again and had no word to say. He too was no doubt thinking that he could have brought this to an end with anger, but it was not easy to do that with a priest.

At last he spoke, but it was with reluctance. I shall see the magistrate, he said.

Then he added heavily, For I too have seen these things that you see.

He sat for a while lost in his thoughts, then he said with difficulty, for such a

thing is not easy to say, I have spoken to the magistrate before.

He sat frowning and perplexed. Kumalo knew that nothing more would come, and he made small movements so that the chief would know that he was ready to be dismissed. And while he was waiting he looked at the counsellors who stood behind the chief, and he saw too that they were frowning and perplexed, and that for this matter there was no counsel that they could give at all. For the counsellors of a broken tribe have counsel for many things, but none for the matter of a broken tribe.

The chief rose wearily to his feet, and he offered his hand to the priest. I shall go to see the Magistrate, he said. Go well, umfundisi.

— Stay well, inkosi.

Kumalo walked down the hill, and did not stop till he reached the church. There he prayed for the chief, and for the restoration of Ndotsheni. The wood-and-iron building was like an oven, and his spirit was depressed, his hope flagging in the lifeless heat. So he prayed briefly, Into Thy hands, oh God, **[228/229]** I commend Ndotsheni. Then he went out again into the heat to seek the headmaster of the school.

Yet there he was not more successful. The headmaster was polite and obliging behind the great spectacles, and showed him things that he called schemes of work, and drawings of flowers and seeds, and different kinds of soil in tubes. The headmaster explained that the school was trying to relate the life of the child to the life of the community, and showed him circulars from the Department in Pietermaritzburg, all about these matters. He took Kumalo out into the blazing sun, and showed him the school gardens, but this was an academic lecture, for there was no water, and everything was dead. Yet perhaps not so academic, for everything in the valley was dead too; even children were dying.

Kumalo asked the headmaster how some of these children could be kept in Ndotsheni. And the headmaster shook his head, and talked about economic causes, and said that the school was a place of little power. So Kumalo walked back again to his church, and sat there dispirited and depressed. Where was the great vision that he had seen at Ezenzeleni, the vision born of such great suffering? Of how a priest could make of his parish a real place of life for his people, and preparation for his children? Was he old then and finished? Or was his vision a delusion, and these things beyond all helping? No power but the power of God could bring about such a miracle, and he prayed again briefly, Into Thy hands, oh God, I commend Ndotsheni.

He went into the house, and there in the great heat he struggled with the church accounts, until he heard the sounds of a horse, and he heard it stop outside the church. He rose from his chair, and went out to see who might be riding in this merciless sun. And for a moment he caught his breath in astonishment, for it was a small white boy on a red horse, a small white boy as like to another who had ridden here as any could be.

The small boy smiled at Kumalo and raised his cap and said, Good morning. And Kumalo felt a strange pride that it should [**229/230**] be so, and a strange humility that it should be so, and an astonishment that the small boy should not know the custom.

— Good morning, inkosana, he said. It is a hot day for riding.

— I don't find it hot. Is this your church?

— Yes, this is my church.

— I go to a church school, St. Mark's. It's the best school in Johannesburg. We've a chapel there.

— St. Mark's, said Kumalo excited. This church is St. Mark's. But your chapel —it is no doubt better than this?

— Well—yes—it *is* better, said the small boy smiling. But it's in the town, you know. Is that your house?

— Yes, this is my house.

— Could I see inside it? I've never been inside a parson's house, I mean a native parson's house.

— You are welcome to see inside it, inkosana.

The small boy slipped off his horse and made it fast to the poles that were there for the horses of those that came to the church. He dusted his feet on the frayed mat outside Kumalo's door, and taking off his cap, entered the house.

— This is a nice house, he said. I didn't expect it would be so nice.

— Not all our houses are such, said Kumalo gently. But a priest must keep his house nice. You have seen some of our other houses, perhaps?

— Oh yes, I have. On my grandfather's farm. They're not so nice as this. Is that your work there?

— Yes, inkosana.

— It looks like Arithmetic.

— It *is* Arithmetic. They are the accounts of the Church.

— I didn't know that churches had accounts. I thought only shops had those.

And Kumalo laughed at him. And having laughed once, he laughed again, so that the small boy said to him, Why are you laughing? But the small boy was laughing also, he took no offense.

— I am just laughing, inkosana. [**230/231**]

— Inkosana? That's little inkosi, isn't it?

— It is little inkosi. Little master, it means.

— Yes, I know. And what are you called? What do I call you?

— Umfundisi.

— I see. Imfundisi.

— No. Umfundisi.

— Umfundisi. What does it mean?

— It means parson.

— May I sit down, umfundisi? the small boy pronounced the word slowly. Is that right? he said.

Kumalo swallowed the laughter. That is right, he said. Would you like a drink of water? You are hot.

— I would like a drink of milk, said the boy. Ice-cold, from the fridge, he said.

— Inkosana, there is no fridge in Ndotsheni.

— Just ordinary milk then, umfundisi.

— Inkosana, there is no milk in Ndotsheni.

The small boy flushed. I would like water, umfundisi, he said.

Kumalo brought him the water, and while he was drinking, asked him, How long are you staying here, inkosana?

— Not very long now, umfundisi.

He went on drinking his water, then he said. These are not our real holidays now. We are here for special reasons.

And Kumalo stood watching him, and said in his heart, Oh child bereaved, I know your reasons.

— Water is amanzi, umfundisi.

And because Kumalo did not answer him, he said, umfundisi.

And again, umfundisi.

— My child.

— Water is amanzi, umfundisi.

Kumalo shook himself out of his reverie. He smiled at the small eager face, and he said, That is right, inkosana.

— And horse is ihashi.

— That is right also.

— And house is ikaya. [**231/232**]

— Right also.

— And money is imali.

— Right also.

— And boy is umfana.

— Right also.

— And cow is inkomo.

Kumalo laughed outright. Wait, wait, he said, I am out of breath. And he pretended to puff and gasp, and sat down on the chair, and wiped his brow.

— You will soon talk Zulu, he said.

— Zulu is easy. What's the time, umfundisi?

— Twelve o'clock, inkosana.

— Jeepers creepers, it's time I was off. Thank you for the water, umfundisi.

The small boy went to his horse. Help me up, he cried. Kumalo helped him up, and the small boy said, I'll come and see you again, umfundisi. I'll talk more Zulu to you.

Kumalo laughed. You will be welcome, he said.

— Umfundisi?

— Inkosana?

— Why is there no milk in Ndotsheni? Is it because the people are poor?

— Yes, inkosana.

— And what do the children do?

Kumalo looked at him. They die, my child, he said. Some of them are dying now.

— Who is dying now?

— The small child of Kuluse.

— Didn't the doctor come?

— Yes, he came.

— And what did he say?

— He said the child must have milk, inkosana.

— And what did the parents say?

— They said, Doctor, we have heard what you say.

And the small boy said in a small voice, I see. He raised his cap and said solemnly. Good-bye, umfundisi. He set off solemnly too, but there were spectators along the way, and it was [**232/233**] not long before he was galloping wildly along the hot dusty road.

* * * * *

The night brought coolness and respite. While they were having their meal, Kumalo and his wife, the girl and the small boy, there was a sound of wheels, and a knock at the door, and there was the friend who had carried the bags.

— Umfundisi. Mother.

— My friend. Will you eat?

— No indeed. I am on my way home. I have a message for you.

— For me?

— Yes, from uJarvis. Was the small white boy here today?

Kumalo had a dull sense of fear, realizing for the first time what had been done.

— He was here, he said.

— We were working in the trees, said

the man, when this small boy came riding up. I do not understand English, umfundisi, but they were talking about Kuluse's child. And come and look what I have brought you.

There outside the door was the milk, in the shining cans in the cart.

— This milk is for small children only, for those who are not yet at school, said the man importantly. And it is to be given by you only. And these sacks must be put over the cans, and small boys must bring water to pour over the sacks. And each morning I shall take back the cans. This will be done till the grass comes and we have milk again.

The man lifted the cans from the cart and said, Where shall I put them, umfundisi? But Kumalo was dumb and stupid, and his wife said, We shall put them in the room that the umfundisi has in the church. So they put them there, and when they came back the man said, You would surely have a message for uJarvis, umfundisi. And Kumalo stuttered and stammered, and at last pointed his hand up at the sky. And the man said, *Tixo* will bless him, and Kumalo nodded. **[233/234]**

The man said, I have worked only a week there, but the day he says to me, die, I shall die.

He climbed into the cart and took up the reins. He was excited and full of conversation. When I come home in this, he said, my wife will think they have made me a magistrate. They all laughed, and Kumalo came out of his dumbness and laughed also, first at the thought that this humble man might be a magistrate and second at the thought that a magistrate should drive in such a cart. And he laughed again that a grown man should play in such fashion, and he laughed again that Kuluse's child might live, and he laughed again at the thought of the stern silent man at High Place. He turned into the house sore with laughing, and his wife watched him with wondering eyes. **[234/235]**

XXXII

A child brought the four letters from the store to the school, and the headmaster sent them over to the house of the umfundisi. They were all letters from Johannesburg, one was from the boy Absalom to his wife, and another to his parents; they were both on His Majesty's Service, from the great prison at Pretoria. The third was from Msimangu himself, and the fourth from Mr. Carmichael. This one Kumalo opened fearfully, because it was from the lawyer who took the case for God, and would be about the mercy. And there the lawyer told him, in gentle and compassionate words, that there would be no mercy, and that his son would be hanged on the fifteenth day of that month. So he read no more but sat there an hour, two hours maybe. Indeed he neither saw sight nor heard sound till his wife said to him, It has come, then, Stephen.

And when he nodded, she said, Give it to me, Stephen. With shaking hands he gave it to her, and she read it also, and sat looking before her, with lost and terrible eyes, for this was the child of her womb, of her breasts. Yet she did not sit as long as he had done, for she stood up and said, It is not good to sit idle. Finish your letters, and go to see Kuluse's child, and the girl Elizabeth that is ill. And I shall do my work about the house.

— There is another letter, he said.
— From him? she said.
— From him.

He gave it to her, and she sat down again and opened it carefully and read it. The pain was in her eyes and her face and her hands, but he did not see it, for he stared before him on the floor, only his eyes were not looking at the floor but at no **[235/236]** place at all, and his face was sunken, in the same mould of suffering from which it had escaped since his return to this valley.

— Stephen, she said sharply.
He looked at her.

— Read it, finish it, she said. Then let us go to our work.

He took the letter and read it, it was short and simple, and except for the first line, it was in Zulu, as is often the custom:

My dear Father and Mother,

I am hoping you are all in health even as I am. They told me this morning there will be no mercy for the thing that I have done. So I shall not see you or Ndotsheni again.

This is a good place. I am locked in, and no one may come and talk to me. But I may smoke and read and write letters, and the white men do not speak badly to me.

There is a priest who comes to see me, a black priest from Pretoria. He is preparing me, and speaks well to me.

There is no more news here, so I close my letter. I think of you all at Ndotsheni, and if I were back there I should not leave it again.

Your son,
ABSALOM.

Is the child born? If it is a boy, I should like his name to be Peter. Have you heard of the case of Matthew and Johannes? I have been to the court to give evidence in this case, but they did not let me see it finish. My father, did you get the money in my Post Office Book?

— Stephen, shall we go and work now?
— Yes, he said, that would be better. But I have not read Msimangu's letter. And here is a letter for our daughter.
— I shall take it. Read your letter first then. And tell me, will you go to Kuluse's?
— I shall go there.
— And would it tire you too greatly to go up to the store? [**236/237**]

He looked out of the windows.
— Look, he said, look at the clouds.

She came and stood by him, and saw the great heavy clouds that were gathering on the other side of the Umzimkulu valley.

— It will rain, he said. Why do you want me to go to the store? Is it something you need badly?

— It is nothing I need, Stephen. But I thought you might go to the store and ask the white man, when these letters come on His Majesty's Service from the Central Prison to hold them privately till we come. For our shame is enough.

— Yes, yes, he said. I shall do that for a certainty.

— Read your letter then.

He opened Msimangu's letter, and heard about all the happenings of Johannesburg and was astonished to find within himself a faint nostalgia for that great bewildering city. When he had finished he went out to look at the clouds, for it was exciting to see them after weeks of pitiless sun. Indeed one or two of them were already sailing overhead, and they cast great shadows over the valley, moving slowly and surely till they reached the slopes to the tops, and then they passed up these slopes with sudden swiftness and were gone. It was close and sultry, and soon there would be thunder from across the Umzimkulu, for on this day the drought would break, with no doubt at all.

While he stood there he saw a motor car coming down the road from Carisbrooke into the valley. It was a sight seldom seen, and the car went slowly because the road was not meant for cars, but only for carts and wagons and oxen. Then he saw that not far from the church there was a white man sitting still upon a horse. He seemed to be waiting for the car, and with something of a shock he realized that it was Jarvis. A white man climbed out of the car, and he saw with further surprise that it was the magistrate, and the foolish jest of the night before came back to him at once. Jarvis got down from his horse, and he shook hands with the magistrate, and with other white men that were climbing out of the car, bringing out with them sticks and flags. Then lo! from the other direction came riding the stout chief, in the fur cap and the riding breeches, surrounded [237/238] by his counsellors. The chief saluted the magistrate, and the magistrate the chief, and there were other salutes also. Then they all stayed and talked together, so that it was clear that they had met together for some purpose. There was pointing of hands, to places distant and to places at hand. Then one of the counsellors began to cut down a small tree with straight clean branches. These branches he cut into lengths, and sharpened the ends, so that Kumalo stood more and more mystified. The white men brought out more sticks and flags from the car, and one of them set up a box on three legs, as though he would take photographs. Jarvis took some of the sticks and flags, and so did the magistrate, after he had taken off his coat because of the heat. They pointed to the clouds also, and Kumalo heard Jarvis say, It looks like it at last.

Now the chief was not to be outdone by the white men, so he too got down from his horse and took some of the sticks, but Kumalo could see that he did not fully understand what was being done. Jarvis, who seemed to be in charge of these matters, planted one of the sticks in the ground, and the chief gave a stick to one of his counsellors, and said something to him. So the counsellor also planted the stick in the ground, but the white man with the box on the three legs called out, Not there, not there, take that stick away. The counsellor was in two minds, and he looked hesitantly at the chief, who said angrily, Not there, not there, take it away. Then the chief, embarrassed and knowing still less what was to be done, got back on his horse and sat there, leaving the white men to plant the sticks.

So an hour passed, while there was quite an array of sticks and flags, and Kumalo looked on as mystified as ever. Jarvis and the magistrate stood together, and they kept on pointing at the hills, then turned and pointed down the valley. Then they talked to the chief, and the counsellors stood by, listening with grave at-

tention to the conversation. Kumalo heard Jarvis say to the magistrate, That's too long. The magistrate shrugged his shoulders, saying, That's the way these things are done. Then Jarvis said, I'll go to Pretoria. Would you mind? The magistrate said, I don't mind at all. It may be the way to get it. Then Jarvis said, [238/239] I don't want to lose your company, but if you want to get home dry, you'd better be starting. This'll be no ordinary storm.

But Jarvis did not start himself. He said good-bye to the magistrate, and began to walk across the bare fields, measuring the distance with his strides. Kumalo heard the magistrate say to one of the white men, They say he's going queer. From what I've heard, he soon won't have any money left.

Then the magistrate said to the chief, You will see that not one of these sticks is touched or removed. He saluted the chief, and he and the other white men climbed into the car and drove away up the hill. The chief said to his counsellors, You will give orders that not one of these sticks is to be touched or removed. The counsellors then rode away, each to some part of the valley, and the chief rode past the church, returning Kumalo's greeting, but not stopping to tell him anything about this matter of the sticks.

Indeed it was true what Jarvis had said, that this would be no ordinary storm. For it was now dark and threatening over the valley. There were no more shadows sailing over the fields, for all was shadow. On the other side of the Umzimkulu the thunder was rolling without pause, and now and then the lightning would strike down among the far-off hills. But it was this for which all men were waiting, the rain at last. Women were hurrying along the paths, and with a sudden babel of sound the children poured out of the school, and the headmaster and his teachers were urging them, Hurry, hurry, do not loiter along the road.

It was something to see, a storm like this. A great bank of black and heavy cloud was moving over the Umzimkulu, and Kumalo stood for a long time and watched it. Out of it the thunder came, and lightning shot out of it to the earth below. Wind sprang up in the valley of Ndotsheni, and the dust whirled over the fields and along the roads. It was very dark and soon the hills beyond the Umzimkulu were shut off by the rain. He saw Jarvis hurrying back to his horse, which stood restlessly against the fence. With a few practiced movements he stripped it of saddle and bridle, and saying a word to it, left it loose. Then he [**239/240**] walked quickly in the direction of Kumalo, and called out to him, umfundisi.

— Umnumzana.

— May I put these things in your porch, umfundisi, and stay in your church?

— Indeed, I shall come with you, umnumzana.

So they went into the church, and none too soon, for the thunder boomed out overhead, and they could hear the rain rushing across the fields. In a moment it was drumming on the iron roof, with a deafening noise that made all conversation impossible. Kumalo lit a lamp in the church, and Jarvis sat down on one of the benches, and remained there without moving.

But it was not long before the rain found the holes in the old rusted roof, and Jarvis had to move to avoid it.

Kumalo, nervous and wishing to make an apology, shouted at him, the roof leaks, and Jarvis shouted back at him, I have seen it.

And again the rain came down through the roof on the new place where Jarvis was sitting, so that he had to move again. He stood up and moved about in the semi-darkness, testing the benches with his hand, but it was hard to find a place to sit, for where there was a dry place on a bench, there was rain coming down on the floor, and where there was a dry place on the floor, there was rain coming down on the bench.

— The roof leaks in many places, Kumalo shouted, and Jarvis shouted in reply, I have seen that also.

At last Jarvis found a place where the rain did not fall too badly, and Kumalo found himself a place also, and they sat there together in silence. But outside it was not silent, with the cracking of the thunder, and the deafening downpour on the roof.

It was a long time that they sat there, and it was not until they heard the rushing of the streams, of dead rivers come to life, that they knew that the storm was abating. Indeed the thunder sounded further away and there was a dull light in the church, and the rain made less noise on the roof.

It was nearly over when Jarvis rose and came and stood in [**240/241**] the aisle near Kumalo. Without looking at the old man he said, Is there mercy?

Kumalo took the letter from his wallet with trembling hands; his hands trembled partly because of the sorrow, and partly because he was always so with this man. Jarvis took the letter and held it away from him so that the dull light fell on it. Then he put it back again in the envelope, and returned it to Kumalo.

— I do not understand these matters, he said, but otherwise I understand completely.

— I hear you, umnumzana.

Jarvis was silent for a while, looking towards the altar and the cross on the altar.

— When it comes to this fifteenth day, he said, I shall remember. Stay well, umfundisi.

But Kumalo did not say go well. He did not offer to carry the saddle and bridle, nor did he think to thank Jarvis for the milk. And least of all did he think to ask about the matter of the sticks. And when he rose and went out, Jarvis was gone. It was still raining, but lightly, and the valley was full of sound, of streams and rivers, all red with the blood of the earth.

That evening they all came out in the pale red light of sunset, and they examined the sticks, but no one understood their purpose. The small boys pretended to pull the sticks out, seizing them near the earth, and turning the whites of their eyes up to heaven in their mock efforts. The small girls looked on, half with enjoyment, half with apprehension. This game went well till the young son of Dazuma pulled one out in error, and stood shocked at what he had done. Then there was silence, and the small boys looked in fear at their elders, and the small girls went to their mothers, some weeping, some giggling with apprehension, some saying, We told you, we told you. The young offender was taken off by his mother, who shook him and said, You have shamed me, you have shamed me. And the grown men that there were in the valley searched round the place, and one said, There is the hole. So they put it in carefully, and one got down on his knees and patted the ground round the stick, so that the place would look as though the stick had never been re- [241/242] moved. But one said, Make it rough, for the ground is wet, and it will look as though it has been patted. So they made it rough, and put grass and pebbles over it, and indeed no one could have said that it had been patted.

Then the cart with the milk arrived, and the mothers of the small children, or some messenger that they had sent, went to the church for their portions.

— What is all this with the sticks? Kumalo asked his friend.

— Umfundisi, I do not know. But tomorrow I shall try to discover. [242/243]

XXXIII

The sticks stood for days in the places where the men had put them, but no one came again to the valley. It was rumored that a dam was to be built here, but no one knew how it would be filled, because the small stream that ran past the church was sometimes dry, and was never a great stream at any time. Kumalo's friend told him that Jarvis had gone away to Pretoria, and his business was surely the business of the sticks, which was the business of the dam.

So the days passed. Kumalo prayed regularly for the restoration of Ndotsheni, and the sun rose and set regularly over the earth.

Kuluse's child was recovered, and Kumalo went about his pastoral duties. The school went on with its work, and they were no doubt learning there about seeds and plants, and the right kind of grass for pastures, and the right kind of stuff to put into the soil, and the right kind of food to give to cattle. More and more he found himself waiting for news of Jarvis's return, so that the people might know what plans were afoot; and more and more he found himself thinking that it was Jarvis and Jarvis alone that could perform the great miracle.

The girl was happy in her new home, for she had a dependent and affectionate nature. The small boy played with the other small boys, and had asked after his mother not more than once or twice; with time he would forget her. About Absalom no one asked, and if they talked about it in their huts, they let it make no difference in their respect for the old umfundisi.

One day the small white boy came galloping up, and when Kumalo came out to greet him, he raised his cap as before, and [243/244] Kumalo found himself warm with pleasure to see his small visitor again.

— I've come to talk Zulu again, said the boy. He slid down from his horse, and put the reins round the post. He walked over to the house with the assurance of a man, and dusted his feet and took off his cap before entering the house. He sat down at the table and looked round with a pleasure inside him, so that a man felt it was something bright that had come into the house.

— Are the accounts finished, umfundisi?

— Yes, they are finished, inkosana.

— Were they right?

Kumalo laughed, he could not help himself.

— Yes, they were right, he said. But not very good.

— Not very good, eh? Are you ready for the Zulu?

Kumalo laughed again, and sat down in his chair at the other side of the table, and said, Yes, I am ready for the Zulu. When is your grandfather returning?

— I don't know, said the small boy. I want him to come back. I like him, he said.

Kumalo could have laughed again at this, but he thought perhaps it was not a thing to laugh at. But the small boy laughed himself, so Kumalo laughed also. It was easy to laugh with this small boy, there seemed to be laughter inside him.

— When are you going back to Johannesburg, inkosana?

— When my grandfather comes back.

And Kumalo said to him in Zulu, When you go, something bright will go out of Ndotsheni.

— What are you saying, umfundisi?

But when Kumalo would have translated, the small boy cried out, No, don't tell me. Say it again in Zulu. So Kumalo said it again.

— That means when you are gone, said the small boy, and say the rest again.

— Something bright will go out of Ndotsheni, said Kumalo in Zulu.

— Something about Ndotsheni. But it's too hard for me. Say it in English, umfundisi. **[244/245]**

— Something bright will go out of Ndotsheni, said Kumalo in English.

— Yes, I see. When I go, something bright will go out of Ndotsheni.

The small boy laughed with pleasure. I hear you, he said in Zulu.

And Kumalo clapped his hands in astonishment, and said, Au! Au! You speak Zulu, so that the small boy laughed with still greater pleasure, and Kumalo clapped his hands again, and made many exclamations. The door opened and his wife came in, and he said to the small boy, this is my wife, and he said to his wife in Zulu, this is the son of the man. The small boy stood up and made a bow to Kumalo's wife, and she stood and looked at him with fear and sorrow. But he said to her, You have a nice house here, and

he laughed. She said to her husband in Zulu, I am overcome, I do not know what to say. And the small boy said in Zulu, I hear you, so that she took a step backward in fear. But Kumalo said to her swiftly, He does not understand you, those are only words that he knows, and for the small boy he clapped his hands again in astonishment and said, Au! Au! But you speak Zulu. And the woman went backwards to the door, and opened it and shut it and was gone.

— Are you ready for the Zulu, umfundisi?

— Indeed I am ready.

— Tree is umuti, umfundisi.

— That is right, inkosana.

— But medicine is also umuti, umfundisi.

And the small boy said this with an air of triumph, and a kind of mock bewilderment, so that they both laughed together.

— You see, inkosana, said Kumalo seriously, our medicines come mostly from trees. That is why the word is the same.

— I see, said the small boy, pleased with this explanation. And box is ibokisi.

— That is right, inkosana. You see, we had no boxes, and so our word is from your word.

— I see. And motor-bike is isitututu.

— That is right. That is from the sound that the motor-bike **[245/246]** makes, so, isi-tu-tu-tu. But inkosana, let us make a sentence. For you are giving me all the words that you know, and so you will not learn anything that is new. Now how do you say, I see a horse?

So the lesson went on, till Kumalo said to his pupil, It is nearly twelve o'clock, and perhaps it is time you must go.

— Yes, I must go, but I'll come back for some more Zulu.

— You must come back, inkosana. Soon you will be speaking better than many Zulus. You will be able to speak in the dark, and people will not know it is not a Zulu.

The small boy was pleased, and when they went out he said, Help me up, umfundisi. So Kumalo helped him up, and the small boy lifted his cap, and went galloping up the road. There was a car going up the road, and the small boy stopped his horse and cried, my grandfather is back. Then he struck at the horse and set out in a wild attempt to catch up with the car.

There was a young man standing outside the church, a young pleasant-faced man of some twenty-five years, and his bags were on the ground. He took off his hat and said in English, You are the umfundisi?

— I am.

— And I am the new agricultural demonstrator. I have my papers here, umfundisi.

— Come into the house, said Kumalo, excited.

They went into the house, and the young man took out his papers and showed them to Kumalo. These papers were from parsons and school-inspectors and the like, and said that the bearer, Napoleon Letsitsi, was a young man of sober habits and good conduct, and another paper said that he had passed out of a school in the Transkei as an agricultural demonstrator.

— I see, said Kumalo. But you must tell me why you are here. Who sent you to me?

— Why, the white man who brought me.

— uJarvis, was that the name?

— I do not know the name, umfundisi, but it is the white man who has just gone.

— Yes, that is uJarvis. Now tell me all. [246/247]

— I am come here to teach farming, umfundisi.

— To us, in Ndotsheni?

— Yes, umfundisi.

Kumalo's face lighted up, and he sat there with his eyes shining. You are an angel from God, he said. He stood up and walked about the room, hitting one hand against the other, which the young man watched in amazement. Kumalo saw him and laughed at him, and said again, You are an angel from God. He sat down again and said to the young demonstrator, where did the white man find you?

— He came to my home in Krugersdorp. I was teaching there at a school. He asked me if I would do a great work, and he told me about this place Ndotsheni. So I felt I would come here.

— And what about your teaching?

— I am not really a teacher, so they did not pay me well. And the white man said they would pay me ten pounds a month here, so I came. But I did not come only for the money. It was a small work there in the school.

Kumalo felt a pang of jealousy, for he had never earned ten pounds a month in all his sixty years. But he put it from him.

— The white man asked if I could speak Zulu, and I said no, but I could speak Xosa as well as I spoke my own language, for my mother was a Xosa. And he said that would do for Xosa and Zulu are almost the same.

Kumalo's wife opened the door again, and said, It is time for food. Kumalo said in Zulu, My wife, this is Mr. Letsitsi, who has come to teach our people farming. And he said to Letsitsi, You will eat with us.

They went to eat, and Letsitsi was introduced to the girl and the small boy. After Kumalo had asked a blessing, they sat down, and Kumalo said in Zulu, When did you arrive in Pietermaritzburg?

— This morning, umfundisi. And then we came with the motor-car to this place.

— And what did you think of the white man? [247/248]

— He is very silent, umfundisi. He did not speak much to me.

— That is his nature.

— We stopped there on the road, overlooking a valley. And he said, What could you do in such a valley? Those were the first words we spoke on the journey.

— And did you tell him?

— I told him, umfundisi.

— And what did he say?

— He said nothing, umfundisi. He made a noise in his throat, that was all.

— And then?

— He did not speak till we got here. He said to me, Go to the umfundisi, and ask him to find lodgings for you. Tell him

I am sorry I cannot come, but I am anxious to get to my home.

Kumalo looked at his wife, and she at him.

— Our rooms are small, and this is a parson's house, said Kumalo, but you may stay here if you wish.

— My people are also of the church, umfundisi. I should be glad to stay here.

— And what will you do in this valley?

The young demonstrator laughed. I must look at it first, he said.

— But what would you have done in that other valley?

So the young man told them all he would have done in the other valley, how the people must stop burning the dung and must put it back into the land, how they must gather the weeds together and treat them and not leave them to wither away in the sun, how they must stop ploughing up and down the hills, how they must plant trees for fuel, trees that grow quickly like wattles, in some place where they could not plough at all, on the steep sides of streams so that the water did not rush away in the storms. But these were hard things to do, because the people must learn that it is harmful for each man to wrest a living from his own little piece of ground. Some must give up their ground for trees, and some for pastures. And hardest of [248/249] all would be the custom of lobola, by which a man pays for his wife in cattle, for people kept too many cattle for this purpose, and counted all their wealth in cattle, so that the grass had no chance to recover.

— And is there to be a dam? asked Kumalo.

— Yes, there is to be a dam, said the young man, so that the cattle always have water to drink. And the water from the dam can be let out through a gate, and can water this land and that, and can water the pastures that are planted.

— But where is the water to come from?

— It will come by a pipe from a river, said the young demonstrator. That is what the white man said.

— That will be his river, said Kumalo.

And can all these things you have been saying, can they all be done in Ndotsheni?

— I must first see the valley, said the demonstrator laughing.

— But you came down through it, said Kumalo eagerly.

— Yes, I saw it. But I must see it slowly. Yet I think all these things can be done.

They all sat round the table, their faces excited and eager, for this young man could paint a picture before your eyes. And Kumalo looked round at them and said, I told this young man he was an angel from God. He got up in his excitement and walked round the room. Are you impatient to begin, he said.

The young man laughed with embarrassment. I am impatient, he said.

— What is your first step that you take?

— I must first go to see the chief, umfundisi.

— Yes, that is the first thing you must do.

Then outside he heard the sounds of a horse, and he got up and went out, wondering if it could be the small boy again, and back so quickly. And indeed it was, but the boy did not climb down, he talked to Kumalo from his horse. He talked excitedly and earnestly, as though it were a serious matter.

— That was a close shave, he said.

— A shave, asked Kumalo. A close shave?

— That's slang, said the small boy. But he did not laugh, he was too serious. It means a narrow escape, he said. You see, if [249/250] my grandfather hadn't come back so early, I couldn't have come to say good-bye.

— You are going then, inkosana?

But the boy did not answer his question. He saw that Kumalo was puzzled, and he was anxious to explain.

— You see, if my grandfather had come back later, then perhaps it would have been too late for me to ride down here again. But because he came early, there was time.

— That means you are going tomorrow, inkosana.

— Yes, tomorrow. On the narrow gauge train, you know, the small train.

— Au! inkosana.

— But I'm coming back for the holidays. Then we'll learn some more Zulu.

— That will be a pleasure, said Kumalo simply.

— Good-bye then, umfundisi.

— Good-bye, inkosana.

Then he said in Zulu, Go well, inkosana. The small boy thought for a moment, and frowned in concentration. Then he said in Zulu, Stay well, umfundisi. So Kumalo said, Au! Au! in astonishment, and the small boy laughed and raised his cap, and was gone in a great cloud of dust. He galloped up the road, but stopped and turned round and saluted, before he set out on his way. And Kumalo stood there, and the young demonstrator came and stood by him, both watching the small boy.

— And that, said Kumalo earnestly to the demonstrator, is a small angel from God.

They turned to walk back to the house, and Kumalo said, so you think many things can be done.

— There are many things that can be done, umfundisi.

— Truly?

— Umfundisi, said the young man, and his face was eager, there is no reason why this valley should not be what it was before. But it will not happen quickly. Not in a day.

— If God wills, said Kumalo humbly, before I die. For I have lived my life in destruction. [250/251]

XXXIV

Everything was ready for the confirmation. The women of the church were there, in their white dresses, each with the green cloth about her neck. Those men that were not away, and who belonged to this church, were there in their Sunday clothes, which means their working clothes, patched and cleaned and brushed. The children for the confirmation were there, the girls in their white dresses and caps, the boys in their school-going clothes, patched and cleaned and brushed. Women were busy in the house, helping the wife of the umfundisi, for after the confirmation there would be a simple meal, of tea boiled till the leaves had no more tea left in them, and of heavy homely cakes made of the meal of the maize. It was simple food, but it was to be eaten together.

And over the great valley the storm clouds were gathering again in the heavy oppressive heat, so that one did not know whether to be glad or sorry. The great dark shadows sailed over the red earth, and up the bare red hills to the tops. The people looked at the sky, and at the road by which the Bishop would come, and did not know whether to be glad or sorry. For it was certain that before this sun had set, the lightning would strike amongst the hills, and the thunder would echo amongst them.

Kumalo looked at the sky anxiously, and at the road by which the Bishop would come; and while he was looking he was surprised to see his friend driving along the road, with the cart that brought the milk. For the milk never came so early.

— You are early, my friend. [251/252]

— I am early, umfundisi, said his friend gravely. We work no more today. The inkosikazi is dead.

— Au! Au! said Kumalo, it cannot be.

— It is so, umfundisi. When the sun stood so—and he pointed above his head —it was then that she died.

— Au! Au! It is a sorrow.

— It is a sorrow, umfundisi.

— And the umnumzana?

— He goes about silent. You know how he is. But this time the silence is heavier. Umfundisi, I shall go and wash myself, then I can come to the confirmation.

— Go then, my friend.

Kumalo went into the house, and he told his wife, The inkosikazi is dead. And she said, Au! Au! and the women also. Some of them wept, and they spoke of the goodness of the woman that was dead. Kumalo went to his table, and sat down there, thinking what he should do. When this confirmation was over he would go up to the house at High Place, and tell Jarvis of their grief here in the valley. But there came a picture to him of the house of bereavement, of all the cars of the white people that would be there, of the black-clothed farmers that would stand about in little groups, talking gravely and quietly, for he had seen such a thing before. And he knew that he could not go, for this was not according to the custom. He would stand there by himself, and unless Jarvis himself came out, no one would ask why he was there, no one would know that he had brought a message. He sighed, and took out some paper from the drawer. He decided it must be written in English, for although most white men of these parts spoke Zulu, there were few who could read or write it. So he wrote then. And he wrote many things, and tore them up and put them aside, but at last it was finished.

Umnumzana,

We are grieved here at this church to hear that the mother has passed away, and we understand it and suffer with tears. We are certain also that she knew of the things you have [**252/253**] done for us, and did something in it. We shall pray in this church for the rest of her soul, and for you also in your suffering.

Your faithful servant,
Rev. S. Kumalo.

When it was finished, he sat wondering if he should send it. For suppose this woman had died of a heart that was broken, because her son had been killed. Then was he, the father of the man who had killed him, to send such a letter? Had he not heard that she was sick and thin? He groaned as he wrestled with this difficult matter, but as he sat there uncertain, he thought of the gift of the milk, and of the young demonstrator that had come to

teach farming, and above all, he remembered the voice of Jarvis saying, even as if he were speaking now in this room, Is there mercy? And he knew then that this was a man who put his feet upon a road, and that no man would turn him from it. So he sealed the letter, and went out and called a boy to him and said, My child, will you take a letter for me? And the boy said, I shall do it, umfundisi. Go to Kuluse, said Kumalo, and ask him for his horse, and take this letter to the house of uJarvis. Do not trouble the umnumzana, but give this letter to any person that you see about the place. And my child, go quietly and respectfully, and do not call to any person there, and do not laugh or talk idly, for the inkosikazi is dead. Do you understand?

— I understand completely, umfundisi.

— Go then, my child. I am sorry you cannot be here to see the confirmation.

— It does not matter, umfundisi.

Then Kumalo went to tell the people that the inkosikazi was dead. And they fell silent, and if there had been any calling or laughter or talking idly, there was no more. They stood there talking quietly and soberly till the Bishop came.

It was dark in the church for the confirmation, so that they had to light the lamps. The great heavy clouds swept over the valley, and the lightning flashed over the red desolate hills, [**253/254**] where the earth had torn away like flesh. The thunder roared over the valleys of old men and old women, of mothers and children. The men are away, the young men, and the girls are away, the soil cannot keep them any more. And some of the children are there in the church being confirmed, and after a while they too will go away, for the soil cannot keep them any more.

It was dark there in the church, and the rain came down through the roof. The pools formed on the floor, and the people moved here and there, to get away from the rain. Some of the white dresses were wet, and a girl shivered there with the cold, because this occasion was solemn for her, and she did not dare to move out of the rain. And the voice of the Bishop said, Defend, oh Lord, this Thy child with Thy heavenly grace, that he may continue Thine for ever, and daily increase in Thy Holy Spirit more and more, till he come unto Thy everlasting Kingdom. And this he said to each child that came, and confirmed them all.

After the confirmation they crowded into the house, for the simple food that was to be taken. Kumalo had to ask those who were not that day confirmed, or who were not parents of those confirmed, to stay in the church, for it was still raining heavily, though the lightning and the thunder had passed. Yet the house was full to overflowing; the people were in the kitchen, and in the room where Kumalo did his accounts, and in the room where they ate, and in the room where they slept, even in the room of the young demonstrator.

At last the rain was over, and the Bishop and Kumalo were left alone in the room where Kumalo did his accounts. The Bishop lit his pipe and said to Kumalo, Mr. Kumalo, I should like to talk to you. And Kumalo sat down fearfully, afraid of what would be said.

— I was sorry to hear of all your troubles, my friend.

— They have been heavy, my lord.

— I did not like to worry you, Mr. Kumalo, after all you had suffered. And I thought I had better wait till this confirmation. [254/255]

— Yes, my lord.

— I speak to you out of my regard for you, my friend. You must be sure of that.

— Yes, my lord.

— Then I think, Mr. Kumalo, that you should go away from Ndotsheni.

Yes, that is what would be said, it is said now. Yes, that is what I have feared. Yet take me away, and I die. I am too old to begin any more. I am old, I am frail. Yet I have tried to be a father to this people. Could you not have been here, Oh Bishop, the day when I came back to Ndotsheni? Would you not have seen that these people love me, although I am old? Would you not have heard a child say, We are glad the umfundisi is back, this other man, we did not understand him? Would you take' me away just when new things are beginning, when there is milk for the children, and the young demonstrator has come, and the sticks for the dam are planted in the ground? The tears fill the eyes, and the eyes shut, and the tears are forced out, and they fall on the new black suit, made for this confirmation with the money of the beloved Msimangu. The old head is bowed, and the old man sits there like a child, with not a word to be spoken.

— Mr. Kumalo, says the Bishop gently, and then again, more loudly, Mr. Kumalo.

— Sir. My lord.

— I am sorry to distress you. I am sorry to distress you. But would it not be better if you went away?

— It is what you say, my lord.

The Bishop sits forward in his chair, and rests his elbows upon his knees. Mr. Kumalo, is it not true that the father of the murdered man is your neighbour here in Ndotsheni? Mr. Jarvis.

— It is true, my lord.

— Then for that reason alone I think you should go.

Is that a reason why I should go? Why, does he not ride here to see me, and did not the small boy come into my house? Did he not send the milk for the children, and did he not get this [255/256] young demonstrator to teach the people farming? And does not my heart grieve for him, now that the inkosikazi is dead? But how does one say these things to a Bishop, to a great man in the country? They are things that cannot be said.

— Do you understand me, Mr. Kumalo?

— I understand you, my lord.

— I would send you to Pietermaritzburg, to your old friend Ntombela. You could help him there, and it would take a load off your shoulders. He can worry about buildings and schools and money, and you can give your mind to the work of a priest. That is the plan I have in my mind.

— I understand you, my lord.

— If you stay here, Mr. Kumalo, there will be many loads on your shoulders. There is not only the fact that Mr. Jarvis is your neighbour, but sooner or later you must rebuild your church, and that will cost a great deal of money and anxiety. You saw for yourself today in what condition it is.

— Yes, my lord.

— And I understand you have brought back to live with you the wife of your son, and that she is expecting a child. Is it fair to them to stay here, Mr. Kumalo? Would it not be better to go to some place where these things are not known?

— I understand you, my lord.

There was a knock at the door, and it was the boy standing there, the boy who took the message. Kumalo took the letter, and it was addressed to the Rev. S. Kumalo, Ndotsheni. He thanked the boy and closed the door, then went and sat down in his chair, ready to listen to the Bishop.

— Read your letter, Mr. Kumalo.

So Kumalo opened the letter, and read it.

Umfundisi,

I thank you for your message of sympathy, and for the promise of the prayers of your church. You are right, my wife knew of the things that are being done, and had the greatest part in it. These things we did in memory of our beloved son. It was one of her last wishes that a new church [256/257] should be built at Ndotsheni, and I shall come to discuss it with you.

Yours truly,
JAMES JARVIS.

You should know that my wife was suffering before we went to Johannesburg.

Kumalo stood up, and he said in a voice that astonished the Bishop, this is from God, he said. It was a voice in which there was relief from anxiety, and laughter, and

weeping, and he said again, looking round the walls of the room, This is from God.

— May I see your letter from God, said the Bishop drily.

So Kumalo gave it to him eagerly, and stood impatiently while the Bishop read it. And when the Bishop had finished, he said gravely, That was a foolish jest. This is truly a letter from God.

He read it again, and blew his nose, and sat with the letter in his hand.

— What are the things that are being done? he asked.

So Kumalo told him about the milk, and the new dam that was to be built, and the young demonstrator. And the Bishop blew his nose several times, and said to Kumalo, This is an extraordinary thing. It is one of the most extraordinary things that I have ever heard.

And Kumalo explained the words, You should know that my wife was suffering before we went to Johannesburg. He explained how these words were written out of understanding and compassion. And he told the Bishop of the words, Is there mercy?; and of the small boy who visited him, the small boy with the laughter inside him.

The Bishop said, Let us go into the church and pray, if there is a dry place to pray in your church. Then I must go, for I have still a long journey. But let me first say good-bye to your wife, and your daughter-in-law. Tell me, what of the other matter, of your daughter-in-law, and the child she is expecting? [257/258]

— We have prayed openly before the people, my lord. What more could be done than that?

— It was the way it was done in olden days, said the Bishop. In the olden days when men had faith. But I should not say that, after what I have heard today.

The Bishop said farewell to the people of the house, and he and Kumalo went to the church. At the church door he spoke to Kumalo and said gravely, I see it is not God's will that you should leave Ndotsheni.

After the Bishop had gone, Kumalo

stood outside the church in the gathering dark. The rain had stopped, but the sky was black with promise. It was cool, and the breeze blew gently from the great river, and the soul of the man was uplifted. And while he stood there looking out over the great valley, there was a voice that cried out of heaven, Comfort ye, comfort ye, my people, these things will I do unto you, and not forsake you.

Only it did not happen as men deem such things to happen, it happened otherwise. It happened in that fashion that men call illusion, or the imaginings of people overwrought, or an intimation of the divine.

When he went into the house, he found his wife and the girl, and some other women of the church, and his friend who carried the bags, busy making a wreath. They had a cypress branch, for there was a solitary cypress near the hut of his friend, the only cypress that grew in the whole valley of Ndotsheni, and how it grew there no man could remember. This branch they had made into a ring, and tied it so that it could not spring apart. Into it they had put the flowers of the veld, such as grew in the bareness of the valley.

— I do not like it, umfundisi. What is wrong with it? It does not look like a white person's wreath.

— They use white flowers, said the new teacher. I have often seen that they use white flowers there in Pietermaritzburg.

— Umfundisi, said the friend excitedly, I know where there are white flowers, arum lilies.

— They use arum lilies, said the new teacher, also excited. [258/259]

— But they are far away. They grow near the railway line, on the far side of Carisbrooke, by a little stream that I know.

— That is far away, said Kumalo.

— I shall go there, said the man. It is not too far to go for such a thing as this. Can you lend me a lantern, umfundisi?

— Surely, my friend.

— And there must be a white ribbon, said the teacher.

— I have one at my house, said one of the women. I shall go and fetch it.

— And you, Stephen, will you write a card for us? Have you such a card?

— The edges of it should be black, said the teacher.

— Yes, I can find a card, said Kumalo, and I shall put black edges on it with the ink.

He went to his room where he did the accounts, and he found such a card, and printed on it.

> With sympathy from the
> people of St. Mark's Church,
> Ndotsheni.

He was busy with the edges, careful not to spoil the card with the ink, when his wife called him to come to his food. [259/260]

XXXV

There is ploughing in Ndotsheni, and indeed on all the farms around it. But the ploughing goes slowly, because the young demonstrator, and behind him the chief, tell the men they must no longer go up and down. They throw up walls of earth, and plough round the hills, so that the fields look no longer like they used to look in the old days of ploughing. Women and boys collect the dung, but it looks so little on the land that the chief has ordered a kraal to be built, where the cattle can stay and the dung be easily collected; but that is a hard thing, because there will be nothing to eat in the kraal. The young demonstrator shakes his head over the dung, but next year he says it will be better. The wattle seed is boiled, and no one has heard of such a thing before in this valley, but those that have worked for the white farmers say it is right, and so they boil it. For this seed one or two desolate places have been chosen, but the young demonstrator shakes his head over them, there is so little food in the soil. And the demonstrator has told the people they can throw away the maize they have kept for the planting, because it is inferior and he has better seed from uJarvis. But they do not throw it away, they keep it for eating.

But all this was not done by magic. There have been meetings, and much silence, and much sullenness. It was only the fear of the chief that made anything come out of these meetings. No one was more dissatisfied than those who had to give up their fields. Kuluse's brother was silent for days because the dam was to eat up his land, and he was dissatisfied with the poor piece of land they gave him. Indeed the umfundisi had to persuade [260/261] him, and it was hard to refuse the umfundisi, because it was through him that had come the milk that had saved his brother's child.

The chief had hinted that there were still harder things he would ask, and indeed the young demonstrator was dissatisfied that they had not been asked at once. But it would be hard to get these people to agree to everything at once. Even this year he hoped, said the young demonstrator, that the people would see something with their eyes, though he shook his head sadly over the poverty-stricken soil.

There was talk that the Government would give a bull to the chief, and the young demonstrator explained to Kumalo that they would get rid of the cows that gave the smallest yield, but he did not talk thus in the meeting, for that was one of the hard things for a people who counted their wealth in cattle, even these miserable cattle.

But the greatest wonder of all is the great machine, that was fighting in the war they said, and pushes the earth of Kuluse's brother's land over to the line of the sticks, and leaves it there, growing ever higher and higher. And even Kuluse's brother, watching it sullenly, breaks out into unwilling laughter, but remembers again and is sullen. But there is some satisfaction for him, for next year, when the dam is full, Zuma and his brother must both give up their land that lies below the dam, for white man's grass is to be planted there, to be watered from the dam, to be cut and thrown into the kraal where the cattle will be kept. And both Zuma and his brother laughed at him, because he was sullen about the dam; so in some measure he is satisfied.

Indeed there is something new in this valley, some spirit and some life, and much to talk about in the huts. Although nothing has come yet, something is here already.

*　　*　　*　　*　　*

— There was another Napoleon, said Kumalo, who was also a man who did many things. So many things did he do that many books were written about him. [261/262]

The young demonstrator laughed, but he cast his eyes on the ground, and rubbed his one boot against the other.

— You can be proud, said Kumalo. For there is a new life in this valley. I have been here for many years, but I have never seen ploughing with such spirit.

— There is a new thing happening here, he said. It is not only these rains, though they too refresh the spirit. There is hope here, such as I have never seen before.

— You must not expect too much, said the young man anxiously. I do not expect much this year. The maize will be a little higher, and the harvest a little bigger, but the soil is poor indeed.

— But next year there will be the kraal.

— Yes, said the young man eagerly. We will save much dung in the kraal. They say to me, umfundisi, that even if the winter is cold, they will not burn the dung.

— How long will it be before the trees are ready?

— Many years, said the demonstrator gloomily. Tell me, umfundisi, he said anxiously, do you think they will bear the winter for seven years?

— Have courage, young man. Both the chief and I are working for you.

— I am impatient for the dam, said the demonstrator. When the dam is made, there will be water for the pastures. I tell you, umfundisi, he said excitedly, there will be milk in this valley. It will not be necessary to take the white man's milk.

Kumalo looked at him. Where would we be without the white man's milk, he asked. Where would we be without all that this white man has done for us? Where would you be also? Would you be working for him here?

— It is true I am paid by him, said the young man stubbornly. I am not ungrateful.

— Then you should not speak so, said Kumalo coldly.

There fell a constraint between them, until the young demonstrator said quietly, umfundisi, I work here with all my heart, is it not so? [262/263]

— That is true indeed.

— I work so because I work for my country and my people. You must see that, umfundisi. I could not work so for any master.

— If you had no master, you would not be here at all.

— I understand you, said the young man. This man is a good man, and I respect him. But it is not the way it should be done, that is all.

— And what way should it be done?

— Not this way, said the young man doggedly.

— What way then?

— Umfundisi, it was the white man who gave us so little land, it was the white man who took us away from the land to go to work. And we were ignorant also. It is all these things together that have made this valley desolate. Therefore, what this good white man does is only a repayment.

— I do not like this talk.

— I understand you, umfundisi, I understand you completely. But let me ask one thing of you.

— Ask it then.

— If this valley were restored, as you are always asking in your prayers, do you think it would hold all the people of this tribe if they all returned?

— I do not know indeed.

— But I know, umfundisi. We can re-store this valley for those who are here, but when the children grow up, there will again be too many. Some will have to go still.

And Kumalo was silent, having no answer. He sighed. You are too clever for me, he said.

— I am sorry, umfundisi.

— You need not be sorry. I see you have a love for truth.

— I was taught that, umfundisi. It was a white man who taught me. There is not even good farming, he said, without the truth.

— This man was wise.

— It was he also who taught me that we do not work for [263/264] men, that we work for the land and the people. We do not even work for money, he said.

Kumalo was touched, and he said to the young man, Are there many who think as you do?

— I do not know, umfundisi. I do not know if there are many. But there are some.

He grew excited. We work for Africa, he said, not for this man or that man. Not for a white man or a black man, but for Africa.

— Why do you not say South Africa?

— We would if we could, said the young man soberly.

He reflected for a moment. We speak as we sing, he said, for we sing *Nkosi Sikelel' iAfrika*.

— It is getting dark, said Kumalo, and it is time for us to wash.

— You must not misunderstand me, umfundisi, said the young man earnestly. I am not a man for politics. I am not a man to make trouble in your valley. I desire to restore it, that is all.

— May God give you your desire, said Kumalo with equal earnestness. My son, one word.

— Yes, umfundisi.

— I cannot stop you from thinking your thoughts. It is good that a young man has such deep thoughts. But hate no man, and desire power over no man. For I have a friend who taught me that power corrupts.

— I hate no man, umfundisi. I desire power over none.

— That is well. For there is enough hating in our land already.

The young man went into the house to wash, and Kumalo stood for a moment in the dark, where the stars were coming out over the valley that was to be restored. And that for him was enough, for his life was nearly finished. He was too old for new and disturbing thoughts and they hurt him also, for they struck at many things. Yes, they struck at the grave silent man at High Place, who after such deep hurt, had shown such deep compassion. He was too old for new and disturbing [264/265] thoughts. A white man's dog, that is what they called him and his kind. Well, that was the way his life had been lived, that was the way he would die.

He turned and followed the young man into the house. [265/266]

XXXVI

This was the fourteenth day. Kumalo said to his wife, I am going up into the mountain. And she said, I understand you. For twice before he had done it, once when the small boy Absalom was sick unto death, and once when he had thought of giving up the ministry to run a native store at Donnybrook for a white man named Baxter, for more money than the church could ever pay. And there was a third time, but that was without her knowledge, for she was away, and he had been sorely tempted to commit adultery with one of the teachers at Ndotsheni, who was weak and lonely.

— Would you come with me, he said, for I do not like to leave you alone.

She was touched and she said, I cannot come, for the girl is near her time, and who knows when it will be. But you must certainly go.

She made him a bottle of tea, of the kind that is made by boiling the leaves, and she wrapped up a few heavy cakes of maize. He took his coat and his stick and walked up the path that went to the place of the chief. But at the first fork you go to the side of the hand that you eat with, and you climb another hill to other huts that lie beneath the mountain itself. There you turn and walk under the mountain to the east, as though you were going to the far valley of Empayeni, which is another valley where the fields are red and bare, a valley of old men and women, and mothers and children. But when you reach the end of the level path, where it begins to fall to this other valley, you strike upwards into the mountain itself. This mountain is called Emoyeni, which means, in the winds, and it stands high above Carisbrooke and the tops, and higher still [266/267] above the valleys of Ndotsheni and Empayeni. Indeed it is a rampart of the great valley itself, the valley of the Umzimkulu, and from it you look down on one of the fairest scenes of Africa.

Now it was almost dark, and he was alone in the dusk; which was well, for one did not go publicly on a journey of this nature. But even as he started to climb the path that ran through the great stones, a man on a horse was there, and a voice said to him, It is you umfundisi?

— It is I, umnumzana.

— Then we are well met, umfundisi. For here in my pocket I have a letter for the people of your church. He paused for a moment, and then he said, The flowers were of great beauty, umfundisi.

— I thank you, umnumzana.

— And the church, umfundisi. Do you desire a new church?

Kumalo could only smile and shake his head, there were no words in him. And though he shook his head as if it were No, Jarvis understood him.

— The plans will shortly come to you, and you must say if they are what you desire.

— I shall send them to the Bishop, umnumzana.

— You will know what to do. But I am anxious to do it quickly, for I shall be leaving this place.

Kumalo stood shocked at the frightening and desolating words. And although it was dark, Jarvis understood him, for he said swiftly, I shall be often here. You know I have a work in Ndotsheni. Tell me, how is the young man?

— He works night and day. There is no quietness in him.

The white man laughed softly. That is good, he said. Then he said gravely, I am alone in my house, so I am going to Johannesburg to live with my daughter and her children. You know the small boy?

— Indeed, umnumzana, I know him.

— Is he like him?

— He is like him, umnumzana.

And then Kumalo said, Indeed, I have never seen such a child as he is. [267/268]

Jarvis turned on his horse, and in the dark the grave silent man was eager. What do you mean, he asked.

— Umnumzana, there is a brightness inside him.

— Yes, yes, that is true. The other was even so.

And then he said, like a man with hunger, do you remember?

And because this man was hungry, Kumalo, though he did not well remember, said, I remember.

They stayed there in silence till Jarvis said, umfundisi, I must go. But he did not go. Instead he said, Where are you going at this hour?

Kumalo was embarrassed, and the words fell about on his tongue, but he answered, I am going into the mountain.

Because Jarvis made no answer he sought for words to explain it, but before he had spoken a word, the other had already spoken. I understand you, he said, I understand completely.

And because he spoke with compassion, the old man wept, and Jarvis sat embarrassed on his horse. Indeed he might have come down from it, but such a thing is not lightly done. But he stretched his hand over the darkening valley, and he said, One thing is about to be finished, but here is something that is only begun. And while I live it will continue. Umfundisi, go well.

— Umnumzana!

— Yes.

— Do not go before I have thanked you. For the young man, and the milk. And now for the church.

— I have seen a man, said Jarvis with a kind of grim gaiety, who was in darkness till you found him. If that is what you do, I give it willingly.

Perhaps it was something deep that was here, or perhaps the darkness gives courage, but Kumalo said, truly, of all the white men that I have ever known—

— I am no saintly man, said Jarvis fiercely.

— Of that I cannot speak, but God put His hands on you.

And Jarvis said, That may be, that may be. He turned suddenly to Kumalo. Go well, umfundisi. Throughout this night, stay well. [268/269]

And Kumalo cried after him, Go well, go well.

Indeed there were other things, deep things, that he could have cried, but such a thing is not lightly done. He waited till the sounds of the horse had died away, then started to climb heavily, holding onto the greatest stones, for he was young no longer. He was tired and panting when he reached the summit, and he sat down on a stone to rest, looking out over the great valley, to the mountains of Ingeli and East Griqualand, dark against the sky. Then recovered, he walked a short distance and found the place that he had used before on these occasions. It was an angle in the rock, sheltered from the winds, with a place for a man to sit on, his legs at ease over the edge. The first of these occasions he remembered clearly, perhaps because it was the first, perhaps because he had come to pray for the child that no prayer could save any more. The child could not write then, but here were three letters from him now, and in all of them he said, If I could come back to Ndotsheni, I would not leave it any more. And in a day or two they would receive the last he would ever write. His heart went out in a great compassion for the boy that must die, who promised now, when there was no more mercy, to sin no more. If he had got to him sooner, perhaps. He knitted his brows at the memory of that terrible and useless questioning, the terrible and useless answering, it is as my father wishes, it is as my father says. What would it have helped if he had said, My father, I do not know?

He turned aside from such fruitless remembering, and set himself to the order of his vigil. He confessed his sins, remembering them as well as he could since the last time he had been in this mountain. There were some he remembered easily, the lie in the train, the lie to his brother, when John had barred the door against him and shut him out in the street; his loss of faith in Johannesburg, and his desire to hurt the girl, the sinning and innocent child. All this he did as fully as he could, and prayed for absolution.

Then he turned to thanksgiving, and remembered with profound awareness, that he had great cause for thanksgiving, and that for many things. He took them one by one, giving thanks [**269/270**] for each, and praying for each person that he remembered. There was above all the beloved Msimangu and his generous gift. There was the young man from the reformatory saying with angry brows, I am sorry, umfundisi, that I spoke such angry words. There was Mrs. Lithebe, who said so often, Why else were we born? And Father Vincent, holding both his hands and saying, Anything, anything, you have only to ask, I shall do anything. And the lawyer that took the case for God, and had written to say there was no mercy in such kind and gentle words.

Then there was the return to Ndotsheni, with his wife and his friend to meet him. And the woman who threw her apron over her head. And the women waiting at the church. And the great joy of the return, so that pain was forgotten.

He pondered long over this, for might not another man, returning to another valley, have found none of these things? Why was it given to one man to have his pain transmuted into gladness? Why was it given to one man to have such an awareness of God? And might not another, having no such awareness, live with pain that never ended? Why was there a compulsion upon him to pray for the restoration of Ndotsheni, and why was there a white man there on the tops, to do in this valley what no other could have done? And why of all men, the father of the man who had been murdered by his son? And might not another feel also a compulsion, and pray night and day without ceasing, for the restoration of some other valley that would never be restored?

But his mind would contain it no longer. It was not for man's knowing. He put it from his mind, for it was a secret.

And then the white man Jarvis, and the inkosikazi that was dead, and the small boy with the brightness inside him. As his mind could not contain that other, neither could this be contained. But here were thanks that a man could render till the end of his days. And some of them he strove now to render.

He woke with a start. It was cold, but not so cold. He had never slept before on these vigils, but he was old, not quite finished, but nearly finished. He thought of all those that were [**270/271**] suffering, of Gertrude the weak and foolish one, of the people of Shanty Town and Alexandra, of his wife now at this moment. But above all of his son, Absalom. Would he be awake, would he be able to sleep, this night before the morning? He cried out, My son, my son, my son.

With his crying he was now fully awake, and he looked at his watch and saw that it was one o'clock. The sun would rise soon after five, and it was then it was done, they said. If the boy was asleep, then let him sleep, it was better. But if he was awake, then oh Christ of the abundant mercy, be with him. Over this he prayed long and earnestly.

Would his wife be awake, and thinking of it? She would have come with him, were it not for the girl. And the girl, why he had forgotten her. But she was no doubt asleep; she was loving enough, but this husband had given her so little, no more than her others had done.

And there was Jarvis, bereaved of his wife and his son, and his daughter-in-law bereaved of her husband, and her children bereaved of their father, especially the small boy, the bright laughing boy. The small boy stood there before his eyes, and he said to Kumalo, When I go, something bright will go out of Ndotsheni. Yes, I see, he said. Yes, I see. He was not shy or ashamed, but he said, Yes, I see, and laughed with his pleasure.

And now for all the people of Africa, the beloved country. *Nkosi Sikelel' iAfrika,* God save Africa. But he would not see that salvation. It lay afar off, because men were afraid of it. Because, to tell the truth, they were afraid of him, and his wife, and Msimangu, and the young demonstrator. And what was there evil in their desires, in their hunger? That men should walk upright in the land where they were born, and be free to use the fruits of the earth, what was there evil in it? Yet men were afraid, with a fear that was deep, deep in the heart, a fear so deep that they hid their kindness, or brought it out with fierceness and anger, and hid it behind fierce and frowning eyes. They were afraid because they were so few. And such fear could not be cast out, but by love. **[271/272]**

It was Msimangu who had said, Msimangu who had no hate for any man, I have one great fear in my heart, that one day when they turn to loving they will find we are turned to hating.

Oh the grave and the sombre words.

When he woke again there was a faint change in the east, and he looked at his watch almost with panic. But it was four o'clock and he was reassured. And now it was time to be awake, for it might be they had wakened his son, and called him to make ready. He left his place and could hardly stand, for his feet were cold and numb. He found another place where he could look to the east, and if it was true what men said, when the sun came up over the rim, it would be done.

He had heard that they could eat what they wished on a morning like this. Strange that a man should ask for food at such a time. Did the body hunger, driven by some deep dark power that did not know it must die? Is the boy quiet, and does he dress quietly, and does he think of Ndotsheni now? Do tears come into his eyes, and does he wipe them away, and stand up like a man? Does he say, I will not eat any food, I will pray? Is Msimangu there with him, or Father Vincent, or some other priest whose duty it is, to comfort and strengthen him, for he is afraid of the hanging? Does he repent him, or is there only room for his fear? Is there nothing that can be done now, is there not an angel that comes there and cries, This is for God not for man, come child, come with me?

He looked out of his clouded eyes at the faint steady lightening in the east. But he calmed himself, and took out the heavy maize cakes and the tea, and put them upon a stone. And he gave thanks, and broke the cakes and ate them, and drank of the tea. Then he gave himself over to deep and earnest prayer, and after each petition he raised his eyes and looked to the east. And the east lightened and lightened, till he knew that the time was not far off. And when he expected it, he rose to his feet and took off his hat and laid it down on the earth, and clasped his hands **[272/273]** before him. And while he stood there the sun rose in the east.

Yes, it is the dawn that has come. The titihoya wakes from sleep, and goes about its work of forlorn crying. The sun tips with light the mountains of Ingeli and East Griqualand. The great valley of the Umzimkulu is still in darkness, but the light will come there. Ndotsheni is still in darkness, but the light will come there also. For it is the dawn that has come, as it has come for a thousand centuries, never failing. But when that dawn will come, of our emancipation, from the fear of bondage and the bondage of fear, why, that is a secret. **[273/275]**

List of Words

Afrikáner
"a" as in father. The name now used for the descendants of the Boers. Some large-minded Afrikaners claim that it has a wider connotation, and means white South Africans, but many Afrikaans-speaking and English-speaking South Africans would object to this extension of meaning. It is used here in its usually accepted meaning.

Afrikáans
the language of the Afrikaner, a much simplified and beautiful version of the language of Holland, though it is held in contempt by some ignorant English-speaking South Africans, and indeed by some Hollanders. Afrikaans and English are the two official languages of the Union of South Africa.

Ingéli
The first "i" as in "pit," the second as "ee." The "e" is almost like "a" in "pane."

Inkosána
The "i" as in "pit," the "o" midway between "o" in "pot," and "o" in "born." The "a" as in "father," but the second "a" is hardly sounded. Approximate pronunciation "inkosáan." Means little chief, or little master.

Inkósi
As above. But the final "i" is hardly sounded. Means chief or master.

Inkósikazi
As above. The second "k" is like hard "g." The final "i" is hardly sounded. Pronounce "inkosigaaz." Means mistress. [275/276]

Ixópo
The name of a village. Its Zulu pronunciation is difficult, and would be considered affected in English speech. It is pronounced in English, "Ickopo," with "o" as in "hole."

Johánnesburg
An Afrikaans word, but pronounced in English as it is written. It is the centre of the gold-mining industry.

Káfferboetie
Pronounce "boetie" not as "booty" but to rhyme with "sooty." A term of contempt originally used to describe those who fraternised with African natives, but now used to describe any who work for the welfare of the non-European. Means literally "little brother of the kaffir." Afrikaans.

Kloof
An Afrikaans word now as fully English. Pronounced as written. Means ravine or even a valley if the sides are steep. But it would not be used of a great valley like the Umzimkulu.

Kraal
An Afrikaans word now as fully English. Pronounced in English "crawl." Means in this book an enclosure for cattle, when they come for milking, or where in the early days they were kept for protection. But it may also mean a number of huts together, under the rule of the head of the family, who is of course subject to the chief.

Kumálo
"u" as "oo" as in "book." "a" as in "father." The "o" midway between "o" in "pot" and "o" in "born."

Lithébe
Pronounced "ditebe," "e" approximately as in "bed." [276/277]

Msimángu

The word is pronounced with the lips initially closed. Therefore no vowel precedes the "M." Pronounced approximately as written.

Ndotshéni

Approximately "Indotsheni." "o" midway between "o" in "pot" and "o" in "born," "e" almost as "a" in "pane," "i" as "ee." Last vowel hardly sounded.

Nkosi sikelél' iAfrika

Means "God bless Africa," though in the book it is taken to mean "God *save* Africa." This lovely hymn is rapidly becoming accepted as the national anthem of the black people. At any mixed meeting therefore, where goodwill prevails, three such anthems are sung at the conclusion, "God Save The King," "Die Stem Van Suid-Afrika," and "Nkosi Sikelel' iAfrika." This is co-operative, but very wearing. But such meetings are rare. Pronunciation, "Nkosi" almost as "Inkosi," "sikelel'" with "k" as hard "g," and "e" approximately as in "bed," "iAfrika" with "a" as in "father," "i" as shortened "ee."

Odendaalsrúst

Pronounced by English-speaking people as written.

Pietermáritzburg

Pronounced by English-speaking people as written. A city founded by the Voortrekkers Piet Retief and Gert Maritz. Capital of the Province of Natal.

Pretória

Pronounced by English-speaking people as written. A city named after the Voortrekker, Pretorius. Capital of the Union of South Africa.

Siyáfa

"i" as "ee," "a" as in "father." Means "we die." **[277/278]**

Titihóya

A plover-like bird. The name is onomatopoeic.

Tíxo

I rejected the Zulu word for the Great Spirit as too long and difficult. This is the Xosa word. It is also difficult to pronounce, but may be pronounced "Teeko," the "o" being midway the "o" in "pot" and the "o" of "born."

Umfúndisi

The last "i" is hardly sounded. Pronounced approximately "oomfóondees," the "oo" being as in "book," and the "ees" as "eace" in the word "peace." Means parson, but is also a title and used with respect.

Umnúmzana

Pronounced "oomnóomzaan." Means "sir."

Umzimkúlu

Pronounced by English-speaking people as "Umzimkóoloo," but the "oo" is very long as in "coo."

Veld

An Afrikaans word now as fully English. Pronounced in both languages as "felt." Means open grass country. Or it may mean the grass itself, as when a farmer looks down at his feet, and says, this veld is poor.

Xósa

The pronunciation is difficult. English-speaking people pronounce it "Kosa," "o" midway between "o" in "pot" and "o" in "born," "a" almost as "u" in "much." A native tribe of the Eastern Cape.

Zúlu

The great tribe of Zululand, which overflowed into Natal and other parts. Both "u"'s are long as in "coo."

PART TWO

THE CRITICS

[Publication Review]*

CHARLES J. ROLO (1916–   ), literary critic for *The Atlantic Monthly* from 1948 to 1960, is the author and editor of several non-fiction books and, at present, a stockbroker on Wall Street.

There is no large area of the civilized world which we have read less about than South Africa. And most of what we have read has been in the vein of adultery on the safari, or big game and Englishmen out in the noonday sun. Yet South Africa shares with the United States an acute racial problem, exacerbated in the Dominion by the great preponderance of blacks over whites and by the existence of a third element—the "coloreds"—a million people of mixed blood.

In Alan Paton's novel, *Cry, the Beloved Country* (Scribner, $3.00), hate and villainy are not personified by any of the main protagonists. Violence is virtually absent; there is a murder but it happens off stage. Yet Mr. Paton has projected with extraordinary poignancy the tragedy of South Africa's blacks, shorn of their moral law by the destruction of tribal society, corrupted by oppression, crowded into squalid slums in Johannesburg, and monstrously exploited by the whites who fear that betterment will make the blacks more conscious of their power.

The mainspring of this unusual book is saintliness. The hero, an old Zulu minister, the Reverend Stephen Kumalo, is a feat of characterization rare in the modern novel: a convincing portrait of a saintly man. The story opens:—

There is a lovely road that runs from Ixopo into the hills. These hills are grass-covered and rolling, and they are lovely beyond any singing of it. The road climbs seven miles into them to Carisbrooke; and from there, if there is no mist, you look down on one of the fairest valleys in Africa. About you there is grass and bracken and you may hear the forlorn crying of the titihoya, one of the birds of the veld. . . . The grass is rich. . . . Stand unshod upon it, for the ground is holy. . . . It keeps men, guards men, cares for men.

But down in the lower valleys the eroded soil cannot keep men. So the young go off to Johannesburg. And to Johannesburg journeys Stephen Kumalo in search of a vanished brother and sister and a vanished son, Absalom. The story of that search is told almost entirely in dialogue, in which the Zulu idiom, rendered in simple English, yields a lyrical cadence sometimes touched with Biblical grandeur.

Kumalo finds that his sister has become a pros- [112/113] titute, his brother a rabble-rouser, and his son a murderer. He has murdered a young white man who is the most ardent champion of the blacks, and the son of the great landowner in his home district. "It seems that God has turned from me," Kumalo says, as he leaves his doomed son. And his torment mirrors that of his people.

Back in his village he meets the sorrowing father of the man his son murdered. The scenes that ensue between the white lord and the humble Zulu achieve a rare intensity and poetic compassion. In them the spiritual and social dramas are entwined, and comfort is wrenched out of desolation. The comfort is unfortunately a trifle pat: milk for the sick child, a new church, a dam for the stricken valley. But if Mr. Paton's symbolism fails him in the final pages, his message loses nothing of its urgency.

* Charles J. Rolo, "Reader's Choice," *The Atlantic Monthly,* CLXXXI (April 1948), 112–113. Copyright © 1948, by The Atlantic Monthly Company, Boston, Mass. 02116. Reprinted with the permission of the author.

Cry, the Beloved Country and the Broken Tribe*

HAROLD R. COLLINS (1915–   ), a professor of English at Kent State University, has published several articles and critiques on West African and South African fiction in English.

Alan Paton's *Cry, the Beloved Country* has been published in Scribner's attractive "Modern Standard Authors" series and is now being studied in college classrooms. There are, of course, several difficulties standing in the way of an informative discussion of this fine novel. Fiction about Africa may conceivably be terra incognita for us. We remember Conrad's great story, "The Heart of Darkness," but that belongs to the earlier era of the scramble for Africa. Olive Schreiner's rather over-rated *Story of an African Farm,* conscientiously reread, turns out to be a feminist novel which scarcely mentions the Africans. We need more information on social conditions in the Union of South Africa than is available in Paton's capsule history of the country, quoted by Lewis Gannett in his useful introduction to the Scribner's edition. More specifically, we need reliable information on race relations in South Africa and the rest of Africa, so we may confidently demonstrate the novel's power and integrity in dramatizing racial problems in terms of human feelings— human hopes, aspirations, fears, and sorrows. Nonfiction [379/380] works on Africa are legion, but many of them are superficial travelogues, and those that look like serious, impartial studies may grind the imperialist ax.

Cry, the Beloved Country is a "story of comfort in desolation." We shall observe that the desolation consists not so much in the crowded native reserves, or the ruin of the reserved land by erosion and overcropping, or the absence of the young men drawn to the mines, or the frightful living conditions of the town natives—terrible as these afflictions are— but in the loss of the old African moral order that gave purpose and meaning to African lives. When Gannett says that *Cry, the Beloved Country* "creates rather than follows a tradition," he is probably putting his case rather too strongly. At any rate, the African novels of Joyce Cary and Elspeth Huxley are helpful toward an understanding of Paton's novel because they are tragedies, or tragicomedies, on the conflict of cultures in Africa and because they treat of the breaking of the tribes which results from that conflict. Likewise, in the jungle of information and special pleading on African conditions, there are dependable nonfiction sources, especially anthropological studies, that document the theme "Cry, for the broken tribe, for the law and the custom that are gone."

We recall that the Zulu preacher's sister Gertrude goes to Johannesburg to find her husband and becomes a prostitute there, that his son Absalom, sent to the great city to find the sister, falls among evil companions, becomes a thief and a murderer. Arthur Jarvis, whom Absalom murders, has been a prominent *kaffirboetie* (or friend of the natives). His bereaved father finds among his son's manuscripts what seems to be an address on native crime, ironically, an explanation of the high incidence of crime among the Africans in the towns:

* Harold R. Collins, "Cry, the Beloved Country and the Broken Tribe," *College English,* XIV (April 1953), 379–385. Reprinted with the permission of the National Council of Teachers of English and Harold R. Collins.

The old tribal system was, for all its violence and savagery, for all its superstition and witchcraft, a moral system. Our natives today produce criminals and prostitutes and drunkards, not because it is their nature to do so, but because their simple system of order and tradition and convention has been destroyed. It has been destroyed by the impact of our own civilization. Our civilization has therefore the inescapable duty to set up another system of order and tradition and convention.[2]

Indeed, one of the most important effects of European civilization in Africa is the deterioration and breakdown of the old African cultures and the consequent breakdown in African personalities. In the past our observation of the striking differences between these native African cultures and those of the Western world, and, perhaps even more, our feelings of racial superiority, have blinded us to the fact of the moral force of the old order. Now we begin to understand what has been happening. In the twentieth century, especially outside the reservations, in the mining compounds, the squatting grounds on the white men's farms, and the native slum "locations," Africans have been "detribalized," as the technical term has it. They have been losing the old moral standards without assuming, or being able to assume, those of the white men. Like Absalom and Matthew Kumalo, they have become social derelicts almost completely without moral guidance of any sort and, naturally enough, criminals.

Before the tribes were broken, the Africans had a good deal of moral guidance in their traditional religions. As an experienced missionary and expert on the West African peoples says: [380/381]

The behavior of Africans is not left to uncharted freedom, but is governed by a system of rules and regulations, so extensive, so complicated, that Europeans who study it stand amazed, and are tempted to declare the Africans to be the slaves of tribal custom. . . . The riotous instincts are restrained by forces that are not of this tangible sphere. In other words, the ethics of the Africans, their customary morality is grounded in their religion.[3]

In the Kumalos' Zululand, the old African religion has gone forever, though witchcraft has not. Absalom and the pitiful young girl he lives with are "Church of England," but their religion has no real hold on them. Their morality is not grounded in Christianity, certainly.

Anyone who wants to learn about detribalization would do well to consult *Africa,* the journal of the International Institute of African Languages and Cultures, which specializes in studies of the problems of culture contact. In this journal we find anthropological studies that confirm Paton's view of the broken tribe. For instance, Miss Ellen Hellman's "Native Life in a Johannesburg Slum Yard" is a study of the conduct of Africans in an environment rather like Claremont, Alexandra, and Orlando, where Gertrude, Absalom, and Matthew Kumalo are corrupted. Her conclusions are precisely those of Arthur Jarvis—and Alan Paton:

In the drive to town, families are separated from their kinfolk and form isolated groups in town. The restraints of tribal discipline do not affect the urban native, and no substitute discipline has, as yet, emerged from out the chaotic welter of transition. The old sanctions have lost their force and the sanctions which order European life are not applicable to native life.

Presuming that Europeans are controlled by public opinion, law, and the precepts of Christianity, Miss Hellman points out that for these Africans there is "no body of public opinion," that conviction and imprisonment carry no social stigma because the criminal sanction has been applied to trivial misdemeanors, and that the great majority of the slum-yard natives have "tacitly rejected Christianity." [4]

2 *Cry, the Beloved Country* (New York, 1948), p. 144. For confirmation of Paton's description of the reserves consult a South African economist's account of a ruin approaching desert conditions, W. M. Macmillan's *Africa Emergent* (London, 1938), pp. 168–72. R. L. Buell's monumental study *The Native Problem in Africa* (New York, 1928) gives the figures for the overcrowding on the reserves (I, 76).

3 Edwin Smith, *The Golden Stool: Some Aspects of Culture Contact in Modern Africa* (Garden City, N.Y., 1928), pp. 188 and 190. See also Diedrich Westermann, *The African Today and Tomorrow* (rev. ed.; London, 1939), pp. 147–49, for a general description of the old African social organization.

4 *Africa,* VIII (January, 1935), 60.

For Absalom Kumalo, there was "no body of public opinion" beyond the promptings of such unimproving acquaintances as his cousin Matthew, Johannes Pafuri, and Baby Mkize. Such acquaintances would not be in much awe of penal sanctions, and who can blame them, really, when an African can be arrested for some irregularity in his passes? It would seem that Absalom has "tacitly rejected Christianity" and taken his uncle's measure of his Christian father— "a white man's dog."

In a culture-contact study of a group of Africans in northwestern Rhodesia, Audrey I. Richards gives a series of case histories of detribalized persons. The history of Jackie Biltong is representative, and Jackie reminds us of the Kumalo boys, though the district in which he lives is an isolated one where the introduction of taxes and the money economy is just beginning to send the men to the distant labor centers, the points from which white influences radiate. Jackie's father, sacked from a job as a cook, went to the mines and took his son with him, and the woman he lived with brought Jackie up. Jackie is "smartly dressed" but somewhat disreputable and irresponsible. "Caught for pilfering," he is living on food cooked by his friend's mother and a relative of his mother. Recently he made ten shillings digging a garden for the local prostitute, and has spent the money on "clothes and beer"; he says he [381/382] will "pay back friend and look for tax later on." [5]

The African novels of Joyce Cary, written out of his seven years' experience as a political officer in Nigeria, and those of Elspeth Huxley, an expert on African colonial affairs and a former Kenya settler, throw considerable light on the process of detribalization. Cary's novels are crowded with strayed souls, tribeless Africans free of the old African sanctions and not controlled by European sanctions. We observe what the breaking of the tribes means in terms of the disorganization of African personalities. Of course Cary is writing about Nigeria, which does not have the large white population of South Africa or the highly developed mining industry. Racial friction and the conflict of cultures are less acute in Nigeria than in South Africa. And yet, as our examples of Cary's detribalized Africans will show, the effects of breaking the tribe are much the same in the two areas.

Cary's Africans, like Gertrude, Absalom, and Matthew Kumalo, get into trouble when they leave the tribe and enter the white man's world. Henry in *An American Visitor* (1933) is a "smooth operator" who finally opens a store in the minefields and does a splendid trade in condemned and slightly blown tinned meats, secondhand caps and trousers, aphrodisiacs, smuggled gin, and abortion drugs. Ajaki in *Mister Johnson* (1947) is a cash-drawer thief. The title character of that novel is a first-rate grafter, extorting his own personal tolls on a new road and embezzling treasury funds. Like Absalom Kumalo, he inadvertently murders a man who surprises him in amateurish housebreaking.[6]

It might be objected that our civilized societies produce such criminals in abundance. Well, surely some of Cary's misguided Africans are peculiar to the African scene. The Reverend Seleh Coker in *The African Witch* (1936) is an irresponsible agitator and spellbinder much bolder than John Kumalo. He preaches a weird juju variety of Christian doctrine and inspires the murder and mutilation of a saintly old missionary. The fanatical and superstitious Christian converts in *Aissa Saved* (1932) provoke a riot that threatens the safety of the native officials of the local government.[7]

[5] "The Village Census in the Study of Culture Contact," *Africa*, VIII (January, 1935), 20–33.
[6] *An American Visitor* (London, 1939), pp. 280–81; *Mister Johnson* (London, 1947), pp. 167–71, 192–93. See William Plomer's story, "Ula Masondo," in *I Speak of Africa* (London, 1927). A young country boy goes to work in a Johannesburg mine, falls among evil companions (an experienced thief, a disreputable "Christian" dandy, and a prostitute), and takes to highway robbery and housebreaking.
[7] *The African Witch* (New York, 1936), p. 391; *Aissa Saved* (London, 1932), pp. 168, 171, 264, 287.

Obai, Fish, and the elders of the Birri people in *An American Visitor* are so deeply distressed by their contacts with white civilization that they can only be described as neurotic. Obai's truculence toward the whites has a strange derivation. He has learned "un-Birri" ways outside his home district, and he boldly breaks a sexual taboo of his people. Then he is terrified to think that he may be denounced. His painful insecurity is partially relieved by his aggressive behavior toward the whites. Fish hates all the whites because the missionaries have given refuge to his estranged wife. Although District Officer Bewsher has tried manfully to protect the Birri from all white influences, even missionary activity, the Birri elders observe the breaking-up of the old culture; in their passionate regret for the old order passing away, they make Bewsher their scapegoat. They blame him for the "misfortunes of [382/383] the time" and the "collapse of their own authority, of all decency and good behavior."

When malcontent Africans rebel against the whites, they merely give the *coup de grâce* to their native society. Bewsher is unable to prevent a mining company from encroaching on tribal land. The Birri, feeling that they have been betrayed to the "interests," kill their benefactor and revolt. In a punitive expedition against this small, backward Nigerian tribe, only thirty natives are killed, but the old society is broken beyond repair. The old cultural forms, already badly undermined, collapse completely under the pressure of routine military operations: "The old patriarchal government disappeared and the people became a mob. Large numbers of the young men drifted away, even during the campaign, to join the flotsam of wandering laborers and petty thieves in the neighboring provinces." After the "war" Bewsher's successor finds it expedient to bring in a mission and a mining company to integrate the mob, make something like a society of it.[8]

The tribeless Africans of the South African towns and cities belong to just such an improvised society. They are essentially a mob, and a mob rejecting the standards of white public opinion, white law, and Christianity.

In Elspeth Huxley's *Red Strangers* (1939), the emphasis is not so much on the antisocial behavior of the tribeless Africans in the white men's sphere, as in Cary's African novels and *Cry, the Beloved Country,* but on the Africans' bewilderment in their tribal areas as they see the white intruders turn their social order upside down. This novel is an account of the effects of the British occupation of Kenya upon one family of a Kikuyu clan. For all the differences in detail such an account suggests what happened in every African community with the advent of the whites, what happened in the Kumalos' Zululand. Kenya, like South Africa, is a "white man's country" where racial friction and culture conflict are acute, though the white agricultural enterprises of Kenya do not break the tribe as quickly as the great mines of South Africa do.

The British "conquer" the Kikuyu easily enough. They muddle badly, however, when they undertake to rule a people they know so little about. They set up the head of the Warriors' Council as the responsible native official in the group, not knowing that the clan has always been governed by the Council of Elders. When the elders, shorn of their judicial power, no longer sit as the clan court, "Men steal and evade punishment, for the thieves no longer pay compensation." The Kikuyu never really understand just what is forbidden by the white men's law; the white men know nothing of traditional Kikuyu law. Because of language difficulties, justice is blind indeed. But even more out-

8 *An American Visitor*, pp. 62, 64, 70, 183, 280. Desperately anxious to protect his Birri from the disruptive force of white civilization, Bewsher invents a synthetic culture for them—a hodgepodge of private property, co-operative marketing, and a neo-pagan religion which is the old creed and ritual with Christian ethics "pumped in." This intriguing scheme sleeps quietly in official files (pp. 102–3, 155–60).

rageous from the native point of view, the "red strangers" force the proud young men, who ought to be warriors, to do portage, always considered "woman's work." There is a disquieting breakdown of parental discipline. One old father complains, "In your youth and mine we could not have insulted our fathers; we feared the wrath of the elders, and only our fathers could provide us with wives." Now the young men have no reason to [383/384] fear the elders, and they can go to work for the white men and earn the bride price themselves.[9]

The missionaries, who "teach their magic to children" even encourage the children to "speak to God," undermine the authority of the *mundu-mugu,* the witch doctor—an authority vital to the community. Besides conducting the sacrifices that rid his people of the evil spirits causing their misfortunes and their ailments and the religious observances involved in the worship of the ancestors, he instructs the young men in the responsibilities of adult life in the clan. He is the guardian of that "system of order and tradition and convention" of which Arthur Jarvis speaks.

Huxley's *mundu-mugu* describes this system himself in a talk to an initiation group:

> Thus some threads link a man to his father's clan and others bind him to his circumcision brothers. Different ties bind him to the elders who rule the country and administer the law. All these threads come together to form a web, and that web is the Kikuyu people. . . . So a man must fulfill his obligations as readily as he uses his privileges; so he must fight with courage and labor with devotion; so he must beget children and respect the elders; and in all things he must act with justice and obey the law.[10]

Such doctrine would have been good for Absalom Kumalo. Yes, but we cannot blame Stephen Kumalo because he has not adequately replaced the witch doctor or "circumcision father" of the old times, nor think poorly of Christianity because it has not done the work of the old African religion.[11] Taxes, the money economy, and the flashier attractions of

European civilization have sent the young men to the labor centers, where they live among indifferent whites and alien Africans, in squalid slums where corrupting temptations are strong. They live in such environments as have produced crime among all races, all nationalities.

What happens when the "threads" bind no longer, when the web is broken, is made plain in the behavior of two young Kikuyu, Karanja and Karioki, who are no longer bound by the old customs, as Gertrude, Absalom, and Matthew Kumalo were not. "I hid behind the door and struck his head with an iron tool. . . . I did not kill him. [He was luckier than Absalom.] . . . A man of experience was with me; he had iron tools with which to open the safe." The young man who describes his adventure thus is thoroughly emancipated from the old ways of tribal life. Karanja and Karioki buy bicycles and European hats and shoes, the outward and obvious signs of white men's magic and puissance. Then, since it seems to these amateur criminals smart and progressive to [384/385] adopt the white men's religion, they set out for the nearest mission. They are in rather a hurry, for Karanja has contracted a bad *thalu* from a prostitute in town and needs to take the cure in the mission hospital.[12]

One might suppose that a good European education would repair the damage

[9] *Red Strangers* (New York, 1939), pp. 176–77, 227, 201, 293–94, 215, 304. The chapter "A Shooting Incident on the Farm," in Izak Dinesen's *Out of Africa* (London, 1936), pp. 93–166, gives a good idea of African jurisprudence, especially the disregard for motives and the long-drawn-out negotiations to establish adequate compensation for bodily injury or homicide.

[10] *Red Strangers,* pp. 236–37, 105. In Beryl Markham's autobiography, *West with the Night* (Boston, 1942), p. 148, a Nandi servant explains to Miss Markham that his circumcision father had told him "how a man should live his life, keeping his voice soft and his anger sheathed until there was just need of it," what a man should eat, and how he should love "so that he remains a man and is yet not like a bull in the herd or a hyena clawing at a feast."

[11] Possibly Islam has been more successful than Christianity as a civilizing agency. Certainly the shrewd, courtly Moslem officials in Cary's African novels and Huxley's *The Walled City* make a striking contrast with the nonentity of a chief in *Cry, the Beloved Country.* Islam outbids Christianity in offering complete social equality, ethical standards more easily assimilated with the old African standards, and a material culture much simpler than that of the West.

[12] *Red Strangers,* pp. 327–28.

to the African personality wrought by the breaking of the tribe, would be the salvation of young men like Karanja, Karioki, and the Kumalo boys. In Huxley's *The Walled City* (1948) we learn what really happens to the educated African. The Nigerian Benjamin Morris, a graduate of an English university and an editor of a small African newspaper, is hurt because the white road foreman and the white sanitary engineer pass him on the street without so much as a nod. It shames him to be patronized by "such inferior persons, who could not explain the differences between the Stoic and Epicurean schools, or outline the quantum theory." Because the Europeans are aloof, Benjamin is acutely unhappy. He loses interest in his liberal magazines from England, relapses into some of the old African superstitions, and prints the most shameless canards against the government. As long as the whites refuse to accord respect to the educated African, the very best European education cannot integrate the African personality. With a good education Absalom Kumalo might not have been a thief and a murderer, but he would have been unhappy and antisocial.[13]

Certainly Paton has been scrupulously fair on the "native problem." His views on the injustice of keeping Africans unskilled to support white supremacy, of developing natural resources at the expense of the welfare of African laborers, of destroying the old African tribal system and letting the Africans deteriorate physically and morally (as dramatically presented in Arthur Jarvis' address on native crime), are set in the context of the old Zulu preacher's agonizing discoveries of the degeneration of his son. Now the African novels and nonfiction sources referred to here have shown that such degeneration is commonplace in modern Africa. Moreover, none of the characters in the novel, not even Arthur Jarvis or the kindly Mr. Msimangu, has a pat and easy solution for the afflictions of South Africa. Paton honestly renders the troubled complexity of the situation— the bewilderment of the whites and Africans caught up in the baffling problems of race conflict, the confusion, the cross-purposes, the frustration of men of good will of both races. *Cry, the Beloved Country* does what no discursive work in political science, sociology, economics, or anthropology could ever do; it makes us understand "how it feels" to be a South African today; it gives us the "form and pressure" of life in South Africa.

[13] *The Walled City* (London, 1948), pp. 255–56, 261, 278–87. See Westermann's unsympathetic description of educated Africans (*op. cit.*, p. 334) and Macmillan's more favorable and more generous one (*op. cit.*, pp. 90–91). Macmillan compares the educated Africans to another "black-coated" class apart, the somewhat disreputable clerks of the European Middle Ages.

Paton's Beloved Country and the Morality of Geography*

SHERIDAN BAKER (1918—   ) is a professor of English at the University of Michigan and editor of the *Michigan Quarterly Review*. He has published three textbooks on prose style as well as essays, reviews, and poems. His most recent work is *Hemingway, an Introduction and Interpretation* (1967).

Alan Paton's *Cry, the Beloved Country* (1948) has earned a place in our literature, at least in the classroom, but as yet has invited no explication. I should like to approach the book as a kind of moral geography, since Paton's title itself shows the land articulate. Kumalo's trials and African sociology all take their ultimate meanings in geographical symbols; and Paton has, in fact, even readjusted South Africa's profile to resemble that moral terrain which both Bunyan and Dante traveled and of which every man knows something, I think, though he has read neither.

Paton does this by allusions both Biblical and primitive. His language leads to the hills, cities, valleys, and green pastures we connect with right and wrong, even when scriptural references are not direct. But Paton uses a moral sensing of geography even more primitive: the sense perhaps in all creatures grounded by gravity that up and down are, by nature, good and bad, that mountains are upright and valleys submissive, that we stand up to live and lie down to die.

Of course, we lie down to rest, too. The valley is a somewhat ambiguous cradle, a nourisher of what Paton calls "deep feelings." Valleys represent maternal comfort and comfortable death; hills, paternal threat and protection. The mountain shadows the valley, brings thunder and water, and has inaccessible heights where the Unknowns live. And a man on the way up is better off than one on the way down. These primeval ups and downs, I think, still alive in our idiom with ambiguities intact, underlie Paton's symbolism.

Paton's moral geography is this: (1) a good valley which has cradled us but which, from social decay and drought, is also the valley of the shadow of death, (2) a beautiful mountain looking down on the valley, sending water and hope, the peak of Omniscience, (3) the city of the plain. The valley is Ndotsheni, the tribal home of the black Reverend Stephen Kumalo. The mountain we may call Carisbrooke, the point at which the reader enters the book to look down on Kumalo's world, the home of the white James Jarvis. The city of the plain is Johannesburg, where black and white pour trouble together:

Water comes out of a bottle, till the glass is full. Then the lights go out. And when they come on again, lo the bottle is full and upright, and the glass empty. . . . Black and white, it says, black and white, though it is red and green. (p. 17, Modern Standard Authors ed.)

Johannesburg's evil has broken the tribe. There Kumalo's sister sells her whiskey and herself. The green valley of home now runs only red earth when it rains, for energy has shifted to Johannesburg. There black and white collide in vio- [56/57] lence, which at last miraculously causes

* Sheridan Baker, "Paton's Beloved Country and the Morality of Geography," *College English*, XIX (November 1957), 56–61. Reprinted with the permission of the National Council of Teachers of English.

water to flow from Carisbrooke down to Ndotsheni.

Because we see mostly through Kumalo's primitive eyes, the symbolism of mountain and valley comes naturally to Paton's book. Kumalo is "a Zulu schooled in English" (15), a Zulu wearing an Anglican collar. The language we are to suppose is Zulu takes on the rhythms and phrases of the English Bible, which Kumalo, of course, uses in its Zulu version. An English priest tells a parable "in that symbolic language that is like the Zulu tongue" (108), and we realize that both languages are simple, concrete, and figurative, the language of tribes living close to the land. The book's idiom both represents and resolves, as does Kumalo himself, the black-white dilemma:

. . . Now God be thanked that there is a beloved one who can lift up the heart in suffering, that one can play with a child in the face of such misery. Now God be thanked that the name of a hill is such music, that the name of a river can heal. Aye, even the name of a river that runs no more.
. . . But this, the purpose of our lives, the end of all our struggle, is beyond all human wisdom. Oh God, my God, do not Thou forsake me. Yea, though I walk through the valley of the shadow of death, I shall fear no evil, if Thou art with me. . . . (62)

The valley of the shadow of death, indeed, is both the valley of Ndotsheni and Kumalo's personal loss of a son, the hope of the primitive tribe where "the dead streams come to life, full of the red blood of the earth" (4). As Kumalo says, only God can save it (233).

But God saves Ndotsheni in the person of James Jarvis, who lives on the beautiful mountain and likewise loses a son to the world. We are told that the ground Jarvis farms is holy; its name is High Place. And whether or not Paton intends "Jarvis" to remind us of "Jahveh" or "Jehovah," we soon find him sitting on a stone at the mountaintop, like an Old Testament God, overlooking the world, remote yet troubled by it. Throughout the book Jarvis receives incidental references as God—a letter from him is a

"letter from God" (262), his grandson is "a small angel from God" (249), his son is admired "as though he were God Almighty" (139), and so forth. Moreover, his son has gone into the world of Johannesburg; he takes up a mission of mercy; he is killed by the very people he comes to save. And through the father the dead son works a Christian miracle: suffered love makes evil good. Jarvis, even like God, does not really become effective until he learns compassion from the loss of his son.

Through these readings, then, Paton works his magic on the mountain at Carisbrooke. The more clearly we see Jarvis as God, the more we see Carisbrooke's supernatural height. The more Jarvis grows in understanding and goodness, the more we see the mountain as symbol of these qualities. But the figurative Godhead which accumulates behind Jarvis does not overshadow Jarvis the man, and, conversely, ordinary events, under Paton's scriptural spell, take on heavenly illumination without losing substance. Kumalo's Biblical vision—emanating from the beautiful mountain—illustrates Paton's ability to give the modern world an easy traffic with the age of miracles. An automobile, not a chariot, swings low, and the effect is in no way ludicrous:

While he stood there he saw a motor car coming down the road from Carisbrooke into the valley. It was a sight seldom seen. . . . Then he saw that not far from the church there was a white man sitting still upon a horse. He seemed to be waiting for the car, and with something of a shock he realized that it was Jarvis. (241)

One suspects that black men converted to Christianity by white men picture God as white, Marc Connelly notwithstanding, and that Paton's symbolic use of Jarvis is particularly apt.

Jarvis's personal growth is paralleled [57/58] by Kumalo's until at the end of the book Kumalo replaces Jarvis on the mountain. Kumalo, too, has a son. In fact, all sons, in Paton's book, bring salvation. The dying valley which runs blood and is resurrected represents the death of both sons, all death, and the life which springs therefrom. The grandson, the nephew, the unborn son, children on their way to school (as if trailing clouds of glory) "coming down from the hills, dropping sometimes out of the very mist" (61)— all bring comfort and hope.

But Kumalo's son brings salvation only at one remove. He kills Jarvis's son, evil making good apparent, black vivifying white. The white son represents the unshakable power of good, transcending death, even increasing; the black son—a kind of Antichrist—represents the hapless innocence of evil in a drifting society. The collision of the two first brings the fathers pain, then mutual sympathy, then some understanding of the good that works in spite of everything. Kumalo's salvation is harder than Jarvis's, and Paton puts his readers closer to Kumalo the Man than to Jarvis the God. Jarvis immediately begins to read his way into the mystery of a good son murdered. But Kumalo has no such comfort. His son is a frightened child, with only a strand of truthfulness left, guilty of mortal sin. Absalom's crime shows Kumalo the hard fact that society may seem the cause but that the individual is responsible. And Kumalo must absorb this bitterness before he can accept the good which flows through the world, even from this tangle. Losing his beloved yet sinning Absalom —a figurative rebel against the righteous father—Kumalo is changed from a kind of primitive tribal leader into the New Testament Father his priesthood indicates. The loss of both sons, the antithesis of both, causes water and milk to flow from High Place down to Ndotsheni, the valley of the shadow, which is, also, this world.

Paton's ancient paradigm of hill and valley as heaven and earth grows clearer as the book progresses. But the more symbolic High Place and Ndotsheni become, the stronger becomes Paton's suggestion that they are Ideals only, remote yet seen, contours to steer by. Only in the evil world is the Son's sacrifice pos-

sible and effective. The simple ups and downs of the country are not enough:

> Cry, the beloved country, for the unborn child that is the inheritor of our fear. Let him not love the earth too deeply . . . nor give too much of his heart to a mountain or a valley. For fear will rob him of all if he gives too much. (80)

Arthur Jarvis first learned to love Africa when, as a boy, he rode "over green hills and into the great valleys" (174), but the city on the plain taught him their meaning. It is in evil Johannesburg that Kumalo says, "I have never met such kindness" (125)—"I have known no one as you are" (215). And Kumalo brings his heightened and deepened perception back to the symbolic mountain and valley.

We come to see that the country represents man and the city represents men. The most insistent image in Paton's book is that of a man—first Jarvis, then Kumalo—alone on a mountain brooding over the depths. Carisbrooke and Ndotsheni denominate the human spirit. Johannesburg is a flat turbulence of good and evil which makes distinctions difficult. Johannesburg is a sociological casebook, with stopgap plans and masses of men. The country is man consulting his soul and learning human inadequacy. When Kumalo comes back from Johannesburg with a son lost and notions of rebuilding the tribe, he consults the ineffective chief and the ineffective schoolmaster. He is left with no one but himself, and prayer and God, finally to rebuild the valley and climb the mountain.

The mountain frames the book at either end. From the first sentence we can feel Paton's moral pressure, and we soon [**58/59**] notice that it has indeed remolded the South African landscape. A map will show that Paton's beloved country has gently heightened and deepened until it quite contradicts the earth's hard surface. We are surprised to find that Johannesburg, at 5,764 feet, is actually more than a thousand feet higher than our high mountain in Natal, which, though heightened each time Paton returns to it, seemed even at first almost the top of the world. In his opening passage, other mountains seem not higher but merely "beyond and behind"; the great Drakensberg range with peaks over 10,000 feet, behind which lies Johannesburg on its high plateau, is merely a place beyond, with no height at all. We are on a mountain that touches the clouds.

The contradiction between morally-high Carisbrooke and actually-higher Johannesburg works Paton no embarrassment. He can even take brief moral advantage of Johannesburg's altitude, suggesting a civilization and complexity looming over simple life along the Umzimkulu. Kumalo's brother speaks both literally and scornfully of his old home as "down." Indeed, Paton makes the city of the plain momentarily higher than it really is. Approaching Johannesburg, he emphasizes climbing: "Climb up to Hilton . . . ," he writes, "Climb over the Drakensberg, on to the level plains" (15). The level plains seem like the top of a table, reached after much climbing, and so this new country seems to back-country Kumalo, overwhelmed by buildings and buses. But Paton has matched his plain to Kumalo's awe, for, actually, after crossing the Drakensberg at more than eight thousand feet, we drop back down some three thousand feet to Johannesburg, though we do not drop so far as the mountain top from which we started.

Nevertheless, with the mountain at Carisbrooke as reference first for the Beautiful then for the Good, we come to think of Johannesburg as sprawling somewhere on a plain even lower than the home valley. And Paton helps us to this illusion. Leaving Carisbrooke, the train suspends us in unreality. We start in the mist. "The train passes through a world of fancy" (11). Finally, sleep separates primitive heights from the city on the plain.

Furthermore, Johannesburg's relative flatness depresses its actual altitude. On the plain Kumalo sees "great white dumps of the mines, like hills under the sun" (181). He hears of buildings as high as "the hill that stands so, straight up, behind my father's kraal" (16). He sees wheels high in the air. And when we are in Johannesburg, in spite of one street corner on a hill (47), in spite of walking "up Twist Street" and "down Louis Botha" (44), the mind keeps the city flat. With Kumalo's thoughts we return to hills, and the hills now seem higher, no matter how the land really lies. His return trip repeats unreality and separation (note especially the stagecraft in "rolls away"): "The white flat hills of the mines drop behind, and the country rolls away as far as the eye can see (219)." Again sleep leaves one world behind.

Paton can now afford to wind explicitly down the Drakensberg because from Pietermaritzburg he can carry his readers up and up again, into the heights at Carisbrooke. This trip from Pietermaritzburg to Carisbrooke helps to explain the slightly puzzling road that begins the book: "There is a lovely road that runs from Ixopo into the hills. . . ." Why do we start from Ixopo, never more than a passing reference, why on the road to Carisbrooke rather than at Carisbrooke itself, Paton's essential scene? There is no reason intrinsic to the book, only the reason in Paton himself. He was born in "Pietermaritzburg, the lovely city." Carisbrooke is the point of vision, we infer, toward which Paton climbed as boy and man. It is not his home. It is in the hills **[59/60]** beyond, higher, wilder, removed from daily streets, a point to dream from. "All roads lead to Johannesburg," he writes (10, 52)—even the one going into the hills in the opposite direction, for so we assume it was in the growth of this man who began life in Pietermaritzburg, taught school in Ixopo, hiked on up to Carisbrooke, turned around to revolutionize a reformatory in Johannesburg, and poured his experience into his book a generation later. Pietermaritzburg is really the place from which, as we enter the book, we are taking our run into spiritual hills, and Kumalo comes home to the good hills of Paton's own experience.

The book ends as it began, at Carisbrooke, though on the peak just above it. From here we first looked down at Ndotsheni and its comic-pathetic little priest, with his dirty collar and leaky church—grand in the eyes of a child—the rustic who fears traffic lights and admires a bus driver's courage. But Kumalo has grown. He himself has even learned amusement at his friend and at Jarvis and the mystery of goodness (238). When he climbs to the mountain he is no longer beneath us; the truth of his experience comes to us directly, at the white reader's own superior altitude. Here, at this new height, Kumalo replaces Jarvis as God the Father, and the hill at Carisbrooke, actually lower than Johannesburg, has now towered up to heaven itself.

Kumalo goes up the mountain to wait for the dawn that will see his son hanged in Pretoria. We think of Christ going into the wilderness, and of Moses, who talked to God on mountains: "But even as he started to climb the path that ran through the great stones, a man on a horse was there, and a voice said to him, It is you, umfundisi?—It is I, umnumzana" (271).

Jarvis goes down the mountain, Kumalo climbs to the top, sits on a stone, and takes Jarvis's position, "looking out over the great valley." Here, above the place where Jarvis first suffered the news of his son's death, Kumalo waits for the sunrise signaling *his* son's execution for the sins of the world.

For, though Absalom is a murderer and we see him childish and frightened, Paton traces suggestions of Christ behind him nevertheless. Father Vincent, referring to Absalom, says, "There was a thief upon the cross" (109). We remember that Christ, too, was executed as a criminal. Absalom is betrayed; there are three culprits; like Christ naming his successor, Absalom wishes his son named Peter. On the Mount of Olives, Christ, like Absalom, prayed his Father not to let him die: "Father, if thou be willing, remove this cup from me: Nevertheless not my will, but thine, be done" (Luke 22:42). Absalom in prison falls before his father "crouched in the way that some of the Indians pray" (207). Kumalo, on the mountain, remembers his words, the conventional Zulu responses: "it is as my father wishes, it is as my father says" (273).

The structure is complete: the two fathers, the two sons, the two mountains, as it were, at beginning and end. It is the black Father, with the compassion of the white man's suffering God, to whom Paton leaves the hope of Africa, and its misgivings, on the highest spiritual mountain imaginable—God in a heaven painful because compassionate, witnessing his son's death and resurrection: "And when he expected it, he rose to his feet and took off his hat and laid it down on the earth, and clasped his hands before him. And while he stood there the sun rose in the east" (277).

The morality Paton writes into his geography, then, is Christian: the salvage of evil through love and suffering. But the geographical pulls are primitive, compelling South Africa's actual geography to match their moral ups and downs. The [60/61] moral heights of Carisbrooke are Paton's dominant symbol. There we begin and there we end, heightened by a kind of kinesthetic moral experience among mountains and valleys long built into our imagining by literature and gravity.

Sheridan Baker's "Paton's Beloved Country"*

HARRY A. GAILEY (1926–   ), professor of African history at San Jose State College, has published articles on colonialism in Africa. He is the author of *History of the Gambia* (1965).

Professor Sheridan Baker's article, which appeared in the November 1957 issue, is deficient in a number of ways. The most obvious fault lies in the thesis that Paton consciously uses the geography of South Africa symbolically. Mr. Baker's suggestion is bold. He predicates three parts to Paton's moral geography: (1) a beautiful mountain—the peak of omniscience, (2) a good valley serving also as the valley of the shadow of death, and (3) the city of the plain—an evil place for black and white. Any connections of this nature between geography and morality must be proved by specific evidence abstracted from the novel or from statements by Paton concerning goals which he sought to achieve in constructing his novel. Logically then we should expect Mr. Baker to show adequate proof for his speculations before he hypothesizes further. This he does not do. The first two divisions of Paton's moral geography are alluded to in the article, but never adequately proved. The third is passed over [143/144] by means of a weak poetic excerpt, out of context, dealing with the feelings of Rev. Kumalo on viewing Johannesburg at night. The quotation does not show the city to be evil. Paton provides more suitable quotations to prove this contention.

I do not believe it was Paton's intent to write a geographical treatise, moral or actual. Rather, the geography and the environment of South Africa serve as the background for a social novel. Any deviation from the actual description of South Africa can be covered by poetic license, but Paton, far from being involved in geographic symbolism, is trying to be as direct as possible in his descriptions of a country with which he is extremely familiar.

There are many objectionable statements and allusions in Mr. Baker's article that give an erroneous view of Paton's social novel and of South Africa: (1) It does not follow that the symbolism of mountain and valley must come naturally to Paton's book because "Kumalo is a Zulu schooled in English" (p. 15). (2) The quotation beginning "Now God be thanked" (pp. 61–62), which according to Baker resolves the black-white dilemma, is taken out of context. Here Paton shows Rev. Kumalo thinking of his son as a child. The hills and the streams are no more, not for a symbolic reason, but because they live in the old man's memory. (3) There is nothing in "the dead streams come to life, full of the red blood of the earth" (p. 4) which indicates that Ndotsheni is the valley of the shadow of death. This quotation from the first chapter is part of a purely descriptive passage of the desolation of much of the formerly good land of the native reserves. (4) I do not see why Mr. Baker was surprised to find Johannesburg's elevation higher than that of Ixopo and Carisbrooke. Johannesburg's relative position to Ndotsheni is accurately defined by Paton: "Climb *over* [italics mine] the Drakensberg, on to the level

* Harry A. Gailey, "Sheridan Baker's 'Paton's Beloved Country,'" *College English*, XX (December 1958), 143–144. Reprinted with the permission of the National Council of Teachers of English and Harry A. Gailey.

plains" (p. 15). The high place at Ndotsheni, like most mountains, could be
cloud wreathed and exalted in the minds
of the natives without rivaling the
Drakensberg. (5) The quotation from
which the book takes its name (p. 80) cannot be construed to prove that Paton attempted to heighten the tension between
the High Place and Johannesburg. (6) I
cannot find any connection between
Paton's beautifully descriptive passage of
Kumalo's first observation of the car which
brings the technicians to the valley (p.
241) and Baker's idea of a modern chariot
swinging low. (7) Paton is convinced, and
he has Kumalo express it for him (p. 61),
that the hope of South Africa is in the
children. Baker has again taken the quotation from context to prove symbolism.
Actually Kumalo is thinking of his son,
soon to die, and the way he looked long
ago on his way to school. (8) Any idea that
Paton correlates Jarvis with God is, like
the article, novel but unproved. Rev. Kumalo is a minister of simple piety. In his
inward struggles he naturally conceives of
many things in terms of God and that He
will fulfill His plan through man. Jarvis
is touched by God and acts accordingly.
A close analysis of the three references
used to show Jarvis in allegorical association with God will show this to be the
case. (9) The quotations concerning Jarvis
riding "over green hills and into the great
valleys" (p. 174) and Kumalo's statements
about goodness in Johannesburg (pp. 125
and 215) have nothing in common and
prove nothing about the "moral geography" of Paton's South Africa. (10) The
opening passage of the novel ("There is a
lovely road that runs from Ixopo into the
hills . . .") should cause no puzzlement.
Paton amplifies it in the lines that follow
and in his introduction. The Valley Umzimkulu, the setting of a great part of the
book, is reached by this road so well
known to Paton.

There are many other criticisms which
could be leveled at the article. There is no
need to analyze these or to expand the
criticisms I have already made. Seldom,
however, have I read a short article with
so much promise that was compounded of
so much unproven speculation.

The "Message" of Alan Paton*

F. CHARLES ROONEY (1939—   ) is a graduate of Sacred Heart Seminary in Detroit, Michigan, and the Gregorian University in Rome. He was ordained into the Catholic priesthood in 1964 and is currently a parish priest at St. Michael's Church in Pontiac, Michigan.

Probably none of the outstanding traditional critics has insisted more rigorously than Coleridge upon the necessary unity of form and content in literature. In his *Biographia Literaria,* chapter XIII, he distinguishes between "imagination" and "fancy." The latter *imposes* a form on what is to be communicated; this form is not the spontaneous outgrowth of an artistic intuition. It is an artificial selection of means to an end. *What* is to be said is primary in the writer's mind; the manner of saying it is quite arbitrary. Imagination, on the other hand, is the faculty of the true artist; it grows up from the subconscious and shapes his work. Here we find no thought of primary and secondary. Imagination, therefore, is natural, while fancy is artificial.

One of the norms generally adopted for poetry and the drama is that the form must be so fitting that it could not be otherwise. This criterion, however, applies less stringently to the novel than to any other literary genre. The scope of the novel and its unmetrical form necessarily allow it more latitude than even the drama or the epic. Yet it is still binding on the novelist to excise unwarranted diversions of both plot and style. He is to tell the story, and whenever he gets sidelined from the story merely to talk, he is weakening his art.

These two standards (the form must grow out of the material and every excrescence must be excised) are the severest guardians of literature from moralizing and propagandizing. For, depending on one's point of view, the distinguishing mark of literature is to **[92/93]** give pleasure, or to appeal to the emotions, or to uplift the reader; and so on. Yet no serious reader will accept these statements as encouraging or even permitting propaganda, be it religious, social, political or economic. Certainly some very good literature can have elements of propaganda; but whatever propaganda there is weakens the work and detracts from it.

It is interesting, yet not altogether surprising, that one of the most skilled and sensitive writers of recent years, Alan Paton, has been suspected of moralizing. Everything about him seems to lend basis to this suspicion. He is an ardent and inspired advocate of racial justice in the most professedly segregationist nation in the world, the Union of South Africa. He is a former reformatory warden and has pioneered for institutional reform in a land not reputed to be especially progressive. And finally (worst of all!) he has written three books, each of which is built upon the foundations of his personal experience. His first two, *Cry, the Beloved Country* (Scribners, 1948) and *Too Late the Phalarope* (Scribners, 1953) unhesitatingly grapple with striking, race-conflict themes.

The third, *Tales from a Troubled Land,* a book of short stories published this spring (Scribners) focuses predomi-

---

* F. Charles Rooney, from "The 'Message' of Alan Paton," *Catholic World*, CIV (November 1961), 92–98. Reprinted with the permission of the author.

nantly on situations in a boys' reformatory. With such an obvious parallel between his life and writing, Paton's readers almost automatically assume that he has a message to put across in his books. And how, one asks, can such a message be anything but propaganda?

With so many counts against him, a writer would have to be especially talented and restrained to keep himself sufficiently out of his stories—to keep his aesthetic distance. Only a highly disciplined writer could keep from haranguing. Yet Paton's readers know that he accomplished exactly that. He tells two taut absorbing stories with characters unmatched in contemporary fiction for their spontaneity and inherent drama for being themselves.

Thus the onlooker is hard put to account for the charge against Paton of propagandizing (except to a limited extent for *Tales from a Troubled Land,* as we will point out below), unless he attributes to the critic either an indiscriminating biocritical method or insufficient objectivity. To bring an author's personal life into the evaluation of his work is fraught with the danger of unjustified assumption. This peril is nowhere more evident than in the criticism of Paton's two novels. A more accurate index of his accomplishment is the warm acceptance of his tender, yet powerful, stories by thousands of perceptive readers. However, the publisher's eulogies of Paton as a humanitarian only bolster suspicions of "preaching." **[93/94]**

The most severe effect of this prejudice about his "purpose" is that it puts a shadow on his stature as a writer. Alan Paton is no mere craftsman though his diction and rhythm are stirring. He is a mature artist telling a story of power, insight and significance. He searches the dilemma of man's fear and disregard of his fellows with all the compassion and force of Steinbeck in *Grapes of Wrath.* Yet he has what Steinbeck never had, a vision of the life of the spirit. He has all Steinbeck's heart, plus *soul.*

For Paton love, supernatural forgiving love, is the imperative of life; without it

life is destroyed. It is the vacuum created by fear and hate that is the cause of all conflict in his novels; his insight into this void has set Paton's novels not only beyond but on a different plane from the bulk of modern fiction.

Cry, the Beloved Country is a great novel, but not because it speaks out against racial intolerance and its bitter effects. Rather the haunting milieu of a civilization choking out its own vitality is evoked naturally and summons our compassion. There are no brutal invectives, no blatant injustices to sear the reader's conscience, no vicious hatred, no righteously unleased passion. It is a great compliment to Paton's genius that he communicates both a story and a lasting impression without bristling, bitter anger.

Restraining himself and the reader within the bonds of probability, he etches the portrait of the family of Stephen Kumalo, a humble colored Anglican parson. The family is separated and destroyed by the advent of an industrial culture in South Africa. Kumalo's son, Absalom, and Arthur Jarvis, the white man whom the son has accidentally killed, are both destroyed by the fear and distrust that have accompanied technological "progress."

But this is a silent destruction, one for which the blame is not pinned down; the directions of real life are not so apparent. The reader's impression of the milieu Paton describes is rather of *corrosion.* Paton's protest to injustice consists in pointing out, not accusing. The South Africa we find in his books is a manifestation of Christian heart that has forgotten what it should be. It has seen itself and has found no love that might embrace all. Therefore it proceeds to exclude, to segregate, to separate, to fear. Self-enclosed, the soul of a nation quickly begins to distort everything it sees until finally it finds that life itself has been squeezed of every value that makes it worthwhile and noble. Indeed the total impression one gets from Paton's work is of a nation frightened by its own shadow. This is the tragedy that elicits our compassion.

Cry, the beloved country, for the unborn child that is the inheritor of our fear. Let him not love the earth too deeply. Let him not laugh too gladly when the water runs through his fingers, nor stand too silent when the setting sun makes red the veld with fire. Let him not be too moved when the birds of his land are singing, nor give too much of his heart to a mountain or a valley. For fear will rob him of all if he gives too much. [94/95]

These are words of a people, forcing themselves up from the well-springs of the human spirit. They are the warning cries of a lover fearing for the beloved. Here, as throughout the novel, there is no maudlin commentary from the author. Rather the innermost emotions of a whole nation are expressed in various ways, in many passages scattered throughout the book to emphasize their independence of any particular figure in the story.

A seeming interpolation by the author (as narrator) in chapter twenty-three provides an excellent example of Paton's technique. The passage is a stinging rebuke to the gold fever of the rich white men who own the mines and unmercifully exploit native labor. It concludes with a mention of the plan of Sir Ernest Oppenheimer, a farsighted white leader, to permit mine workers to live in villages with their families instead of in compounds:

They want to hear your voice again, Sir Ernest Oppenheimer. Some of them applaud you, and some of them thank God for you in their hearts, even at their bedsides. For mines are for men, not for money. And money is not something to go mad about, and throw your hat into the air for. Money is for food and clothes and comfort, and a visit to the pictures. Money is to make happy the lives of children. Money is for security, and for dreams, and for hopes, and for purposes. Money is for buying the fruits of the earth, of the land where you were born. . . . No second Johannesburg is needed upon the earth. One is enough.

It is not hard to imagine a socially conscious writer stepping beyond the legitimate limits of the novel form to express such sentiments. But Paton does not do this. Chapter twenty-three is a natural and integral part of his story, a sequel to the brilliant ninth chapter which describes the overnight rise of a shanty village. To deny the kind of judgment expressed in the above passage a legitimate place in literature is surely to take such an exclusive and rarified view of the writing art that it no longer touches life.

Another startling reflection on the inner corruption of South Africa might seem, at first, open to criticism as extraneous to the story, put in simply to make a point.

In the deserted harbour there is yet water that laps against the quays. In the dark and silent forest there is a leaf that falls. Behind the polished panelling the white ant eats away the wood. Nothing is ever quiet, except for fools.

Yet here too we are eventually forced to admit Paton's genius to express his nation's pulse and his people's conscience. Here we see not a lone angry commentator but a compassionate sufferer witnessing the decline of that which he loves. We do not hear the clear voice of the author telling us what to think; these "asides" always spring from the story: In fact we might wonder at the reticence if they were unsaid, for the very rocks cry out. . . .

PART THREE

THE AFRICAN BACKGROUND

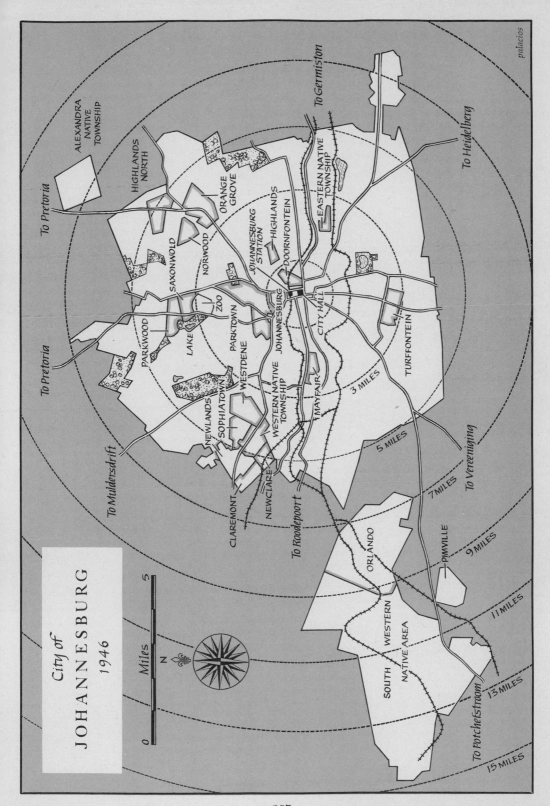

City of
JOHANNESBURG
1946

Miles

To Pretoria

To Pretoria

ALEXANDRA NATIVE TOWNSHIP

HIGHLANDS NORTH

ORANGE GROVE

SAXONWOLD

NORWOOD

HIGHLANDS

JOHANNESBURG STATION

DOORNFONTEIN

EASTERN NATIVE TOWNSHIP

To Germiston

To Heidelberg

ZOO

PARKWOOD

LAKE

PARKTOWN

WESTDENE

JOHANNESBURG

CITY HALL

TURFFONTEIN

To Muldersdrift

NEWLANDS

SOPHIATOWN

WESTERN NATIVE TOWNSHIP

MAYFAIR

3 MILES

5 MILES

To Vereeniging

CLAREMONT

NEWCLARE

To Roodepoort

7 MILES

ORLANDO

PIMVILLE

9 MILES

11 MILES

SOUTH WESTERN NATIVE AREA

To Potchefstroom

13 MILES

15 MILES

palacios

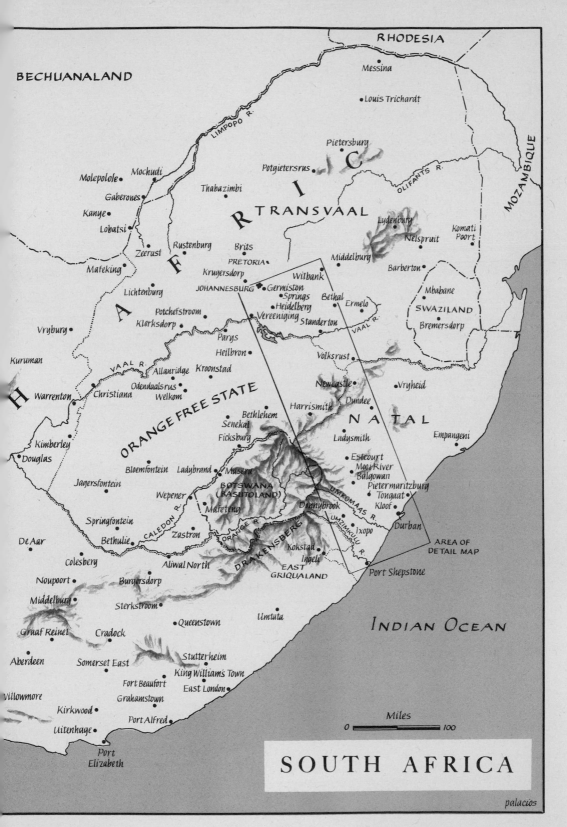

RHODESIA

BECHUANALAND

Messina

Louis Trichardt

Pietersburg

Potgietersrus

OLIFANTS R.

LIMPOPO R.

Molepolole
Mochudi

Thabazimbi

Gaberones

TRANSVAAL

Lydenburg

Komati
Poort

Kanye

Nelspruit

Lobatsi

Rustenburg

Brits

Barberton

Mbabane

Zeerust

PRETORIA

Middelburg

SWAZILAND

Mafeking

Krugersdorp

Witbank

Lichtenburg

JOHANNESBURG
Germiston

Springs

Bethal

Ermelo

Bremersdorp

Potchefstroom

Heidelberg

Vereeniging
Standerton

Klerksdorp

VAAL R.

Parys

Vryburg

Heilbron

Volksrust

Kuruman

VAAL R.

Allanridge
Kroonstad

Newcastle

Vryheid

Warrenton

Odendaalsrus

Welkom

Harrismith

Dundee

NATAL

Empangeni

Christiana

ORANGE FREE STATE

Bethlehem

Ladysmith

Senekal

Kimberley

Ficksburg

Estcourt

Mooi River

Douglas

Bloemfontein
Ladybrand

Maseru

Balgowan

Pietermaritzburg

Jagersfontein

BOTSWANA
(BASUTOLAND)

Tongaat

Wepener

Kloof

Mafeteng

Donnybrook

UMKOMAAS R.

Springfontein

CALEDON R.

ORANGE R.

Ixopo

Durban

De Aar

Bethulie

Zastron

UMZIMKULU R.

Colesberg

Aliwal North

DRAKENSBERG

Kokstad

Ingeli

Port Shepstone

Noupoort

Burgersdorp

EAST
GRIQUALAND

Middelburg

Sterkstroom

Umtata

INDIAN OCEAN

Graaf Reinet

Cradock

Queenstown

AREA OF
DETAIL MAP

Aberdeen

Somerset East

Stutterheim

King William's Town

Fort Beaufort

East London

Willowmore

Grahamstown

Kirkwood

Port Alfred

Miles

Uitenhage

0   100

Port
Elizabeth

SOUTH AFRICA

palacios

159

[The Peoples of South Africa]*

DUDLEY C. LUNT (1896–   ) is a columnist for the *Wilmington* (Delaware) *Morning News.* He is the author of two books on conservation and wildlife, *Thousand Acre Marsh* (1959) and *The Woods and the Sea* (1965), and the editor of several volumes of Thoreau's writings.

A rudimentary knowledge of the origins and development of the four dominant racial groups in South Africa is essential to an appreciative understanding of the biography of Jan Hendrik Hofmeyr.

For all practical purposes the franchise in South Africa is limited to the whites, or Europeans as they are known. This first racial group comprises slightly in excess of three million persons and all political power is concentrated in their hands. Broadly speaking they are divided into two groups. On the one hand there are the descendants of the early Dutch, German, and French Huguenot settlers, who, known today as Afrikaners, are said to comprise sixty percent of the white population. Then there are the other Europeans who are for the most part of English extraction including Jews, who, though insignificant in numbers, are potent in influence.

In the mainstream of South African history, there flows the rivalry and accommodation between the Dutch and the English. The Dutch came first—in 1652 in consequence of the setting up of a victualing station by the Dutch East India Company. Comparable to the Dutch seats in New Amsterdam and on the Delaware River, there was little immigration and the growth was slow. As a matter of fact South Africa has never experienced the ameliorating influence inherent in successive immigrations such as those into the North American continent. At the end of a century and a half there were only about 33,000 people in the Cape Province. Significantly, a little over half of these were slaves, the consequence of importations from East Africa, Madagascar, Ceylon, India and Malaya. Miscegenation at the outset involving both white people and the local Hottentots with the slaves set in train the development of a mixed race, the members of which are variously known today as the "Coloured" or the "Cape Coloureds." They number about a million and a half, are concentrated for the most part in the Cape Province and constitute one of the racial groups that are the major concern of the public policy of South Africa. [vii/viii]

Significant also in this first century and a half, was the existence and expansion of the northern frontier. Two facets of this deserve notice. The first was the pushing upward into the interior by the *voortrekkers* (pioneers) on the treks that have exercised so vast a formative influence in the development of the character of the modern Afrikaner. Psychologically the traditions of the treks are akin to those that stem from the sweep across the continent of the American frontier.

Secondly, in the course of this early expansion, the trekkers came into contact with the native tribes that were pushing down out of the interior vastness of the dark continent. And in conflict as violent as any that characterized the American struggles with the Indians, they encountered and overcame the largest of the four racial groups within the confines of present-day South Africa. These are the natives, the Africans, who are known officially today as the Bantu, and who number nearly eleven million people.

The Napoleonic Wars marked a turning point in the history of South Africa for in their train came the establishment of the British, temporarily in 1795, permanently in 1806, and reinforced in 1820 by the emigration from England of 5,000 settlers. Then commenced what General Smuts called the Century of Wrong. The points of conflict between British colonial rule and the Boers were many and often violent. The year 1836 saw the commencement of the Great Trek. This migratory movement up into the interior was the attempt by the Boers, fortified by the authoritarian strength of their Calvinist religion, to remove themselves from British rule and to isolate themselves from British influence. Its consequence was the establishment of the two Boer Republics —the Transvaal and the Orange Free State. Prominent among the causes of the Great Trek was the freeing of the slaves in 1834 and the sharp conflict of views in the area of race and colour.

The fourth group complicating the area of race relations, which is the major concern of South African politics, comprises the so-called "Asians." These people derive from the policy initiated in 1860 by the early sugar planters in the east coast colony of Natal of importing indentured labour from India. These Indians, or Asians, today number approximately half a million persons, who are still largely resident in Natal.

Until well into the last half of the nineteenth century, the economy of South Africa was pastoral and agricultural. Then the discoveries first of diamonds in Kimberly in 1870 and later in 1886 of gold on the Witwatersrand (Ridge of White Waters) set in train the course of events [viii/ix] that has led to the modern industrial development of the country. More immediately there was ushered in the era of Rhodes and Milner, and this high tide of British imperialism led ultimately to the Boer War (1899–1902).

The modern consequences of these economic and social changes in the structure of South African society are of particular significance in relation to the largest population and racial group—the 11,000,000 Bantu. The natives traditionally had been located on what are known as Reserves. These are areas that have been set apart for them and they are not unlike the reservations of the American Indians. But there is a significant difference. The Bantu are the source of the large force of unskilled labor that is needed on the farms, in domestic service, and in the mines and industries of the South African economy. The inevitable consequence is that a very considerable proportion of the blacks—over a third according to the 1960 census—are at all times located outside the Reserves in urban and semi-urban areas. Moreover, the successive census figures show that this proportion is increasing.

In the decade that followed the Boer War with the accession to power of the Liberal Party in England, self-government was restored to the two Boer Republics, and in 1910 the four provinces—the Transvaal, the Orange Free State, Natal, and the Cape Province—formed the Union of South Africa within the then British Empire. In the Act of Union were two significant provisions that were, in South African constitutional terminology, "entrenched." This means that they could only be altered by a two thirds majority of both houses of the South African parliament in a joint session. One of these so-called entrenched clauses guaranteed the dual existence of the two languages— Dutch, now called Afrikääns and English; the other protected the limited franchise which had existed in the Cape Province in favor of the Coloureds. Another clause provided for what might be called a legalized gerrymander in that the votes cast in rural and urban constituencies should be weighted to the extent of fifteen percent in favor of the rural vote, and this was destined to have far-reaching effects on the outcomes of future elections.

Thereafter there followed the successive premierships of the Boer generals, Louis Botha and Jan Christian Smuts. The opposition was lead by another general, J. B. M. Hertzog, whose policy stemmed from a speech in 1912 in which he argued that the two groups in white South African society—Afrikaans and English-speaking—should each enjoy a separate development until each achieved full stature. This so-called "two- [ix/x] stream" concept is the modern political premise from which the present day Afrikaner Nationalism has derived and developed.

Through a Tribal Reserve*

ALAN PATON wrote *South Africa and Her People* (London, 1957), from which this selection is taken, at the invitation of the Lutterworth Press, London, to be the fourth volume in their Portraits of Nations Series. Paton addresses "you young people from other countries" directly, as he takes you on an imagined tour of South Africa. "It is very important that you should understand the problems of as many countries as possible," he writes in conclusion, "because your nation is one of the community of nations, and bears a responsibility for the whole world."

. . . .
. . . This is the famous South Coast of Natal, and seaside resorts are found every one or two miles, rejoicing in Zulu names like Isipingo, Amanzimtoti, Illovo, Umgababa, Ifafa, Umtwalumi, Umtentweni. The sun is bright, the sands golden, the sea blue, the water warm. This is the playground of South Africa, and indeed of our northern neighbours who have no coasts of their own. Here on this road can be seen cars from Southern and Northern Rhodesia, from Mozambique, Kenya, and the Belgian Congo, even sometimes from Nigeria.

At Port Shepstone we turn inland into the rolling hills of Natal, cross the Ingeli Mountains, and soon after enter the Transkei. After passing Kokstad we say good-bye to white man's country, and are in the largest tribal reserve in South Africa. Its area is over sixteen thousand square miles (which is roughly the size of Denmark), and it has a population of one and a quarter million Africans, with some eighteen thousand white people, and some fourteen thousand coloured people.

We soon know that we are in another kind of country. We are soon passing thousands of the thatched huts of the Mpondo people; these huts lie amongst the fields, empty now, but in the summer,

[116/117] green with maize and millet. It is a beautiful country, but the signs of soil erosion are frequent and alarming, and are more clearly seen in these winter months when the veld is brown and bare.

Most of these huts now have windows, which is a result of education and European influence. They are in groups called Kraals, and in each Kraal is a man with his wife or wives, and his unmarried children, together with his young married sons and their wives and children.

The Mpondo people are divided into patrilineal clans; that is to say, the children belong to the clan of their father. Some of these clans are several thousand strong, and all the members are regarded as related, and they may not marry inside the clan. A tribe is composed of a group of related clans, and is ruled by a chief.

The Kraal, and not the family, as among Western peoples, is the important unit. The head of the Kraal was treated with great respect, but so indeed was any older person; and above all was, of course, the Chief. Custom was obeyed unquestioningly, and the individual was spared many duties of choice and decision that often weigh so heavily upon members of a Western culture. It was this, I think, which gave rise to the strange appearance of self-confidence and docility, of pride

* Alan Paton, from "Through a Tribal Reserve," *South Africa and Her People* (London: Lutterworth Press, 1957), pp. 116–120. Reprinted in a revised edition, Alan Paton, *The Land and People of South Africa* (Philadelphia: J. B. Lippincott Company, 1964). Copyright © 1964 by Alan Paton. Copyright 1955 by Alan Paton. Published in the United States by J. B. Lippincott Company.

and innocence, which is to be seen so often in the eyes and bearing of tribal people, and which has been captured so well by Duggan-Cronin in his photographs. I also think that it is this lessening of individual responsibility which makes laughter and merriment so characteristic of the African communities.

I have often seen tribal women in the reserves, suddenly startled by the sound of a car on the road behind them, go running into the grass of the veld with laughter and enjoyment. But you would never see such a sight in any town or city; for a white person to drive carelessly in a city is to invite resentment, to drive carelessly in a city "location" is to invite violence. To injure someone in a location is to invite death.

Here, too, the children wave to us cheerfully as we pass. They love to call out the letters on our number plates, especially if they are TJ (which letters stand for Transvaal, Johannesburg, and mean the One and Only City to these children who have never seen it). Nothing could be more friendly, more open, than these children's greetings. [117/118] No one could look more friendly, more open, than they. What a great treasure of good will is here, if only we white South Africans do not let it waste away.

The religion of the Mpondo people is based on a belief in the survival of their ancestors, who have great power to help or to harm the living. Disobedience to parents or authority or custom is punished by the ancestors, who bring down illness or bad luck on the offender. At times of serious illness, of birth, marriage, and death, offerings are made to the ancestors. The head of the Kraal slaughters an ox or goat at the entrance to the cattle fold; he calls on the ancestors by name, and asks their blessing. Some meat is burnt for them, and the rest is eaten by the people.

All this is done in reverent fashion, though not with the Christian or churchly kind of reverence to which we are accustomed. These observances were performed with great humility and simplicity, which are the characteristics of all true religious behaviour. This humility and simplicity, as I have told you before, were shown first to one's parents and indeed to all older persons, then to the head of the clan, then to the chief of the tribe, and finally to one's ancestors. God himself, the Creator, was considered by some tribes to be remote from human affairs, and was not prayed to; by other tribes God was merely the Oldest Ancestor, the Ancestor of the tribe itself, and he himself emerged from the reeds of the river at some remote but definite point in history.

When Africans become Christians, and carry this humility and simplicity over into their new religion, then they restore to Christianity one of the great qualities of worship.

Added to this simple religion of the ancestors is the deep-seated fear of witchcraft, which, when it strikes, can turn these proud people into abject and melancholy creatures. Witchcraft is a weapon in the hands of one's enemies, of the jealous, covetous, and quarrelsome. Bad luck comes, and the witch doctor is called in. He smells out the wrongdoer, who in the old days before the white man's law was often killed. Even today a person who believes himself bewitched can waste away and die, and no white doctor can help him.

Witchcraft and the belief in it, like all other elements in African culture, is today in the transitional stages. Many Christianized [118/119] Africans have conquered such fears, but many are still subject to them, and in spite of their faith will consult the witch doctor.

Cattle play an important part in tribal life. *Lobolo,* or the *bride price,* is paid in cattle to the father of the bride. Many of the early missionaries made the mistake of supposing that wives were *purchased* in this manner, but the bride price is something much more important than that. It signifies a contract every bit as important as our own marriages, a contract not between two persons, but between two kinship groups.

Cattle play an important part in the

religious life of the Bantu people, and in the worship of the ancestors. It is the cattle fold that is the scene of important religious ceremonies. Because of this importance of cattle, quite apart from their value as providers of milk and meat, it is difficult to get the Bantu people to reduce the overgrazing of their reserves. Educators and administrators do their best, but it is difficult to interfere with this deep and religious custom, especially when so much else is seen to be withering away.

But this simple idyllic life is undergoing great changes. Many of the able-bodied men are away at the mines, many young boys and girls have gone into domestic service in the white homes of the cities. Missions and schools have done much to change habit and custom. The white man's doctors and hospitals command an increasing confidence from people who once relied on the skill, part scientific, part dangerous, of their own medicine men.

Nevertheless, if you have eyes to see, you will note that this vast reserve of the Transkei offers a truer picture of tribal life than the Valley of a Thousand Hills. The reason for this is that the Transkei is remote from any great city.

We pass through the town of Umtata, which has a population of 9,000 people, and is the capital of the Transkeian territories. Umtata was at one time the seat of the Bunga, the General Council of the Transkei, composed of the twenty-seven white magistrates of the territory and eighty-two representatives of the people. But it is the policy of the Government to restore the authority of the tribal chiefs, and the Bunga has now been abolished.

Is it possible to restore the authority of the chiefs, and the unity of the tribes? I myself think it is impossible, but it remains one of [119/120] the controversial questions facing our country. In my opinion tribal solidarity and chieftainly authority do not belong to the world of modern man, and it is the deepest desire of the more advanced Africans to join the world of modern man, and to do it on a basis of equality. Many of the young people of modern African society, imbued with the political ideas of the West, no longer respect the authority of the chiefs. They regard any attempt to restore tribal unity and authority as a device to prevent them from entering the modern world.

They are also suspicious of the fact that the education of the African people has been taken away from the four Provincial education authorities, and handed over, not to the National education authority, but to the Department of Native Affairs. They do not wish to have a different kind of education from that enjoyed by white children. But the Minister of Native Affairs has made it clear that the African people must not look forward to a position of equality with white people, and they must be given an education which will fit them for the kind of life they may expect to lead.

I wish to make it clear that this opposition to the continuance of tribal authority, and to a separate kind of education, is the opposition of the more highly educated and more politically conscious Africans. There are still many millions who give these matters little thought.

I think it is clear that the Bunga provided a kind of education for democratic government. But of course the real government of South Africa is in the hands of the white Parliament of Cape Town, and I think it should be clear from a reading of our history, that there is in the minds of most white South Africans no intention whatever to share that power. The majority of white South Africans fear such an eventuality; they are outnumbered almost four to one by nonwhite people, and they fear that if they shared their power, they in turn would be subjected to a race domination. That is why some white people feel that a total territorial separation of white and black is the only possible solution of our difficulties. Yet they find great immediate advantage from having black people in their midst. So far, the advantage of the present has triumphed over the fear of the future. . . .

[The Urban South African Woman]*

LAURA LONGMORE was born in South Africa and was a lecturer on African life at the University of Witwatersrand in Johannesburg from 1949 to 1959. She has done archaeological and anthropological field work in Africa, Europe, the Middle East, India, and Russia.

. . . .

Premarital pregnancy

In tribal times youths were gradually prepared for adult life. A premium was put on physical fitness and from the age of ten onwards boys were toughened until they could endure climatic conditions of all kinds. They could walk for miles. They could overpower untamed oxen for ploughing. Their progress to the state of manhood, though arduous, taught them dignity, restraint and rigid discipline.

Girls underwent similar forms of instruction and were warned to remain chaste. There was no unregulated association and entertainment of young women by young men as occurs in urban areas today.

. . . .

[46/48] . . . .

. . . it was generally agreed that in tribal areas in olden times pregnancy was not prevalent among single girls. For in the country, when a boy and girl fall in love, everyone knows about it, and the age mates of the couple help but also watch them to prevent disgrace coming upon them.

But in urban areas, living next door to strangers—people from many different tribes who know nothing of one another's customs—boys from [48/49] these strange tribal families never care what they do to a girl as long as their desires are met; they take no precautions to protect girls. And because their customs differ many parents will not agree to the couple marrying when pregnancy occurs.

It was stated that in tribal times in the old days there were no diseases and life was sweet. Today the biggest test one can meet in life in town is sexual temptation, for most women are not being checked and controlled in towns today. So many women are out to tempt men and so many men seek new women. In olden times Bantu civilization was noted for *obedience* to chiefs, to parents and to the rules and customs of the tribe. There existed a discipline that it is impossible to find in European civilization. Many informants maintain that the impact of these European ideas has unsettled the African and helped to undermine confidence in the old Bantu ways and civilization.

. . . .

[49/50] . . . One of the most striking symptoms of social disintegration and economic disorder is the fact that practically every girl has one or more children before marriage, a state of affairs that is found even in the best homes, including those of pastors and school-teachers. Indeed, very few girls marry before having had children. So common is premarital conception that, as has been previously stated, urban men do not marry a girl unless she has had a child to show that she is not barren. Abortion would seem to be wholly repugnant to African opinion, al-

* Laura Longmore, from "Preliminaries to Marriage," *The Dispossessed, A Study of the Sex-Life of Bantu Women in Urban Areas in and around Johannesburg* (London: Jonathan Cape, 1959), pp. 46, 48–49, 50–53. Reprinted by permission of Jonathan Cape Ltd., publishers.

though there can be no doubt that it is resorted to. In this respect accuracy is hardly obtainable, for suspicion of my motives would have led to much wrong information.

Many informants were confident in expressing the view that out of every hundred urban families there were ninety-five who had children born before marriage. In some cases the children were born at the home of the girl, because the fathers were unknown. When the mothers of such children marry, they have invariably had one or two children who were by men other than the man the women eventually married. The man who married such a woman who has had children already by other men might do so either out of genuine love for her or because he knew that she was not only his choice but she was also capable of bearing children; for many men stressed that the usefulness of a woman lay in her ability to bear children. If she was beautiful and came from a good home, she was useless if she were barren. The remark that beautiful women of urban areas today rarely have children because they have been admired by too many men who have deprived them of their productivity is common. It is seldom that the blame for the sterility of a woman is placed on the man. Women and men stated that this demonstrates the necessity for polygyny in that a man with a number of wives is readily blamed if they are all barren.

My own impressions were that illegitimacy rates were very high, both for the township in which I worked to secure statistical data, and also in Johannesburg and its environs as a whole. But when considering the [50/51] problem of unmarried mothers and women who have children by men who abscond, it is as well to remember that illegitimacy has been found in all periods of social upheaval; it everywhere accompanies great changes in social standards, more especially the meeting of two or more cultures with divergent standards of sexual morality.

Nevertheless, the ever-increasing irresponsibility of Bantu men in the urban areas is a factor that merits the attention of the authorities. It would seem that many of them, grown accustomed to ease, abandon all sense of family responsibility, and prefer to live as single men in the towns. This is bound up with the lack of restraints and protection for women in domestic service. With the preponderance of unattached males on the Witwatersrand these women are being subjected to temptations beyond their capacity to resist. There is always a large class of unattached males ever ready to form loose unions with women in town. It was openly acknowledged that a man may have plenty of women who would grant him any favour in return for money and presents. The urban Bantu male, under present conditions, seems to have neither the opportunity nor the inclination to cultivate an intimate attachment to places and persons, or to indulge in early marriage and family life; his is the characteristic of the mobile group, a mobility fostered by the migrant character of native employment. Extraordinary sex ratios result from the system of maintaining the reserves as reservoirs of labour for the various industries. It is the magnetic pull of the Witwatersrand on the African male worker that largely accounts for the abnormal sex ratio in the urban population. Then also it must be remembered that a number of factors, economic, legal and administrative, cultural, all combine to discourage the migration of women to these areas.

The adverse moral effect of a superfluity of males has made itself felt very strongly in the township, and illegitimate children are found in all types of homes. In all strata of township life so many unmarried women have borne children that it seems to be accepted as an everyday occurrence and to cause little untoward comment. But with regard to the moral aspect what can be expected when thousands of men are quartered in compounds and hostels surrounding the townships, men separated by hundreds of miles from any home influence and restraint. In Johannesburg, as in other societies, the major vices under such circumstances pertain to liquor and sexual immorality. While E.N.T.[1] and its population are comparatively small, it caters for the worst passions of thousands who live elsewhere, hence their far-reaching power of corruption. Three or four or even five children born of the same mother each have a different [51/52] and unnamed father. Girls of only fourteen and fifteen are already earning money by prostitution. Let it be frankly admitted that E.N.T. is the happy hunting ground for the unattached male, free from family responsibility and with no public opinion to check his behaviour. These men from the areas surrounding the township enter it in large numbers during the weekends especially. It is inevitable that they corrupt the women.

It is unnatural to divorce working men from family life, and where it operates and is practised there will result inefficiency, discomfort and almost certainly, in the long run, immorality and degeneration. In view of the appalling results, it is highly questionable whether it is economically and socially desirable to employ male labour separated from normal family life and family responsibilities. The system of migrant labour has become a tremendous power in the economic, social and moral transformation of thousands of Africans.

With so many cases of illegitimacy the general attitude to it cannot be very strongly disapproving. Public opinion, though it exists, is incipient and inarticulate on this matter and, owing to the mixture of tribes, the infusion of degraded European values and the circumscribed extent of its operation, public disapproval is hardly an integrating power. In the absence of public sanctions, the only remaining deterrent, parental control, has very little force. Thus not only do parents not receive the same respect and exercise the same influence as under tribal conditions with their patriarchal age distinctions, but the growing economic independence of children and the separation from their parents entailed in employment are seriously undermining parental control. Township girls seek domestic employment with Europeans, away from the control of their parents, and during this time they come into contact with the large element of unattached males which is to be found in European employment in town. These men find it easy to form attachments with urban women. Marriage, moreover, has become so much of an economic burden, and money can purchase so many pleasures and luxuries, that men and women often prefer to retain their freedom to indulge themselves. It may well be that the new urban African generation is dispensing with marriage in its old forms.

Then again, the comparative isolation of many town families from their relatives, and the instability of marriage in urban areas, where a large number of men leave their wives and children for long periods without support, often abandoning them altogether without the formality of a divorce, have operated to foster the spirit of independence in the urban woman. She belongs to every tribe and to none, for, whereas she may [52/53] have the instincts and prejudices of her particular tribe bred strongly in her, she finds in the town none of the protection which her chief and the customs of her tribe provided. She is left adrift in strange surroundings and foreign customs. Her children grow up very often as slum-dwellers knowing nothing of the ordered life of the tribe, feeling the lure of the town about them. Thus it is that in a township such as E.N.T. strange variations of womenkind may be seen—here a tribal woman, weighed down with bangles and anklets, and there, passing her in the street, a city-bred girl, dressed in the latest European fashion, sometimes with a face made pathetic by its lipstick and powder, seeking no less than her white counterpart the thrill of new adventure, represented for her by the strange ways of the white woman, and the imitations of white

[1 Eastern Native Township]

amusements in native dance-halls and cinema houses. The African woman has been awakened out of a somewhat blank if pleasant existence to question and seek her destiny in the strange allurement of the European world. In such an environment she finds no hand to guide her; there is little to help her build up a new code of morality, a new discipline, or new moral sanctions.

Many, in fact, of the women in town are runaways, their whereabouts often unknown to their parents. Because of economic pressure the African woman begins to take her place more and more beside the man as a co-wage-earner. Widows seek work to support themselves and their children, but are more often lured by the excitement of urban life. But the African woman stands between the customs, sanctified by tradition, of her own people, the protection of which is increasingly denied her, and new standards and values of which she is not herself quite sure. Gone is the protection of group life, and she stands an inexperienced competitor in a highly organized competitive world. The change is devastating, for she must fend for herself; she must fight her own battles in a world in which, at best, women are economically handicapped. Marriage is no longer the universal and automatically achieved calling for her. Indeed, perhaps the unmarried African woman is one of the greatest contributions of the western world to the confusion of Africa, with particularly serious social implications in that the European administration all too frequently refuses to recognize her very existence and make the requisite provision accordingly. . . .

The Tsotsi*

TREVOR HUDDLESTON, C.R. (1913—   ) spent twelve years in South Africa. A member of the Community of the Resurrection, an order within the Anglican Church, Father Huddleston was the priest in charge of the Sophiatown and Orlando Missions in the diocese of Johannesburg from 1943 to 1949 and head of the Community in South Africa from 1949 to 1955. He is now Bishop of Masasi in Tanzania.

. . . *"Tsotsi"*—what does it mean? It is a familiar enough name in every urban African township: familiar enough to have become a term of abuse when applied by a European to an educated African, a term of contempt tinged with fear when used by one African boy of another. Yet it means something of quite tremendous importance to all those whose job is to care for the young of Christ's flock. Every country in its large cities has its "cosh-boys," its "wide-guys," its "gangsters," its "Teddys." And the "tsotsi," the real genuine "tsotsi," is all of these, though first and foremost he is just a boy. The origin of the name is interesting, for it is a corruption of "Zoot Suit," and the "tsotsi," like the Teddy-boy, is supposedly characterised by the cut of his clothes. In this case, because not many African youngsters can claim to have clothes which are "cut," the tight-fitting drain-pipe trousers are the distinctive mark. But today, in Alexandra and Sophiatown and Pimville and Moroka, it is not the clothes, it is the number, the gang, the weapons which are so terrifyingly evident. The tsotsi is youth rotting away, and rotting with fear the society around him. He is problem number one in urban Africa.

One Saturday evening in Sophiatown I was on the stoep of the mission-house after Evensong and Rosary. A boy came running across the school playground, one of the servers. "It's the Principal, Father, come please quickly, he's been stabbed. . . ." I got someone to help me with the stretcher (we always kept it handy and often had to use it) and went as quickly as I could, the boy directing me, to a house hard by the school. Elias Mokoetsi lay on the stoep unconscious and with blood staining his open shirt. There was little excitement. We [81/82] got him on to the stretcher and down to the clinic. The doctor gave him an injection. There was one tiny wound in the breast, no more than a quarter of an inch long. But it was enough, for it was just over his heart. He died within ten minutes. On Sunday after High Mass a woman asked to see me: with her was a young lad of nineteen, who said, "I've come to give myself up to you, Father: I stabbed the Principal. I didn't mean to kill him, Father. He hit me and I got mad. I had a knife. . . ."

. . . .

[82/83] . . . .
Woven into the whole pattern of fear, which is the pattern of so much of South Africa's life, is this fear which is ever present in the locations and townships of the Reef. And it is a by-product of a whole attitude of mind: of something which could undoubtedly be cured, if it were not for the irrational and morbid obsession

over colour which so entirely petrifies constructive work in the social field. For the "tsotsi" is symbolic of something other than a simple social evil, common to all countries. He is, I believe, more than a juvenile delinquent, more than a "case" for an approved school. Like them he is aggressively anti-social: but unlike them he has a profound reason, as a rule, for being so. He is the symbol of a society which does not care. He is in revolt against the frustration which, apparently, cannot be cured, cannot be relieved. He turns upon his own people and uses his knife against [83/84] them because he is caught in that trap from which there is no escape —the trap which Nature seems to have set for him by giving him a black skin. Alan Paton, in his picture of Absalom, has given one story of the typical tsotsi boy. But it is not the only one: it is not the most common. Absalom comes up from the country to find his sister, and is caught in the life of the city, bewildered by it, his standards destroyed by it, and he himself eventually becomes the criminal and the victim of it. No doubt there are many such. But the "tsotsi" I know best has never set foot in the country. He is a "cockney" by birth, and so, possibly, are his parents before him. The only life he knows is the life of the town. The only standards he recognises are those provided by an urban, industrialised society. He would be as much a stranger in the kraals of Zululand as I would be in Tibet. What is it, then, which makes him what he is? How can it be that that lovely little boy of six, with the sparkling eyes and the friendly smile, has become a killer at sixteen? And how is it that there are so many like him? So many that, in the most modern locations in South Africa, people are scared to go out of their homes at night except in groups. In the first place, it must be recognised that Social Welfare work in South Africa amongst Africans is hamstrung from the first not so much by lack of money, as by the attitude of mind which racialism inevitably produces. The most common phrase, I suppose, in use in

this country is "The Native Problem." By this phrase everything is summed up. It is an abstraction—and so, to the average white man, is the African. It is a "problem"—never an opportunity. In some strange way, one has to avoid thinking of black men as if they were persons at all. And so the "tsotsi" [84/85] is just part of this great abstraction too. He is not a boy who has gone wrong: he is a native skellum. He doesn't belong to a family, with a father and mother and brothers and sisters—he is a "problem." White society has to solve the "problem" if it can, because crime is an expensive and unedifying commodity. But white society should not be asked to take a personal interest in it, still less provide money for its solution —for it lies altogether outside the sphere of human relations. It belongs to that other world, which it is easiest to forget. This was brought home to me very forcibly by the murder of Elias Mokoetsi. . . . [85/86]

. . . Incidentally, when Elias Mokoetsi's murderer was tried it was discovered that he had six previous convictions, several of them of a serious nature, although he was only nineteen. The charge was reduced to culpable homicide. He was sentenced to one year in jail. So far as I know he is still walking the streets of Sophiatown. After all, it was only another stabbing in a native area: part of the "problem": why worry too much? Neither the boy who murdered, nor the man who was murdered, had real value as a [86/87] person. Both were natives: a different category, another species living in a world apart.

. . . .

[87/88] . . . In a recent comprehensive survey of one of the African townships it was discovered (though those of us who lived there knew it from first-hand experience) that the average family had to face a gap between income and expenditure of over £2. 10s. per month. How is this gap to be closed? In the answer to that question there lies another answer to the reason for the "tsotsi." It is poverty. In Johannesburg more than half the total population of the city is non-European. Apart from those thousands of migrant labourers employed by the mines and living in compounds, quite separate from the locations of the city, there are at least 350,000 Africans who belong to Johannesburg and upon whose labour Johannesburg depends. Taking the survey I have referred to as an accurate index (and I have every reason to believe that it is), it would not be an exaggeration to say that at least half the African families in the city must live below the bread line—UNLESS THEY CAN CLOSE THAT GAP. African families—thank God—are large as a rule. The average number of children in a [88/89] family is anything between four and seven. Quite often it is more. So, clearly, if they are to be fed and clothed, it is necessary for both parents to go out to work. With their strong sense of "family," this is an unnatural and most undesirable thing for the African people. But it is nowadays an accepted thing also. And it might be all right if there were compulsory education: if the parents could be sure that their children were in school whilst they were out at work. That is the one thing they cannot be sure of. In the urban areas about one child in three can find a place in school. The remaining two-thirds of the child population has only the street or the empty room for its long day. And, in places like Sophiatown or Alexandra Township, that is not so good. "Father, I've come to give you my child, you must take care of him. Father—he is naughty, very, very naughty. I can do nothing with him. He dodges school. He is a 'loafer.' He stays out at night. . . ." How often I have heard these words. And they are spoken over the head of a child of eight or ten. He is "out of control." And he really *is* out of control. I know that the chances are that he is already with a gang. Probably he has taken part in quite a few minor burglaries—fruit or sweets or cigarettes from the "China" shops. When I look down at him I can see a hardness already forming round his mouth, in his eyes. And there is so little I can hope to

do. "Father must get him to school." But all the schools are full, and over-full. "Father must send him away from Johannesburg, to a boarding school." But there are no boarding schools for boys of his age and of his standard in education. "Father must take him to Diepkloof" (The Reformatory which Alan Paton once supervised, and from which he learnt about Absalom [89/90] and old Kumalo) —but Diepkloof already has seven hundred boys and in any case cannot take any boy unless he is committed by a magistrate. There is too much competition: there are too few probation officers. Above all, there are too few people who even begin to care. Sometimes in Johannesburg at night when the cinema crowds are flooding out on to the pavements, I have watched African children—some of them certainly not more than eight years old— hanging about the lighted entrances, darting through the legs of the emerging throng, watching the Greek shops with their brilliant windows. They are filthy dirty. They are hungry. They hold out their hands—"Penny, baas, penny, baas" —and sometimes they get what they ask and run off in search of more. But nobody cares what happens to them or from where they come. Nobody cares that these children, who belong to someone, somewhere, will soon be in those same Johannesburg streets with knives, or with stolen revolvers: will be, in fact, the "tsotsis" of tomorrow. White South Africa lives in fear: but it does surprisingly little to remove the causes. It prefers burglar-proofing: private watchmen: the revolver by the bedside, to any kind of constructive approach to the problem of the "tsotsi." And if half the money which is spent on keeping pass offenders in prison were spent instead on building schools or equipping boys' clubs, the crime-wave would soon become less menacing.

There is, however, another cause of "tsotsi-ism." It is illegitimacy. And this is also something which White South Africa views with a sickening complacency and with a Pharisaical shrug of the shoulders.

"These Kaffirs. Breed like rabbits." Or, "My 'girl' has a lot [**90/91**] of boy-friends, of course. But what can you do? It's their nature." Or, "She's pregnant again. She'll have to go. I can't have an infant in the house. What a nuisance these girls are. I'd almost sooner do the work myself." Or, more rarely on the telephone, "Father, I don't know you and you don't know me. I've got a girl here, and we've had her working for us for a long time. Now she's got two children and they're growing up. I can't keep them in the servant's room. Is there a school, or an institution? . . . Nothing? . . . Oh, but surely there's *some* place. . . . I thought you'd be sure to know of somewhere. . . . Can't you help at all?" No, I cannot. I cannot because the thing is far too big, and its roots go far too deep in the rottenness of a social order which White South Africa tolerates and more than tolerates, desires. I cannot because in the whole Union there is only one Institution that will take pregnant African girls and their babies, and that is always over-full. I am its Chairman, and I know. I cannot, because you, the "Missus," accept your servant for the work she will do: you do not give a thought to where she comes from, how she lives or what she needs in the way of protection. You say (how many hundred times have I heard you?) that you do everything for her and she is ungrateful. What you mean is that you pay her her wages: give her enough to eat: sometimes give her clothing which you can no longer wear yourself. But what of her life in that back-room, at the bottom of your yard, completely separate (by law) from the house? That is, for the time being, her home. The door does not lock properly and the windows are not barred. There is no security. In the white suburbs of Johannesburg there are thousands of African servants of both [**91/92**] sexes. They must live sufficiently close to their work to be on call six days out of seven, and seven nights out of seven. But they must live in "Kayas"—single rooms of varying quality built away from the house. There are no recreation centres of any kind in any of the European suburbs for African servants. . . . [**92/93**]

. . . Indeed nothing can so swiftly arouse the wrath of white suburbia as a plan for providing African servants with recreational facilities. Protest meetings are planned with great swiftness and are attended in force. The English immigrant who has, for the first time in his life, a servant and a car, is perhaps more ready to support such a protest than his Afrikaner neighbour. But both are united in a fierce determination to prevent their suburb becoming attractive to the native servant they employ. So, in fact, the "girl" or the "garden-boy" live in their separate rooms. But they do not always, in the hours when their work is done, stay by themselves or sleep alone. And their employers do not care what goes on, provided that it does not involve a police raid, provided that the morning tea is brought in on time, provided there is no "cheekiness."

What it really means is easy to understand. It means that Eva, who has a home in Sophiatown, or Grace, who lives in Orlando, soon has a babe in her womb: loses her job: returns, disgraced, to her family —and there is another child whose father is unknown, another child who, in all probability, Granny will have to look after: another child who, in the coming years, may be "nobody's business." These are the children who run the streets when they ought to be in school—if they could get into school. These are the "tsotsis" of tomorrow. And White South Africa shrugs its shoulders and complains that servants are not what they used to be. Nobody cares. Except, of course, the municipal authorities and the Government. But they care in a strange and cynical way. They are determined, for [**93/94**] instance, that the life of domestic servants shall be regulated and controlled. There must be an absolute enforcement of the law of registration. The moral law is another matter altogether. So we have reached the stage, in White Johannesburg, where a man and his wife, married by Christian rites, may not live together as man and wife unless they work for the same employer. "Whom God hath joined together, let no man put asunder . . ." but don't dare to go and visit each other: don't be discovered together in the same room, or you are liable to arrest for trespass. Is it so very surprising if a child, conceived and born in illegality, technically non-existent, according to the law of the land a trespasser from birth, becomes in later life a rebel against society, black and white? I do not claim that every lad who becomes a "tsotsi" begins his life in this fashion: nor do I believe that it is environment alone which makes the criminal. There is such a thing as evil: there is sin in a fallen world. But I do not exaggerate when I say that the tsotsi is a symbol of society which does not care. . . .

[Government Report on the 1943 Bus Boycotts]*

The commission appointed to inquire into the operation of bus services for non-Europeans met between September 1943 and January 1944. The following selection from the report of that commission is a part of a history of non-European bus transportation which precedes an investigation into bus boycotts by Africans. The first mention of a boycott comes in Paragraph 26, which describes the bus service to Alexandra Township in the 1930's and the formation, in 1935, of a Bus Owner's Association, which laid down the conditions of running the service.

. . . In 1939 the fare was raised to 5d. and is said to have continued at that figure until August, 1940, when a boycott of the buses took place and the fare was reduced to 4d. again. In October, 1942, the operators applied to the local Road Transportation Board for permission, which was granted, to raise the fare to 5d. This move met with opposition and eventually led to an appeal against the decision to the Central Road Transportation Board. The appeal was heard in July, 1943, and was dismissed. It was, thereupon, decided to introduce the fare of 5d. as from the beginning of August, 1943, but the opposition then organised another boycott which continued for a week. In the negotiations, which ensued, the operators agreed to accept the fourpenny fare pending an inquiry into the whole position.

Immediately thereafter, two buses broke down and a third was late at Atteridgeville, Pretoria, which led to a boycott of the buses there. This matter was, however, settled on the same day and the service was resumed.

On the 15th day of the same month (August, 1943) the Africans at Eersterust and Riverside, Pretoria, decided to boycott the buses on their route on account of an increase in the weekend fare. This boycott was accompanied by some violence and intimidation with the result that the buses did not enter Eersterust for a fortnight.

It was in these circumstances that this Commission was appointed to inquire into the running of the whole of the non-European bus services on the Reef and in the districts of Pretoria and Vereeniging.

There is evidence that to some extent advantage was taken of the dissatisfaction of the Africans over the bus services to push a certain type of political propaganda among them but your Commissioners have no doubt after hearing all the evidence that quite independent of any organised political agitation the root causes of the Africans' dissatisfaction lie deep in their present sub-economic condition.

A number of complaints were placed before us, e.g. overcrowding, incivility of conductors, irregularity of service, breakdowns, and the like, which will be dealt with later in this report, but underlying all these complaints were certain major considerations which were continually finding expression.

These major considerations can be stated as follows: The Europeans have forced a policy of segregation on the Afri-

* From "Report of the Commission Appointed to Inquire into the Operation of Bus Services for Non-Europeans on the Witwatersrand and in the District of Pretoria and Vereeniging" (Pretoria: The Government Printer, 1944), pp. 1–2, paras. 26–35.

cans. The transportation of the Africans is, therefore, very much a financial obligation of the Europeans. As this policy of segregation also enters the sphere of labour to the disadvantage of the Africans, they should be allowed to engage in and keep to themselves all work, skilled as well as unskilled, required for the service of their own people. That is their feeling. As an illustration of the strength of this feeling it may be pointed out that where an African is supplying a service in competition with a European, as for example, between Germiston Station and the location, the African is patronised in preference, though his charge is higher than that made by the European.

In keeping with this attitude, objection was taken by African witnesses to the employment of European drivers and conductors on non-European trams and buses and similarly an attack was made on the appointment in 1942 of a European inspectorate on the City-Alexandra bus route.

Your Commissioners were informed that, as is to be expected, some Africans do not hesitate to take advantage of this reaction to the "segregation policy" to exploit their own people for private gain. Thus, opposition to the entry of European-owned buses into Eastwood, Pretoria, was organised by an African who was planning to obtain certificates from the Road Transportation Board in order to introduce a bus service of his own. The result was that owing to the obstruction offered by the inhabitants to the passage of the buses, the operators were compelled to turn their buses at the entrance to the township and the inhabitants deprived themselves of the convenience of the bus service within the township.

It is, however, clearly established in evidence before your Commissioners that the following facts must be faced:

(a) That a large urban and peri-urban African population in the areas under consideration has come into existence and is increasing by natural growth and by accessions from elsewhere;

(b) That this population is becoming increasingly race-conscious;

(c) That it does not regard the establishment of locations by local authorities with the restrictions which the Africans regard as irksome as the proper solution of the housing problem;

(d) That it cherishes the desire to own property and to "live like human beings";

(e) That it has not the money to manage its own communal affairs.

[Gold at Odendaalsrust]*

THE LONDON *TIMES* was founded in 1785 by John Walter. Since the mid-nineteenth century it has been distinguished for its broad daily coverage of home and foreign news. The *Times* also publishes several supplements, including *The Times Literary Supplement* and *The Times Educational Supplement*. Its present circulation is 290,485.

SOUTH AFRICAN GOLD TESTS

—— • ——

HOPES OF PROSPERITY FOR THE
ORANGE FREE STATE

———

Development of Research Area

From our Bloemfontein Correspondent

The Orange Free State goldfields came into the news with a rush recently when the astounding assay result of 23,037 inch-dwt. on a borehole south of Odendaalsrust, in which the Blinkpoort Gold Syndicate and Western Holdings are jointly interested, was announced. The core showed some visible gold.

The writer has visited the northern areas of the Free State, at the heart of which lies the sleepy village of Odendaalsrust. Odendaal is an old South African family name, and it was at this village that one of the original Odendaals rested. It has a European population of just over 300 and is off the beaten track, not yet linked by rail with the rest of the country. The nearest track is the main Bloemfontein-Johannesburg line, which passes through the small town of Hennenman, some 23 miles to the east. Odendaalsrust has few pavements, corrugated iron buildings, and probably more horse-carts than

motor-cars. Sandy tracks serve as roads. In the middle of the village the market square, a piece of grass-covered veld, is lined with trees and has only one building upon it. This is the Municipal Office, no larger than a single office in a large Johannesburg mining house. Dominating the village, as is usual in the Free State, is a modern and imposing Dutch Reformed Church, recently completed at a cost of £13,000.

Immediately around the village are about 20 derricks with modern drilling machines. Working day and night, and manned by a European overseer and a squad of natives, these drills, with their diamond-studded fingers, are probing thousands of feet below the surface, bringing geological samples to the top. These are minutely examined by expert geologists, on whose pronouncements so much depends. Every now and again the village celebrates when one of the drills inter-

---

* "South African Gold Tests," London Times, May 13, 1946, p. 5. Reprinted with the permission of The Times.

177

sects the gold-bearing reef, usually at a depth of some 5,000 ft. Occasionally water is struck, and the drilling may have to be discontinued: or the experts decide that there is more chance of striking the reef by deflecting the drills by some small angle.

DRILLING METHODS

The derricks, super-structures supporting the drilling machines, are 84 ft. high and cost £4,000 to erect with all their accessories. The drills are driven by steam. At every 10 ft. that the drill descends a new iron cylindrical rod is added to the lengthening support for the actual drill. When 60 ft. has been added to the depth the hollow cylindrical rods are brought to the surface and the tubular sample is extracted. The sample has usually cracked and crumbled, but the geologist always examines it, with the hope of finding evidence of gold.

In the old days the only way to discover whether gold lay buried deep in the earth was to sink a shaft about 6 ft. square, so that samples could be hauled to the surface. Now these slender drills pierce neat holes to a depth of over 8,500 ft. if necessary to bring to the surface samples the size of a garden hose, which provide all the information necessary before a costly shaft-sinking and mining venture is launched. The depth of the Free State holes varies from about 600 ft. to nearly 9,000 ft. Large areas of gold-bearing reef have been located, much of it in payable quantity. Early drilling took place in 1933 and continued spasmodically until 1938, when a large strike was made at St. Helena. Since the end of the war there has been intense activity.

A leading geologist, with a full background of experience and practical knowledge obtained from years of work on the Rand goldmines, stated recently that shafts would be sunk within about six months, that the first of the mines might well be in production in the initial stages within 12 months, and that in about four years'

time there should be at least 10 new goldmines in full production. It is estimated that each mine will employ 600 Europeans and 6,000 natives, and that the next five years will see the population of the Odendaalsrust district increase from its present 300 to over 15,000 Europeans and possibly as many as 100,000 natives.

Meanwhile mining options have been taken over vast tracts of the northern Free State, mainly in the districts of Odendaalsrust, St. Helena, Bothaville, Hoopstad, Ventersburg, Theunissen, Winburg, Brandfort, and Dealesville. The area extends south of Bloemfontein, the capital, with a small number of options taken up on farms in the southern Free State. Many farmers have been paid large sums for these mineral options, which still leave them free to pursue their farming, as surface rights are not necessarily involved.

Main attention at Odendaalsrust is shifting gradually away from share speculation and is concentrated on the buying of property. Plots and stands have risen spectacularly in price. The record price of £12,000 has been paid for a small building plot in the centre of Odendaalsrust which 14 days earlier had changed hands at £2,700. An offer of £7,000 has been rejected for a building plot formerly worth less than £100. One sold 10 years ago for £52 is priced £5,000 to-day. Most people are banking heavily on the assumption that, with the news that 10 mines have been opened, large armies of white employees, business men, and native labourers will descend upon Odendaalsrust in the fairly near future, and so are buying property as fast as they can. Sir Ernest Oppenheimer's statement about a large influx of population has been seized on joyously by speculators.

In the immediate neighbourhood of Odendaalsrust the highest prices have been paid, averaging £15 a morgen (600 square roods), but increasing to £25 in parts. One farmer with 867 morgen of land adjoining the town commonage was paid £16,857 for the mineral rights alone. The mining companies have taken up all the "erven" they can. Before the war a municipal "erf" in the village, measuring a modest 100 by 150 Cape feet, could be bought for £4 or £5, but to-day the same erf would cost about £1,000. Before gold can be mined as an economic proposition, however, the whole area will have to be developed on a grand scale. The main requirements are communications, water, electric power, housing, equipment, materials, and labour.

IRRIGATION PLANS

Already railway engineers are planning a coordinated system of transport to serve the entire region, while irrigation experts have plans to divert water in quantity to the prospective goldfields. There is talk of major schemes of damming the Zand and Vet rivers, leading off the water by canals to those parts where it is indispensable, and of leading water down from the Vaal river, which forms the boundary between the Free State and the Transvaal. Much new equipment, primarily from America and Britain, will be needed, and delays in delivery might hold up the development of these new goldfields.

Housing in South Africa remains extremely problematical, and competent authorities can see no easy or sudden solution to the problem of general shortages throughout the country. Yet a large-scale housing plan is indispensable to the production of gold. Complete new townships will have to be laid down. Native labour, that bulwark of South African economic life, will be necessary on a great scale. Whence is it to come? South Africa depends largely on native labour from outside its borders. These are some of the difficulties that lie plainly ahead, but this country has overcome similar difficulties before.

There are four main reasons why some experts do not believe that the Free State fields will ever outstrip those on the Rand, the greatest in the world. The proved area is relatively small: the gold-bearing reefs lie at great depth: the temperature underground increases more rapidly in the Free State: the area is faulted. The mining experts are satisfied, however, that gold exists in payable quantity in the northern Free State. The large Johannesburg mining houses are prepared to go ahead, and the financial reserves necessary to start large-scale mining will be forthcoming. The State will lend all possible assistance.

The past has brought the Free State more than its share of economic strain and racial strife and less than its share of industrial and mining activity. Now the scales may be about to tip. Bloemfontein the capital, has just ended its centenary celebrations, and hopes the second century on which it is now entering may bring peace and prosperity, economic activity on a scale undreamed of, and a general lifting of horizons. Where mealies now grow undisturbed and sheep and cattle graze in idle laziness may one day be transformed into the hustle and bustle of modern cities.

The Golden Semicircle*

THEODORE GREGORY (1890—   ) has been Dean of the Faculty of Economics and a professor of economics at the University of London (1927—1937). From 1938 to 1946, he served as Economic Advisor to the government of India. An Honorary Fellow of the London School of Economics, Dr. Gregory has written extensively on economics.

. . . It was hoped initially to accommodate about 10 per cent of the Native labour force. This modest proportion reflected the fact that of the total number of mine workers, a large proportion came from outside the Union and for obvious reasons the scheme could not apply to them. Moreover, of the Union Natives, judging from Witwatersrand experience, though 55 per cent were married, only 25 per cent of these married men had no allotments of arable land in the reserves, and even of these many enjoyed some rights to land or shared occupation with their relatives. Such men were reluctant to lose rights and to become permanent town-dwellers.[98] It was decided to begin with a 'Native village' of 100 houses, to be increased subsequently to 500.

On 12 June 1952 Harry Oppenheimer, then Member of Parliament for Kimberly, asked the Minister of Native Affairs (then Senator Verwoerd) in the course of a parliamentary discussion, 'whether he would be good enough to define his attitude in regard to the experiment which is being made on certain of the new gold-mines in the Orange Free State by the establishment of villages on the mines for married Native employees.' The Minister replied[99] on 13 June:

In regard to married quarters at the mines on the Free State gold-fields I want to state quite unequivocally that I am opposed to that development. I, too, have objections, and my department has been instructed to investigate the position very thoroughly and to stop the development of such villages as far as possible. Let me give my reasons for this. Within that Free State gold-mining area every mine can then establish its own Native town with married quarters. That will then mean a series of Native towns. While we are already establishing Native towns in the vicinity of the big cities to provide housing for the Natives, it will mean that in addition a large number of black spots will be spread out throughout the whole Free State mining area. Now we must bear in mind that when the mines stop working one day that large number of towns will remain there spread out over that area. [578/579] They may amount to 20 or 30 or 40 within that area! They do not fall under our control either. The Department of Native Affairs has no jurisdiction over those Native towns on mining land. We do realize that the mines need a certain limited number of experienced married Natives such as boss boys, but our view is that there should be married quarters only for those who are needed on the mines for night duties or for emergency duties. The others who are needed there but who need not live on the spot because of the nature of their work should find their accommodation in the neighbouring locations or in Native areas where locations may be established. There are such location areas near each of those mining areas. That is possible in practice. In addition it is our view that it must be borne in mind that the Natives who work in the mines are not the sophisticated Natives. They are usually Natives who have been recruited by agents in the reserves, but usually their children who grow up in those mining towns do not want to work on the mines. So when the married quarters have been created the Native fathers will use them and the children will be

[98] Mr. Rheinallt Jones, the Native labour adviser to Anglo American Corporation, in an interview reported in the Johannesburg *Star* on 25 February 1949.

[99] *Hansard*, vol. 80, cols. 8030–I.

* Theodore Gregory, from "The Golden Semicircle," *Ernest Oppenheimer and the Economic Development of Southern Africa* (Cape Town, London, New York: Oxford University Press, 1962), pp. 578–582. Reprinted with the permission of Oxford University Press.

pushed on to the neighbouring general community. They will disappear from those mining towns in the course of time and they will become a burden to the neighbouring towns or cities where they will have to be accommodated in the locations. They will be pushed off on to others. If such a mine-worker Native himself contracts tuberculosis or silicosis the mines will not keep him there in their housing scheme. He is paid compensation, but he is also pushed off on to another housing scheme because they need his house for the new mine worker. So it means that those married quarters become a channel through which the rest of the non-European population in the cities becomes greater and greater. It is an unhealthy development if it occurs without control for the sake of the non-European labour of one industry. We feel that this industry must be treated like other industries and that its married Native labourers must be accommodated as in the case of the other industries.

This attitude, as Harry Oppenheimer was subsequently to point out, was inconsistent with the policy favoured for industry in general, whereby industry was to assume the responsibility for housing its own labour, and not the local authority. The argument that married mine labour should be housed in the municipal locations[100] seemed to cut across this general policy.

A long correspondence was subsequently conducted with the appropriate government department. Government adhered to the view that

while the establishment of a mine of villages for Native married mine workers with their families is wholly disapproved, the continuance of the [579/580] traditional policy of the use of migrant labour on the gold-mines, accommodated in compounds, which has been advocated consistently by the Gold Producers' Committee, has the approval of the Department of Native Affairs.

But, as the official letter of September 1953 continues:

As a special concession, Native personnel, who are employed on a permanent basis because of specialized training and experience and who are required to be continuously on the mine property, may be accommodated in a limited number of married quarters on each mine. No foreign Natives may be permitted this privilege and they may under no circumstances be allowed to import their families.

The general principle laid down in this and subsequent correspondence was an absolute limit of 3 per cent of the total Native labour complement of any mine and it 'must be clearly understood that the department will only agree to additional married quarters up to the said 3 per cent when it is satisfied that the extension of the concession is fully justified by the circumstances of each case.'

Though the opposition of Government thwarted the efforts of Ernest Oppenheimer and Anglo American Corporation to create mining villages for the married Native labour force in the Orange Free State, Ernest Oppenheimer was yet able, in the penultimate year of his life, to assist powerfully in an effort to improve housing conditions for the Native population in the Johannesburg area. Living conditions in certain Native areas were admittedly appallingly bad, and it was the reading of Father Trevor Huddleston's *Naught for your comfort*—a brilliant piece of propaganda, which Ernest Oppenheimer, 'like most South Africans . . . considered biased and unfair and . . . gave an untrue impression of conditions in South Africa'— which nevertheless 'led him to wish to come and see again for himself the conditions under which our urban African population was living,'[101] and indirectly led to a scheme by which the mining houses placed a sum of £3 million at the disposal of the Johannesburg City Council for slum clearance. Dr. Boris Wilson, M.P.C., first proposed the scheme, but the part played by Ernest Oppenheimer can be gathered from a letter sent to him by Dr. Wilson on 17 August 1956:

It is impossible to really put down in print my thanks to you for the wonderful way in which you reacted to my proposal to you for a loan of £3 million to remove the slums. What makes it even more remarkable is [580/581] that you had already thought of doing something tangible in the matter, and circumstances conspired to bring us together so that we could lay down the foundation for the removal of the Moroka shanty town slums and the worst of the Pimville area.

[100] *Rand Daily Mail*, 14 June 1952: 'Imagine the position if the mines are prevented from housing their married employees, while secondary industries are compelled to bear the cost of housing theirs.'
[101] All these citations are from a speech delivered by Harry Oppenheimer on 11 March 1958, when a memorial tower, a tribute to his father, was unveiled by him.

In this letter I must pay tribute to your whole humanitarian approach to the problem of living and, although I have said it in public before, I believe that this was the motive which inspired you to go to your mining finance colleagues and ask them to undertake the task with you.

There is no doubt that your magnificent gesture and that of your mining colleagues will be of the greatest benefit, not only to the 80,000 Africans, but to the whole of South Africa.

By March 1958, nearly 10,000 houses had been built out of the 15,000 which it was intended that the scheme should finance. Out of the bricks of the demolished shanty town a memorial tower was erected mid-way between the new African townships of Zondi and Jabulani to commemorate the part which Ernest Oppenheimer had played.

In one other important respect Ernest Oppenheimer's aspirations were not defeated: that was in the sphere of the improvement of the health of the Native employees. No more magnificent memorial to his memory can be imagined than the great hospital at Welkom, the foundation stone of which he laid on 18 December 1950, and which bears his name. Speaking to the Anglo American Corporation shareholders on 22 June 1951, he discussed the problem of the health of Native mine workers in its broadest aspects:

Both from the humanitarian viewpoint and from the standpoint of the practical interests of the industry, it is important that the closest attention be given to the health and well-being of our Native employees. The industry already has a well-deserved reputation for the care it devotes to the health of Native mine workers. It is well established that Natives return to their kraals generally in far better physical condition after their periods of service with the mining industry. But I believe there is still great scope for the development of health services among our Native employees. Especially is this the case in the sphere of what is called preventive medicine. There is also real need for a more active and positive attack upon the prevalent and frequently disabling diseases among the Natives offering themselves for employment in the industry. An advance in this direction is being made on the new mines of the group in the Orange Free State. We have introduced a system of mass miniature radiography as standard practice for all Native employees on our mines; we have set up clinics at the mine hostels for the day-to-day treatment of diseases which, owing to earlier neglect, have hitherto frequently developed so as to require hospitalization and conse- [581/582] quent loss of manpower and in some cases irreparable damage to the individuals concerned; and we have established a system of routine health inspection at all mine hostels under the control of trained and qualified sanitarians. Similar services and welfare centres are about to be established in the mine Native villages. We are also building a very large hospital at Welkom for our Native employees and their dependents, which will incorporate the most modern equipment for the treatment of all forms of disease and accident, and which will be staffed by specialists in the various branches of medicine and surgery.

These improvements do not exhaust the possibilities of ensuring that the highest standards of health are attained among our Native employees, and it is as much in our own interests as in the interests of the Natives themselves that we should be continuously active in applying within the industry all the latest approved ideas that current developments in medical science and hygiene may suggest.

Higher standards of comfort and hygiene in Native housing and accommodation, better feeding and nutrition and better health and medical services will all combine to make employment in our gold-mining industry increasingly attractive to Natives themselves and to those authorities in other territories outside the Union who have the welfare of their Native populations at heart. . . .[102]

[102] The design and lay-out of the hospital was decided upon after a comprehensive tour of overseas hospitals, particularly in Sweden, Great Britain and the United States of America, undertaken by Dr. J. H. G. van Blommestein, the medical consultant of Anglo American Corporation. As recommended by an eminent Swedish authority, standardization of materials and equipment was the keynote of the plans and this greatly contributed to economy. 'Medical and technical visitors from overseas have stated that they could not build a hospital to compare with the Ernest Oppenheimer Hospital for less than £3,500 a bed, yet this hospital, with all its amenities and modern equipment, cost less than £1,130 per bed . . .' (cited from a descriptive pamphlet *The Ernest Oppenheimer Hospital*, published by Anglo American Corporation). The hospital is intended to serve all the mines of the Anglo American Corporation group, and there are women's and children's and maternity sections.

[Sophiatown]*

TREVOR HUDDLESTON, C.R. For biographical information see "The Tsotsi" (p. 170).

Sophiatown! How hard it is to capture and to convey the magic of that name! Once it is a matter of putting pen to paper all the life and colour seems to leave it: and failing to explain its mysterious fascination is somehow a betrayal of one's love for the place. It is particularly important to me to try and paint the picture that I know and that is yet so elusive, for in a few years Sophiatown will cease to exist. It will be, first of all, a rubble heap, destruction spreading like some contagion through the streets (it has begun already), laying low the houses, good and bad alike, that I have known; emptying them of the life, the laughter and the tears of the children—till the place is a grey ruin lying in the sun. Then, I suppose, the factories will begin to go up, gaunt impersonal blocks of cement, characterless and chill, however bright the day. And, in a few years, men will have forgotten that this was a living community and a very unusual one. It will have slipped away into history, and that a fragmentary history of a fraction of time. Perhaps it will awaken faint echoes in the memory of some who recall that it was to Sophiatown that Kumalo came seeking Absalom, his son. But they will never remember what I remember of it: and I cannot put [117/118] my memories on paper, or, if I do, they will only be like the butterflies pinned, dead and lustreless, on the collector's board. Nevertheless, I must try.

Sophiatown! The name has about it a certain historical and almost theological sound. It recalls Sancta Sophia, Holy Wisdom, and the dreaming city where her temple is built. I have never heard of another Sophiatown in the world, though I suppose there must be one: it is such a euphonious name, for one thing. And, of course, it has a history and a meaning as romantic in its way as anything connected with the Eastern Mediterranean. As romantic, but also about as different as it could well be.

Some fifty years ago, when Johannesburg was still a mining "dorp," a planned and growing town, yet small and restricted in area, a certain Mr. Tobiansky dreamed of a European suburb in the West, on the rocky outcrop which is shadowed by the spur known as Northcliff. It is quite a long way from the centre of town, about four and a half miles in fact, but not an impossible distance. It was a most attractive site in every way, for it had "features": it was not like the flat and uninteresting central area of the city. It could hold its own in natural beauty with Parktown and Houghton, soon to become the most fashionable suburbs, and, like them, it had iron-red rock for a foundation and for a problem in civil engineering. Mr. Tobiansky bought a large plot of ground, and named it in gratitude and admiration after his wife, Sophia. As he pegged out the streets he named many of them after his children; Edith and Gerty and Bertha and Toby and Sol. So, from the very beginning, Sophiatown had a homely and "family" feel about it. There

* Trevor Huddleston, from "Sophiatown" and "Out Damned Spot," *Naught for Your Comfort* (New York: The Macmillan Company, 1963), pp. 117–124, 126–127, 128–129, 133–137, 182–194. Copyright, 1956, by Ernest Urban Trevor Huddleston. Reprinted by permission of Doubleday & Company, Inc. and William Collins Sons & Company Ltd.

was nothing "up-stage" or snobbish about those names, just as there was nothing [118/119] pretentious about the kind of houses which began to spring up. In fact, there was nothing very planned about it either. Still, the veldt and the rock were more noticeable than the houses: the streets ran up and down the kopje and stopped short when the kopje became too steep. There was, on one side, a wide sweep of what you might call meadow-land: an empty plot of ground which provided clay for the bricks and a good playing-field for the children. There seemed to be no reason on earth why Sophiatown should not be as popular a suburb as Parktown itself: perhaps even more popular because it was more open, higher up on the six-thousand-foot pla-teau which is Johannesburg. But Mr. Tobiansky had reckoned without the Town Council: or perhaps already that mischievous and unpredictable voice had whispered something about the future. Whatever it was, the Council decided that a growing town must have sewage disposal facilities: and it decided further that those facilities must be in the Western area of the young Johannesburg. The natural and immediate consequence of this de-cision was the end of Mr. Tobiansky's dream. Sophiatown ceased to be attractive in any way to those Europeans who wished to buy land and to build homes in the suburbs. Mr. Tobiansky could not sell to White Johannesburg and, for a while, he could not sell to anyone else. Then, once again, the Town Council intervened. The First World War brought a wave of in-dustrialisation, and with it the need for African labour. The only existing loca-tion, Pimville, had been planned and planted some ten miles from the centre of the town. There was certainly need for another location which would house the African workers and which might be a little more conveniently sited for their [119/120] work. The Western Area was once more chosen. Sewage disposal and a native location seemed to go together. The Western Native Township, with ac-

commodation for some three thousand families, was built. A tall iron fence was erected all round it. The Africans moved in. So, some forty years ago, began the African occupation of the Western sub-urbs. As soon as the location was estab-lished, Tobiansky found himself in an area where the non-European was in the majority. There was nothing to prevent him selling his land to Africans, coloureds and Asiatics. Under one of President Kruger's laws he was perfectly safeguarded for doing so, and, as a good business man, he did the obvious thing. The obvious thing but not the most usual in South Africa. For when Tobiansky sold freehold properties to African purchasers, he was in fact establishing a unique situation. He was making possible an African—or at least a non-white—suburb in Johan-nesburg. He knew, no doubt, what he was doing. He could hardly have known the far-reaching consequences of his action. For as Johannesburg expanded, so did its need for African labour. Apart from the squalid slums of Vrededorp and the dis-tant corrugated-iron location of Pimville, there was nowhere for the people to live except the Western Native Township and the suburbs of Sophiatown, Martindale and Newclare which surrounded it. Houses sprang up in Edith Street and elsewhere: houses of all types, all sizes, all colours. They crept up towards the rocks on top of the hill: they spread out to-wards the brick-fields. By 1920 or there-abouts it had become quite obvious that here was an area which belonged by right of possession to the non-European half of Johannesburg. It was not so evident at that time that white suburbia was also [120/121] spreading rapidly westwards, and that it was becoming especially the residential area of the European artisan. Sophiatown had come to maturity: had a character and an atmosphere of its own, and in the succeeding thirty-odd years that character and that atmosphere deep-ened and became only the more perma-nent. When I arrived to take over as priest-in-charge of the Anglican Mission in September, 1943, the place had for many years assumed the appearance it has to-day. It is that which I wish so greatly to put into words. Yet I know I cannot succeed.

They say that Sophiatown is a slum. Strictly in terms of the Slums Act they are absolutely correct: for the density of the population is about twice what it should be, 70,000 instead of 30,000. But the word "slum" to describe Sophiatown is grossly misleading, and especially to people who know the slums of Europe or the United States. It conjures up immediately a picture of tenement buildings, old and damp, with crumbling stone and dark cellars. The Dickensian descriptions come to mind, and the gloom and dreariness which he could convey so vividly are there in the imagination as soon as the word "slum" is read or recognised. In that sense Sophiatown is not, and never has been, a slum. There are no tenements: there is nothing really old: there are no dark cellars. Sometimes looking up at Sophiatown from the Western Native Township, across the main road, I have felt I was looking at an Italian village somewhere in Umbria. For you do "look up" at Sophiatown, and in the evening light, across the blue-grey haze of smoke from braziers and chimneys, against a saffron sky, you see close-packed, red-roofed little houses. You see, on the farthest skyline, the tall and [121/122] shapely blue-gum trees (which might be cypresses if it were really Italy). You see, moving up and down the hilly streets, people in groups: people with colourful clothes: people who, when you come up to them, are children playing, dancing and standing round the braziers. And above it all you see the Church of Christ the King, its tower visible north, south, east and west, riding like a great ship at anchor upon the grey and golden waves of the town beneath. In the evening, towards the early South African sunset, there is very little of the slum about Sophiatown. It is a human dwelling-place. It is as if old Sophia Tobiansky herself were gathering her great family about her: watching over them before they slept. Essentially Sophiatown is a gay place and, for all the occasional moments of violence and excitement, a kindly one too. But like every other place with a character, you have to live in it, to get the feel of its life, before you can really know it. And in the whole of South Africa there are only a handful of white citizens who have had that privilege. The decision to move the Western Areas; to destroy all the properties built there, and to transplant the whole population to Meadowlands, four miles farther away from the city, was taken by people who had no first-hand knowledge of the place at all. How could they be expected to know it, when in their eyes it represents the very antithesis of a sound "native policy"? Freehold rights and permanence: the building up of a living community; these things are contrary to the whole doctrine of apartheid. They assume that the African has a right to live in the city as well as to work in it. Such an assumption is heresy to Dr. Verwoerd. It cannot be allowed. But what is it that makes Sophiatown so [122/123] precious? Why should we care so much to preserve what, on any showing, is two-thirds a slum area? I have asked myself that question a thousand times as I have walked its streets, visited its people in their homes, taken the Blessed Sacrament to the sick and dying. I have asked it when the dust was flying and the wind tossing the refuse about in those sordid and over-crowded backyards, and I have asked it when, looking for someone at night, I have stumbled in the dark across children asleep on the floor, packed tight together beneath a table, to make room for others also to sleep. I have asked it when, on a blisteringly hot December day, the sun has beaten down on the iron ceiling of a shack and the heat has mercilessly pressed its substance upon that old, frail creature lying on the bed. I have asked it as I lay awake at night listening to the drunken shouts and the noisy laughter from the yard behind the Mission. In other words, I know Sophiatown at its worst: in all weathers, under all conditions, as a slum living up to its reputation. I still love it and believe it has a unique value. But why? In the first place, because it is not a "location." Part of the meaning of White South Africa's attitude to the African is revealed in that word "location." In America it generally has reference to part of the technique of the cinema industry. A film is made "on location" in order to give it the genuine flavour and atmosphere required by the story. But everywhere else in the world, so far as I know, the word just means a place; a site; a prescribed area. That is why, no doubt, it was chosen by the European when he decided that the African must have somewhere to live when he came to work in the towns and cities of his own country. He could not live in a suburb. He [123/124] could not live in a village. He could not live in the residential area of the town itself. He could only work in those places. And because he is an abstraction—"a native"— he must have an abstraction for his home. A "location" in fact: a place to be in, for so long as his presence is necessary and desirable to his European boss. A place from which to move on when it ceases to be necessary or desirable that he should stay. The "locations" of South Africa for the most part live up to their name. They are abstract, colourless places. Every town has one on its outskirts. To-day it is necessary by law that there should be a buffer strip at least five hundred yards wide between any location and the town it serves. There must be the same distance between a location and a main road. Nothing must be erected on the buffer strip— not even a pair of football goal-posts. It must mark that tremendous and vital distinction between civilisation and barbarism upon which the doctrine of white supremacy rests. No one of either race may linger on that strip of land, for in that way it might become a meeting-place. It is, in exact and literal terms, a no-man's-land: and it is meant to be just that. There is a noticeable and depressing simi-

larity about all locations. It is not only that, for the most part, the houses are built on mass-production lines and at the lowest cost compatible with minimum housing standards. It is that, at the same time, they are sited in the most monotonous way imaginable, as if to say: "There must be no variety in a location. Variety is a characteristic of the human being. His home is a reflection of that characteristic. But because the African is a native, it is a quality which simply does not exist.". . . [124/126]

Sophiatown is not a location. That is my first reason for loving it. It is so utterly free from monotony, in its siting, in its buildings and in its people. By a historical accident it started life as a suburb, changed its colour at an early moment in its career and then decided to go [126/127] all out for variety. A £3,000 building jostles a row of single-rooms: an "American" barber's shop stands next door to an African herbalist's store, with its dried roots and dust-laden animal hides hanging in the window. You can go into a store to buy a packet of cigarettes and be served by a Chinaman, an Indian or a Pakistani. You can have your choice of doctors and clinics even: for they also are not municipally controlled. There are churches of every denomination and of almost every imaginable sect. There is one, for example, known as "The Donkey Church," upon whose squat, square tower there stands in place of the traditional weathercock, an ass. I would not know its real origin, except that it is, I believe, a schism from the Methodist Church. Nor do I wish to suggest any approval for schism as such: for nothing has done so much damage to African Christianity than its fissiparousness. But somehow or other that little donkey represents the freedom that has existed down the years in Sophiatown. . . . [127/128] Basically White South Africa has the same benign or unbenign contempt for the African as man for the donkey. Was it not Smuts himself who said once that "the African has the patience of the ass"? And so Sophiatown is written off as a slum area: its values must be those of the slum: its people must be dirty, undesirable and, above all, unseen. Like the donkey that stands as a symbol above their streets, they are useful for their labour, for they are strong. But, as Dr. Verwoerd says, there is no place for them above that level in society itself. "I keep my secret still . . ." The secret of Sophiatown is not only its variety, it is its hidden heroisms, or rather its unknown heroes and heroines, its saints uncanonised and unsung. I know very many.

In the first place, let me say it frankly, any young person who keeps straight when the dice is loaded so heavily against him, needs virtue of a heroic quality. The over-crowded rooms of Sophiatown, wherein whole families must sleep and must perform all their human functions as best they may, do not make morality an easy thing. The lack of opportunity for fulfilling his personality in any productive way does not make it easy, either, for a lad to escape the street-corner gang and the excitement of gambling. The endless, grey vista of an existence which is based upon poverty is not the kind of outlook which helps to keep a boy or his girl-friend alive to ultimate standards of beauty, truth and goodness. Again and again, hearing confessions, I have asked myself how I could advise these children, how warn them, how comfort them when they have fallen. ". . . I have since sinned exceedingly in thought, word and deed, by my own fault, my own most grievous [128/129] fault. . . ." Have you *really*? No doubt the actual sin is grave enough; fornication or stealing or fighting, but what would I have done in your place? And whose fault is it in the sight of God? And what anyway, can I advise? "Don't let yourself get into bad company . . . don't be idle . . . find some other interest than gambling . . . love? Well, it's not so easy to describe it . . . it must have the quality of unselfishness." God forgive me! I find myself giving advice that, in those circum-

stances, I *know* I could not follow. And yet, again and again those gentle men and women: those fresh, gay lads and girls try to follow, try desperately hard to obey it, and even in their failures do not make environment or circumstance an excuse. To keep your self-respect when you are *expected* to have less than your white "baas"; to keep your home neat and tidy and to dress your children in fresh clothes; to pay for their school-books regularly and to see that they are fed properly. All this against a background of overcrowding, of the need to be up and away to work before you have time to eat your own breakfast or to clean the room that is your home. It needs the kind of virtue which most European Christians in South Africa have never come within a mile of. And it is common in Sophiatown. I do not refer just to our own church people, though naturally, they are the ones I know best and most intimately. There is, in that "black spot" (to use the Minister's offensive title) a great well of courage and cheerfulness in face of adversity which has been through the years an inspiration and a challenge to at least one Christian priest. . . . [129/133]

. . . I have said that Sophiatown is a gay place. It is more. It has a vitality and an exuberance about it which belong to no other suburb in South Africa: certainly to no white suburb. It positively sparkles with life. Sometimes when I have been depressed by the apparent success of the present Government in selling the idea of white supremacy, I have pulled myself up by thinking just for a moment or two of the African people as I know them in Sophiatown. There is something so robust and strong about their way of dealing with each frustration, which is each day, that it is even laughable to think that such an idea can endure. And in fact it is by laughter, so often, that the problems and the sorrows are fronted and overcome. It is by that magnificent sense of humour and by the fitness with which it is expressed that victory is won in the daily struggle, and will ultimately be won in the struggle for true nationhood. A good example of the kind of humour I have known and loved is to be seen in Sophiatown any week-end, when the "Sophiatown Scottish" are on the march. In the distance, on a Sunday afternoon, you will hear the beating of a drum and the sound of a far trumpet. Soon, at the farthest end of Victoria Road, you will see a small crowd moving towards you and becoming a large crowd as it moves. Then, if you are wise, you will wait, and witness the unique and heartening sight of an all-African all-female band: dressed in tartan kilts, white gloves, bandsman's staff and accoutrement, swinging down the road with marvellous gusto. Behind them will come the spectators, not marching in step but dancing with complete abandon, and, surrounding them, as [133/134] always when there's a sight, a crowd of the children, dancing, too, and singing as they dance. Somehow the "Sophiatown Scottish" stands for so much more than a happy Sunday afternoon. They stand for the joy and gaiety which is *there*, deep in the heart of the African and ready to break out in one form or another whenever and wherever he is at home. Another example of the same thing I have seen very often at political meetings, especially when European police are present to take names and to record speeches. What could so easily, in other circumstances, become a dangerously tense situation through the provocative and contemptuous attitude of the authorities, becomes a ridiculous and irrelevant matter. "After all," the Africans seem to say, "this is only an incident, and a minor one, in our progress to freedom and to fulfilment. Why not laugh at it, shrug it off with a song?" and so they do. Sophiatown! It is not your physical beauty which makes you so lovable; not that soft line of colour which sometimes seems to strike across the greyness of your streets: not the splendour of the evening sky which turns your drabness into gold—it is none of these things. It is your people. Yet somehow I do not think it can be the same when you yourself have been de-stroyed and your houses are just rubble and the factories begin to go up and to smother you with their bulk and size. Even though your people will still be here in Johannesburg, in the wide symmetry of some location such as Meadowlands, there will have been a loss immeasurable. The truth is that Sophiatown is a community: a living organism which has grown up through the years, and which has struck its roots deep in this particular place and in this special soil. So have I known it to be. A community with all [134/135] the ordinary problems of a community, and made up of people and families both bad and good. A community, not an abstraction, and therefore *personal* and real in all its aspects. And because it is an African community, living in a city of South Africa, it has to grow together in a unique way. Xosa and Mosotho, Shangaan and Motswana, Indian and Chinese, coloured and white, have all contributed something to it. And, in my opinion, they have all had something of value to contribute. The place is cosmopolitan in a real sense and has about it that atmosphere which belongs to cosmopolitan towns the world over. It is, in that sense, unique. The most unlikely and unexpected things can happen there and not appear at all unlikely or seem incongruous. So you have to be prepared, if you live in the midst of it as a priest, for every conceivable problem at every hour of the day or night. How, then, can you fail to love it?

A great deal is said by sociologists and others of "the breakdown of tribal custom" and "the disastrous impact of Western Industrialism upon the urban African." That sentence itself is stiff with the jargon of the race-relations text-book. But when you live in Sophiatown you don't see it that way at all. You see Mrs. X who has a drunken husband and five children to support—and what must she do? You see Mr. Y, whose wife left him two years ago and the kids are growing up; what is he to plan for them, can the "Father" help him? You see young Joel

who has just left school and got a "tea-
boy" job in the city, but he longs to do
his Matric. and can't find the time or the
money or the quietness for work that he
needs. You are called to that room in
Tucker Street, where Joseph is fighting
for his [135/136] life against advanced
TB. and in spite of all your efforts you
can't get a bed anywhere and you wonder,
well, you wonder what it all means within
the Providence of God. And you hear
that Jane has got into trouble and the
boy won't admit his fault; and you run
post-haste to see her father before he goes
out with a sjambok. . . . And then there's
George, arrested for carrying "dagga" and
there's Michael whom you've not seen for
weeks, but you hear he's drinking. . . . But
behind them all, behind the "problems"
which come the way of every priest in
every parish in Christendom, there is that
great mass of folk who live ordinary lives
in extraordinary conditions, and who *are*
the Christian community in Sophiatown.
And a more vital Christian community it
would be hard to find anywhere. I wonder,
for instance, how many parishes in England to-day would have a Mass in the
dark of a winter morning at half past five
and get a congregation of twenty or thirty
people? And that not just once, but week
after week? I wonder how many churches
to-day are full on Sunday morning at six
o'clock and again at eleven? Yet this is
but the outward form of something far
deeper and more profound. It is in fact
the answer to the sociologist's question
—at least it is part of the answer. The
only thing which is meeting the need for
a sense of "community," of "belonging,"
in the broken and shattered tribalism of
the town-dwelling African is the Church.
It is for that reason that these present
years of crisis are of such tremendous
significance. If the Church fails in bearing her witness on the colour question
now, she will never, in my opinion, have
a second opportunity. Here, in Sophiatown, over the past thirty years and more,
we have been engaged in building a Christian community. [136/137] It is that

community which is now being smashed
to pieces in the interests of a racial
ideology. And as we watch our people's
homes being reduced to heaps of rubble,
we watch also the destruction of something which cannot be built again so
easily or so fair. When Sophiatown is
finally obliterated and its people scattered,
I believe that South Africa will have lost
not only a place but an ideal.

> *"Day that I have loved, day that I
>   have loved,*
>   *The night is here. . . ."* [137/182]

. . . The first lorries began to move off
for Meadowlands eight miles away to the
west. The rain poured down. The removal was definitely under way. Two
thousand police, armed; many foreign
correspondents; dozens of photographers;
a total ban on all gatherings, including
(as was thought at the time) attendance at
a church service. All this, to effect a slum-
clearance scheme which would be of lasting benefit to the "natives"; all this to
carry through a plan which anyone could
see to be a good plan; all this excitement
and fuss and publicity over a project
which, to any sensible European in South
Africa was a crying necessity if white
civilisation was to be preserved. What
was it all about? What were the principles
involved? What was the Western Areas
Removal Scheme anyway? These questions
must be answered here in view of the
immense interest shown in this matter by
the world at large. Nothing, [182/183]
since Michael Scott's revelations about
farming conditions at Bethal, has made so
great an impact on the international Press.
Yet to-day, when the removal of 60,000
people to Meadowlands is proceeding
rapidly, and Sophiatown begins to look
like a blitzed area in London, the moral
and ethical implications of this scheme
are barely understood, and if once they
were debated, they are now forgotten. Yet
I believe that the Western Areas Removal
Scheme—to give it its official name—will

one day be recognised as a major issue of race-relations in South Africa. We would do well to learn the lessons it has to teach.

In the first place, the Removal Scheme is no new idea. It was not even the invention of the Nationalist Government. It emerged as soon as the white suburbs of Johannesburg began to spread westward and to make their first contact with old Tobiansky's "mixed" estate. It is now fifty years since Sophiatown was first occupied by Africans. It is over forty since New-clare (which is part of the Western Areas) was established and whites were specifically restricted from residing in the Township. It is nearly forty years since the Johannesburg Town Council was so convinced of the non-European nature of that part of the city that it built its own location, the Western Native Township, in the heart of the area, and ringed it with an iron fence. By 1920, no one would have questioned the fact that Sophiatown, Martindale and Newclare were and always would be black. And by 1920 the industrial expansion of Johannesburg had also begun, and the Africans drawn into the city as its labour force needed homes. They found them, as they must, in Sophiatown and its neighbourhood. What was more important to many of them, they found [183/184] an opportunity—rare indeed in urban Africa—for investment in real estate. Instead of living in a municipally-owned location, they could live on their own plot in their own homes. And their children, and their children's children could live there too. Freehold rights, even if amenities were lacking, were worth having. That was undoubtedly one of the great attractions of Sophiatown. The other was its nearness to the city. Instead of spending time and money on transport, as those who lived way out at Pimville Location had to do, they were within cycling distance of their work. Altogether it was a good place to be, combining the freedom of the country with the convenience of the town. And it was healthy, too, for it stood high on a ridge of rock and you could look away towards Pretoria over open, rolling country, where fresh breezes blew. The only problem, as the years passed, was that of overcrowding. Industry continued to respond, particularly when South Africa went off gold. Labour was needed for the factories and the business houses of the city in a big way. And it had to be black labour, for that alone was both cheap and plentiful. Unfortunately it did not occur to Johannesburg citizens that the labour force also had to live somewhere, had to have houses. One of the effects of the race situation in South Africa has always been that blindness. Labour is labour: it is not human, if it is black. It must be there, standing ready in your factory or your kitchen, or your office, but it must make no demands for the necessities of life: a roof-tree or an income large enough to support the home. It must have strong muscles for the job: but how they are to become strong is its own concern. It must have clean clothes and a tidy appearance in your [184/185] home: but it doesn't matter where or how it is to get the water for washing or the space for drying. So Johannesburg built its factories, its flats and its fun-fairs: it forgot to build houses for its African citizens. And Sophiatown, with its eighteen hundred "stands," began to crack at the seams with its growing population. There was some relief when another municipal location at Orlando was started. But that was needed far more rapidly than it was built. The density of population in Sophiatown continued to increase every year, even though new families moved into Orlando as soon as the houses were finished: even though there was soon a waiting-list of thousands registered with the civic authorities for vacant homes.

The expansion of Johannesburg was not restricted to its non-European labour force. The white population, too, increased, drawing men from the country by the same economic forces which have operated in every part of the world since the industrial revolution. And it chose to spread westward. New suburbs sprang up beyond Ferreirastown. Brixton, New-lands, Westdene: an encirclement of the non-European area had begun. White artisans occupied these suburbs for the most part: and in Westdene they were predominantly Afrikaners. By a strange irony, the group most strongly anti-African (because it has most to fear from African competition) occupied houses only a few yards from the last street in Sophiatown and looked across a strip of grass at the homes which had been es-tablished there. By 1937 the first sounds of battle were heard, and by 1939 a city councillor whose constituency abutted on Sophiatown demanded the total removal of all non-European "settlements" in the Western Areas. But [185/186] in view of the total failure of the City Council to build houses fast enough anywhere in Johannesburg to meet the needs of the African labour force, and also in view of the demands made on the country by the war, nothing was done. In 1944, a year after my arrival in Sophiatown, the Coun-cil approved in principle the removal of all Africans and coloureds from the area. But no attempt was made in the following years to implement the scheme, and no attempt was made either to proceed with slum-clearance or to build sufficient houses for those who desperately needed them. It was during the period 1944-1949 that the shanty towns emerged, and it was during that period also that the number of African families without any proper home reached catastrophic proportions. The idea of uprooting sixty thousand peo-ple who at least had a roof over their heads became ludicrous in view of the vast mass of the homeless who had to make do with shacks and shanties all round the western perimeter of the city.

The "problem" of the Western Areas was added to all the other "problems" of South Africa. But basically the issue was dead simple. It was just this: that white Johannesburg had encroached upon black Johannesburg, and so, naturally, black Johannesburg must move on. MUST MOVE ON. That is why the Western Areas Scheme

is so terribly important to the Christian: or rather, why it ought to be. An African freehold township, established for fifty years, can be uprooted and totally de-stroyed, because it is contiguous with a European suburb. The question of right or wrong does not have any relevance. The story of Naboth's vineyard rings no bell. Arguments soundly based on eco-nomics, or town-planning and on history, have no meaning [186/187] whatsoever. If a black township stands where a white suburb wants to stand, the township must go. We can think up a justification for it afterwards.

When the Malan Government was re-turned to power in 1948, it wasted no time in elevating the Western Areas Scheme to the level of national impor-tance. Mnr. Mentz, M.P., speaking in the House of Assembly, stated solemnly that "there is not a single strand of barbed wire between my constituency (Westdene) and Sophiatown." Obviously such an ap-palling danger to European security could not be allowed to continue any longer. The City Council was ordered to get a move on, and to implement its recom-mendations of 1944.

It should not be forgotten that during the long years when the removal scheme was under discussion by the authorities, it was never once discussed with the peo-ple who were going to be removed; with the ratepayers of Sophiatown who, though they paid their rates, had no other contact with the municipal authorities to whom they paid them than the privilege of pay-ing. For nearly twenty years the threat had hung over the Western Areas. Those who had invested their savings in homes for themselves and their children might lose everything: those who wanted some security, some assurance of a future, dared not risk basing it on such shifting founda-tions. Always, in those years, we were living in a place which was besieged by the forces of fear and uncertainty. It was this, added to the overcrowding, which imposed slum conditions on an area which, in every possible respect, was most suited to be and to remain an African suburb. It is not much of an encouragement to improve your property if, any morning, you open your newspaper and see headlines, "Western [**187/188**] Areas Plan Approved: Black Spots to be Removed." I am convinced, from my experience in Sophiatown, that a great deal of the crime and of the juvenile delinquency was directly due to this sense of insecurity. If you're going to lose what you've got anyhow, why worry too much about other people's rights and property? But that is another story.

Our chief difficulty in fighting the removal was two-fold. In the first place we had to demand, and to go on demanding, a genuine slum-clearance scheme. That is to say, the building of houses in a sufficient number at Orlando or elsewhere to make it possible for the sub-tenants of Sophiatown to move out and thus reduce the density of population to reasonable proportions. On the other hand, we had to keep the citizens of Johannesburg awake to the plain truth that the Government's scheme was not slum-clearance but robbery: robbery carried out in the interests of and under pressure from the neighbouring white suburbs: a political manoeuvre. The South African Institute of Race Relations called a conference in August, 1953, to which fifty-one organisations sent representatives. The Government and the City Council were also invited to attend. Both refused. "Such a conference," said the Secretary of State for Native Affairs, "should not take place . . . it will not in my opinion serve any useful purpose." Obviously, as in every other issue affecting the African people, the Government had no intention of consultation and no desire to hear their point of view. THEY MUST MOVE. Being natives, the Government always knows what is best for them, and does it.

Soon after this, a group of us, including Helen Navid, formed the Western Areas Protest Committee, of which [**188/189**] I was chairman, and went into the fight for the conscience of Johannes-burg. It was our aim to work in the closest conjunction with the African National Congress and the Transvaal Indian Congress. They were to organise the people in the Areas themselves: we were to reach the European suburbs and try to educate the white citizens on the true implications of the Scheme. Our hope was that in this way we might at least succeed in forcing the City Council to refuse to co-operate with the Government. In the meanwhile the Bishop of Johannesburg and the Citizens' Housing League were attacking the Council fiercely and persistently over its failure to build houses. It was not too difficult to point to the "Shelters" at Orlando and to the Moroka Emergency Camp and to show that at least ninety thousand people were living under slum conditions quite obviously worse than anything in Sophiatown: and these slums were municipally owned. What WAS difficult, was to make Johannesburg realise that there were moral issues involved: for ninety per cent of its people had never seen the places we were talking about and could not care less what happened to them.

We campaigned in the suburbs, with varying success. But at least we made some progress: we made the city aware of the possible dangers involved in a compulsory removal scheme. After a great deal of shilly-shally the Council announced that it would not co-operate with the Government.

Dr. Verwoerd reacted promptly and characteristically by creating a new local authority with plenary powers which would be directly responsible to him for carrying through his plans. The "Black Spot" of Sophiatown became for the Native Affairs Department its chief [**189/190**] priority. Every possible use was made of propaganda to prove that those who opposed the removal were in fact opposing slum-clearance; and Meadowlands—the area chosen for the new location—became a symbol of all the paternal charity and foresight which Dr. Verwoerd so loves to proclaim as the fruit of an apartheid policy. This was exactly what the conscience of Johannesburg was waiting for: to be able to relax again in the comforting thought that, after all, Sophiatown was a filthy slum: Meadowlands would be a tidy and controlled location. The natives would be better off, even if they had lost freehold rights, even if they had to travel farther to their work, even if they were now in a place where Government regulations and restrictions could be most vigorously imposed. It became increasingly difficult for us to get a favourable Press. And naturally in consequence it became difficult to maintain European opposition. In Sophiatown itself, Congress carried on a campaign of public meetings (always attended by the political branch of the C.I.D.) and of house-to-house visits. But they, too, were running into great practical difficulties. It was all very well to explain to people the meaning of the removal and the loss of rights it must entail. It was more difficult to work out any constructive plan of opposition: for, if people resisted removal to Meadowlands, at least some alternative accommodation must be provided. And in the Western Areas there had been no accommodation for years.

Such was the position when, in February, the Government acted. It acted with great efficiency, with overwhelming force and with a surprise move, two days earlier than was expected. Perhaps we had done our [190/191] job more effectively than we knew, for the Press of the world was there on that February morning, and if South Africa and Johannesburg were largely unconcerned, Sophiatown became for a time world news.

I think many people expected violent resistance to the removal, and were surprised when the lorries moved off to Meadowlands so safely and with such apparently happy travellers. I was attacked in the House of Assembly by both the Minister of Native Affairs and the Minister of Justice for having attempted to invite gangsterism and to encourage the use of armed force. Although I challenged

the two Ministers to repeat their statements outside the privileged forum of Parliament, neither did so. Nor did any of my ecclesiastical superiors (the Bishop of Johannesburg was away in England at the time) attempt to come to my defence. Indeed I cannot honestly say that in the whole struggle for the upholding of principle and the resistance to oppression which the removal meant to us, there was any very noticeably Christian opposition to the scheme. And as soon as the move to Meadowlands had begun, the Press and the people of Johannesburg made every effort to justify what they had both previously condemned. The seduction of power had worked effectively once more.

As I write these words, some thousands have left Sophiatown (the Government claims ten thousand) and have settled in the new location. Many of the streets are becoming heaps of rubble. The squalid shelters, the sordid rooms have been pulled down and the places where they stood lie open to the sun and to the sky. Beside them also lie the remains of houses which I have also known, where families lived happily and in pride of ownership. The good and the bad are destroyed [191/192] together: their occupants live in the neat monotony of Meadowlands.

I do not weep for the destruction of the material which was Sophiatown. At least two-thirds of it would have to be destroyed in any scheme for the renewing of that area which we always dreamed might come to pass. I do not weep, either, simply because what I have known and greatly loved is no more. Living through two world wars at least teaches one a measure of detachment and is a reminder to all men that "here we have no abiding city." Nor do I condemn Meadowlands as a place to live. It has a pretty name. It is a pleasant site. And if you are used to locations, I suppose it bears comparison with any other. At least it is just as dull. But I weep because the Western Area Removal Scheme, and the uprooting of sixty thousand people, is being carried out with the connivance of the Christian conscience of Johannesburg. I weep because in spite of all we have tried to do, we have failed so utterly to uphold principle against prejudice, the rights of persons against the claims of power.

"But after all, Padre," said a B.B.C. correspondent sent to make a recording for his programme, "you must admit that Sophiatown was a slum. It was a jolly good thing it was cleared away. And I've seen Meadowlands: it's fine. They're quite happy. What are freehold rights anyway? Surely the principle isn't as important as all that? And most of the property in Sophiatown was mortgaged too. Don't you think all the fuss was a bit of a mistake? Was it fair? Is the Government always wrong?" I should have liked to answer those questions over the air. But apparently that was not considered desirable. Now, when the removal is to [192/193] most people a thing of the past, it is a little late to make comments. Yet, late or not, I must try for the sake of the future, and for the sake of truth itself.

Sophiatown WAS a slum. Those of us who have lived there would never wish to deny that. We have seen with our own eyes the heroism of so many of our own Christian people in their battle to fight and to overcome their environment. It would be treason to them to deny that Sophiatown was a slum. But slum conditions can be removed without the expropriation of a whole area. Indeed the greatest experts in town-planning would agree that only in the last resort should you uproot people from the place they know as home: for in such uprooting you destroy not only the fabric of their houses, you destroy a living organism—the community itself. Sophiatown, then, could have been replanned and rebuilt on the same site: a model African suburb. It could have been, but for the pressure of three things. First, the pressure of white opinion and the political force it represented; secondly, the existence of freehold tenure, and the threat of permanence which it implied; thirdly, that which underlies every event of any

racial significance in South Africa: the assumption that white "civilisation" is threatened by the very existence of an African community in any way similar to itself. The African in the kraal is in his right place: so is the African in the kitchen. But the African in a "European" suburb, in a "European" house which he himself owns and is proud of: he is a menace: he must be removed.

They are happy in Meadowlands. I do not doubt it. For even in a location you can have your family and your friends about you, and that is a home of sorts, [193/194] even if it is not your own. And maybe it is a far better home than the single room or the corrugated-iron shack that you have left. But beneath your happiness you know, or perhaps you only feel without knowing, a deeper uncertainty and a more profound unrest.

You have been moved to Meadowlands to-day. Where will you be moved to tomorrow? When white Johannesburg once more creeps up to your doorstep and you in turn become a threat to its peace and to its security, what will happen? Where does the process stop? It never stops in South Africa. There is no rest, no permanence, no future you can be sure of: for domination is an insatiable hunger. It is never satisfied, for it is never certain of itself. It can never rest, for it never knows its own final end or purpose. They are happy in Meadowlands. All right, all right, let us admit it. But one day Sophiatown will be a white suburb: or perhaps a white industrial zone, with factories and workshops standing where the rubble now lies. Its life as an African township will be forgotten. Perhaps only the names of Tobiansky's children at the street corners will remind men of its past. But it will be stolen property. And nothing that man can do will alter that. Nor, I believe, will the African people ever forget it: however happy they may be in Meadowlands, however long the years since that February morning when an army came to Sophiatown and destroyed it for ever.

You Are Wrong, Father Huddleston*

ALEXANDER STEWARD (1917—   ) was born in South Africa and spent his childhood in Zululand. He was on the crime beat of the *Rand Daily Mail* in Johannesburg and since then has served abroad with the Department of External Affairs, in Kenya, the territories of the African subcontinent, and North America. He is currently Director of Information at South Africa House in London.

. . . .
It was in the neighbourhood of Port Elizabeth that the process had its far-away beginnings, for it was there that White men and Black men first met. The Europeans had established themselves in the southern extremity of the continent in the mid-seventeenth century, and the Bantu were in the northern parts of what is now the Union in the 16th century. The Europeans moved north-east along the coast, and the Bantu south-west, and in the mid-eighteenth century they came into contact. For many decades there were clashes along the ill-defined border that separated them and then, in despair of a satisfactory solution, the White frontier farmers struck north, away from civilisation, into the hinterland. There, in largely uninhabited country, they established the Orange Free State and Transvaal Republics.

For a long time after that the White people and the Black continued, broadly speaking, to occupy the land which they themselves had chosen in their respective migrations. During these decades South Africa was a predominantly agricultural country, and in the beginning there was the space and the opportunity for the various groups to live their own lives, in their own way, in their own areas. But with the civilised techniques which the White man brought, the population increased fast. Then diamonds were discovered and then gold. Steel and power industries were established to exploit the mineral resources of which South Africa has so many, and factories sprang up to process the raw materials. An industrial revolution began, and it is continuing to-day.

This development was necessary for the country's economic well-being, but it shattered the old, easy going pattern. White, Black and Brown were thrown together, often by forces over which they had little control, and a new phase in race relations had begun.

Port Elizabeth, with all its industrial attraction, was one of the first cities to feel the effect of the revolution. Bantu streamed in from the neighbouring Reserves—their [32/33] traditional home—to the new and glamorous centres of employment. Members of other races, Coloureds and Indians, joined them—and when plague broke out at the turn of the century, Port Elizabeth became acutely aware of the social implications of industrialisation.

The epidemic might have been anticipated, but industrialisation and urbanisation were a new phenomenon in South Africa; and as the subsequent history of South Africa (and of all other industrialised countries) has shown, it is one that raises the most complex and intractable problems.

* Alexander Steward, from *You Are Wrong, Father Huddleston* (London: John Lane, The Bodley Head, 1956), pp. 32—35, 39—40, 41—42, 44—45, 46—49, 69—74. Reprinted with the permission of Howard B. Timmins, publisher.

And so all the conditions for plague were there. In the five non-White locations, the over-crowded houses had been thrown together with old corrugated iron, rotten boards, tattered cloth and paraffin tins. The disease spread rapidly, and the 8,000 inhabitants had to be moved out—within 24 hours. When they had gone fire was let loose among their shacks. The plague was halted but the people had nowhere to go. There had been no time to build other accommodation, so they trekked over the city boundary, and at a place called Korsten they built more shanties very much the same as those the rats had infested and the flames had burnt down.

* * * * *

They multiplied fast. Within a generation their numbers had doubled, and misery kept pace. In 1918 there was the world influenza epidemic. In Cape Town, Parliament passed a new Housing Act, and, assisted by it, the Port Elizabeth Council began building homes for its citizens. But they were homes for those who could afford to pay an economic rent, and for the bulk of the non-White people they offered no solution.

For a long time South Africa continued to minimise the implications of what was going on. Legislators toyed with the situation. They believed that somehow or other things would right themselves, that this was a passing phase: that a regulation here, an administrative control there, would be enough.

Meanwhile, the industrial expansion of Port Elizabeth continued. Great automobile companies established their assembly plants there; more and more jobs became available, [33/34] and so more and more people came to Korsten. Overcrowding and higher rents hurried after one another, and so did squalor and unhappiness and disease and crime. There was a boom in the illicit liquor trade. Every device for securing and storing supplies was used, and the trade was the more difficult to control because of the presence in Kor-

sten of Coloureds who, unlike the Bantu, were allowed to buy liquor.

Aggravating the whole sorry situation was the friction between the race groups that had been thrown together.

"There were a few Whites in Korsten," Mr. Schauder explains, "but the really difficult racial antagonisms were those which existed between the non-White elements themselves. There, in that mass of humanity, lived Bantu and Coloureds with some Indians and Chinese thrown in for good measure. The Bantu heartily disliked the Coloureds, Indians and Chinese. The Coloureds were strongly prejudiced against the Bantu but tolerated the Indians and Chinese, while the Indians and Chinese considered themselves superior to both the Bantu and the Coloureds.

"I ask you frankly," says Mr. Schauder, "how should an idealistic man or woman tackle such a problem?"

It seemed to many of the inhabitants of Port Elizabeth that the problem was past tackling. And there were powerful vested interests who did all they could to prevent a solution. They were the professional agitators and the landlords who had this in common—that the elimination of the slum would close down their respective businesses. They had their pawns whom they pushed out into the limelight and into trouble; and generally it seemed that only a miracle could save the situation.

* * * * *

Well, despite the alliance of racketeer and agitator, the miracle has happened. A great Bantu town has arisen at Port Elizabeth in the place of Korsten which gives hope to all who see it. It gave hope to Mr. A. Z. Baker, head of Rotary International, when he saw it in the beginning of 1956. "Flowers, trees and sparkling cleanliness make it a joy to behold," he said.

Shining homes now shelter some 35,000 people there. [34/35] Among the facilities are modern sanitation, electric light, playgrounds, children's crèches, churches, halls, a swimming pool, a social centre, special homes for old people and free medical attention for all. A Bantu child can go from nursery school to matriculation without leaving the township, and his parents are provided with unlimited electric power at a flat rate of 2s. a month —water and sanitation being free. Round the individual properties the municipality has planted 65 miles of hedges, and it has built 45 miles of roads, 95 miles of sidewalks and 45 miles of sewerage.

Responsible for the achievement is the common sense of the South African people who to-day make available some £30,000,-000 a year for the upliftment of the non-White groups—that and the tireless efforts of men like Mr. Schauder.

In a lifetime of non-partisan service and achievement this Austrian-born South African has accumulated a vast experience of the problems of urbanisation, and his are the sort of views—unbiased, practical, tested—that are worth listening to.

"Fifty years of experience have proved to me beyond doubt," he says, "that nothing but evil can come from mixing the races. Each racial group, instead of benefiting from the particular cultural or national virtues of the others, in practice picks up only the vices. In Korsten the various groups mated indiscriminately to produce new combinations of mixed offspring who grew up to be a greater social problem than their parents.

"The result of the experiment in free race mixture was a gross failure. It was at this point we had to become realists. We separated the races into different townships. The success of the project is already evident, and it has been recognised not only by ourselves but equally by experts and friends from overseas. Our experience in Port Elizabeth in this great social experiment has proved that the separation of the races has been the greatest blessing that we could confer on all concerned."

. . . .

[35/39] What happened at Port Elizabeth represents a process which was taking place, in various stages of advancement, in cities and towns throughout the country. And in the immediate post-war years Mr. Schauder's question was being asked on all sides—How shall we tackle this problem?

The issue was put to the electorate in 1948, and the answer was Apartheid.

Apartheid, says Father Huddleston, is un-Christian, an insult to God himself. Time and again in his book he condemns the policy. He attacks it with all the old, familiar generalisations, but nowhere is there a reasoned exposition of the conditions which surround it or of the principles and intentions and facts which motivate it.

Nor is any attempt made to define a practical alternative.

In this, more than anything else, the emptiness of Father Huddleston's case is disclosed.

Here is a man who has seen fit to discredit and blacken the policy of South Africa in the eyes of millions. Here is a man who has set himself up, after twelve years in a Johannesburg slum, as the arbiter of a nation's destiny. But what is his answer to the burning question—How shall we tackle this problem? He gives none. He gives no practical guide or help or encouragement to those who must face and control the realities of the South African situation. His argument is destructive and hollow through and through. In reply to the basic challenge, to what must be done, he offers a profound vacuum echoing only with self-righteous and pious platitudes.

Even where he makes lengthy and detailed attacks on specific aspects of policy, such as the Pass Laws, he suggests no practical alternative. And what *is* the alternative to the Pass Laws? No-one likes them —least of all those who have to administer them. In recent years they have been greatly simplified and numerous expert inquiries have been [39/40] made as to the feasibility of eliminating them. But in present circumstances they simply cannot be eliminated. Where large numbers of people flock to densely populated centres, many of them illiterate, many without employment and many without permanent homes, some form of identification is indispensable. It must be there in the interests of Black and White alike. It is necessary for maintaining law and order, and that is the first duty of any responsible authority.

However, the main issue is not the Pass Laws but the over-all policy which the country must pursue. It is impossible to meet Father Huddleston in this essential area of the controversy because he has shied clear of it. But his defection has its advantage—the field is left open for a calm and uninterrupted examination.

. . . .
[40/41] . . . .
In South Africa, as we have seen, the White man and the Black man arrived at approximately the same time: the Black man somewhat earlier in the north-eastern regions and the White man somewhat earlier in the south-western. The White man brought with him the potentiality of enriching the country; the Black man, because particularly of his unscientific methods of agriculture, the potentiality of impoverishing it. Since then the country has been enriched. Where, a hundred years ago there was brutal tribal warfare, there is to-day peace and order; corn waves to-day where [41/42] there were bloody massacres only yesterday, and where there was famine and ignorance among the Black people there is now food and fast-spreading enlightenment.

Perhaps nowhere in the world has so small a group of men brought into being so progressive a state. The enterprise of a community no larger than that of a London suburb has developed a country twice the size of France; it has built 13,000 miles of railways and roads as fine as any —one of them 1,250 miles long. It brings gold from two miles beneath the earth's surface and raises cities as modern as America's. South Africa, in addition to being the world's largest producer of gold, is the largest producer in the Southern Hemisphere of electric power, coal and cement and the second largest producer of steel: South Africa is developing industrially faster to-day than any other country, with the exception of Western Germany. South Africa has produced scientists of international repute, statesmen who help shape the course of history, poets and writers who are read throughout the English-speaking world and elsewhere.

*   *   *   *   *

In much of this the assistance and co-operation of the Bantu people has been indispensable; but it is the White man who has provided the initiative, the guidance, the dynamic power. And behind this achievement is the fact that South Africa is the South African's only home. He has been inspired by a motive that cannot be shared by the ablest administrators who have their homes elsewhere, and this inspiration has led also to the creation of his own language, his own religion and his own system of law. For him there is no possibility of withdrawal; there is, and can be, no other home. There is no force on earth (let alone a boycott of South African sportsmen as suggested by Father Huddleston) which will persuade him to adopt policies which will endanger his only home.

Thus, in those parts of Africa with permanently settled White communities, and particularly in South Africa, there are only two possible conclusions—assimilation or separation. . . . [42/44]
. . . .
Economic assimilation contains many hazards for White and Black alike. For the White man it would represent a persistent threat to his civilised standard of living because for a long time the Bantu will be prepared to sell his labour for wages considerably lower than the White man requires to maintain that standard. And here it is interesting to observe that, in and out of South Africa, the more skilled workers tend to resist the infiltration into their ranks of the less skilled.

Commenting on this in the *Handbook of Race Relations,* H. J. Simons writes: "To the trade unionist with overseas experience, much of what appears to be inter-racial friction (in the Union) is recognisable as a somewhat aggressive form of the familiar conflict between skilled, semi-skilled and unskilled workers, or between unions organised on a craft basis and those organised for all workers in a given industry. Of the British Trade Unions, for example, it has been said that 'the skilled unions virtually claim the right to do such work as they think fit, and, so far as they can enforce their claim, to exclude the less skilled where they think fit.' " [44/45]

In South Africa, because of historic controls, the more skilled workers are white and the less skilled, black. Thus a policy of economic assimilation would give to what is a normal phenomenon of labour relations the appearance, in South Africa, of racialism.

Dr. P. A. W. Cook, professional adviser for Bantu education, says on this point: "Most trade unions in South Africa do not admit Natives to their ranks and as a consequence the Native who has completed a five year course in an industrial school finds it difficult to establish himself as a tradesman in an urban area. European employers tend not to recognise such training and offer wages very little better than those offered to the untrained . . . . Briefly, the opportunities for employment are too restricted to encourage the growth of industrial education to any great extent."

For his part, the Bantu is not acquainted with the machinations of Trade Unionism and he would understandably believe that he was being deprived of opportunities to advance himself simply because he is black.

But the disadvantages for the Bantu of economic assimilation go much deeper than any action which skilled unions might take to protect the position of their members. The fact is that in a mixed society the less developed people are con-

tinually handicapped. In such a society the Bantu, whether he is a shopkeeper, a lawyer, a doctor or a plumber, would find the competition of the White man, or the Indian, overwhelming. The advantages which the more advanced groups enjoyed would impose a rigid ceiling to the realisation of his aspirations. . . . [45/46]

. . . .

And so it is necessary to take a look for a moment at race prejudice. Above all things a successful policy for [46/47] South Africa must face the realities of human nature, and one of those realities is the expression in certain circumstances of race prejudice. This may be deplored, but it cannot be ignored. Given certain circumstances race prejudice operates among many people in many countries.

Molema (the grandson of a Bantu chief) remarks in his book, *The Bantu,* that he is often struck by the way well-informed people in Britain minimise the gravity and reality of race prejudice and misunderstand its nature. But people who live in South Africa and the United States, he comments, know the facts. He points out that colour antagonism is most acute in those parts of the United States where the Negroes are concentrated, whereas the 'feeling' hardly exists in the Northern States where the Negroes are seen only in isolated numbers. He comes to the conclusion: "It seems clear that the first necessary condition for the production of race conflict is that two races differing greatly in strength and civilisation shall live side by side, *both in large numbers,* and be brought into constant contact."

This is the opinion of a South African Bantu, and it indicates an important feature of prejudice: namely, that it is caused not by any kind of race contact, but by a particular kind. Many contacts are pleasant and stimulating. The foreigner visiting Paris is charmed at the difference of the Parisian; the European travelling in Asia is fascinated by the strangeness of the people about him; close friendships at universities between students of different races are common.

Moreover, race contact, particularly between civilised and backward people, has time and again called forth high qualities of service and humanitarianism which otherwise might not have expressed themselves. Of this the record of missionaries, administrators, educators and welfare workers among the Black people of Africa, and among backward people all over the world, is strong proof. And the friendly and kindly treatment of individual Black people by individual White people throughout South Africa is more proof. There is scarcely a White family in the land that cannot speak with deep affection of one or other, or more, of the Black people it has known.

And so it is perhaps too harsh a judgment of humanity (and particularly of White men in Africa) to assume that [47/48] contact between members of different races necessarily has unpleasant manifestations. Prejudice is, as a rule, the result of a special kind of contact—one in which the presence of one group threatens the identity, the institutions, the culture, the standard of living or the general way of life of the other.

A socially assimilated society in South Africa would provide the condition described by Molema: There would be two races differing greatly in strength and civilisation living side by side, both in large numbers, and being brought into constant contact with one another. The threat would be there day after day and year after year, and with such an association manifesting itself in prejudice there could be no possibility of harmony.

In circumstances such as these men will not respond to a call to love their neighbour. They are too imperfect: they must be given help to enable their affection to overcome their misgivings. This help can, and in South Africa's conditions must, come from the State: and it can be given by ensuring as far as possible that the presence and progress of one group will not threaten the position of the others.

Moreover, the removing of the threat to the separate existence of White and Black would have, not only the negative effect of lessening prejudice, but also the positive effect of releasing the great reservoir of goodwill that there is, throughout Africa, among the White men for the Black. With proper arrangement and control race distinction could cease to be a source of friction and become one of inspiration.

Another important social implication which policy must take into account is the shattering impact which urbanisation has made on the Bantu personality.

The whole world knows that one of the effects of South Africa's industrialisation was the creation at its main centres of employment of slums and shanty towns. Journalists, novelists, commentators, film producers and priests have been proclaiming this fact in season and out for years. And it is true that many of the physical conditions which have resulted from haphazard urbanisation are deplorable. These, however, can be removed and (as I shall show later) are being removed.

It is the psychological and sociological effect of the situation that is more serious and more difficult to remedy [48/49] — and it is doubtful whether it could be remedied at all without an intimate knowledge of the whole history and background of the Bantu people.

We have seen how, for hundreds and thousands of years, the Bantu lived out his life as a member of a most closely-knit unit, the tribe, and how he was peculiarly dependent, physically and spiritually, upon his place within it. Suddenly he has left it. He has been rocketed into the outer space of a totally alien environment, and in the cities he and his two million fellows have become a hopelessly fragmented, inchoate mass of humanity.

The outside observers are, of course, aware of this; and time and again one hears their charge (which Father Huddleston repeats) that the White man's policies have broken down the tribal structure of the Bantu and "put nothing in its place." The charge is devoid of meaning. One might as well accuse a European government of failing "to put something in the place" of yesterday's concept of marriage and family life. The fact is that such things cannot be arranged and legislated for—they are simply not "puttable." They are organic, with an existence of their own, and all that can be done is to provide an environment for their being and growth.

The assimilation of the Bantu into European society would provide the most unlikely of all environments for the creation and growth of something to take the place of the traditions, customs, sanctions and security of the old Bantu tribe.

* * * * *

It was considerations such as these that were engaging the attention of South Africans in the immediate post-war years. The industrial revolution of their country, about which they had been hearing and reading for a long time, had become a demonstrable fact. It confronted them and surrounded them and there was no escaping its implications.

The nation knew now, beyond doubt, that it was at the cross-roads. In 1948 it was asked to choose its direction. It chose separation, and the notice that went up was "Apartheid." [49/69]

. . . During a visit to a new Bantu township on the Witwatersrand at the end of 1954, I saw the combined effect of these two Apartheid Acts. We were making a general tour of the township when we came upon a house in the course of construction. It was larger than most of the others and I noticed it especially on account of the two handsome bay windows which faced the road. There was a Bantu in white overalls standing in what was to be the front garden surveying the operations. I asked him if it was his house. He said no, he was the contractor and that he was building it for the grocer up the road—a Bantu whose shop I had probably seen earlier in the tour. I asked him how business was. He didn't say it was flourishing, but he smiled neverthe-

less with satisfaction when he told me that he was busy on another 14 (I think it was) properties. He took me round the house and showed me with a good deal of justifiable pride the workmanship of his team of Bantu artisans.

This is the new promise which Apartheid holds out: a Bantu building contractor, a Bantu grocer, Bantu artisans and Bantu homes *at a cost which the Bantu can afford*. Before Apartheid, the contractor would have been White, the grocer would have been a Chinese or an Indian, the artisans would have been White, the labourers would have been Bantu—and the home would have been priced far beyond the Bantu's means.

Father Huddleston is rightly concerned at the inadequacy of houses for Bantu in Johannesburg: but he leaves the impression that the cause of the shortage was the indifference of the Europeans. The true cause, however, was not disinterest but interest—interest on the vast capital sums involved. The Bantu could not afford to pay economic rentals for homes built with expensive White labour; and the country, and especially the ratepayers, simply did not have the resources to go on endlessly subsidising them. Until 1949, virtually all Bantu housing was sub-economic; the situation demanded over 30,000 new homes a year, and [69/70] the enormous subsidy-bill which, on the old basis, was involved was simply beyond the capacity of the nation to pay.

* * * * *

Since the country was given direction in 1948 the entire approach to Bantu housing has been revolutionised. The aim now is economic housing and it has been brought within reach by the training and employment of skilled Bantu labour and by the tireless work of the National Building Research Institute in reducing construction costs (and so successful have the scientists been, that their designs are used as the basis of low-cost housing schemes in other parts of Africa and in other parts of the world).

And with the building of homes placed on a sound economic basis, it became economically possible for more money to be made available. During the years 1953–55, the Minister of Health approved schemes costing over £14,000,000; and in the period 1951–54, 21,131 houses were completed. This brought the number of approved homes for Bantu in the 16 main cities and towns to 88,184, of which 32,054 were owned by Bantu. And the number is being added to by, literally, scores daily. By the middle of June last year, Pretoria alone was building 15 houses a day and Johannesburg, 12. (The over-all total of new homes for Bantu during the 1951–54 period, including those built by municipalities, was 50,922.)

In addition to this programme of home building, the Government has evolved what is termed the "site-and-service" scheme under which a levy on employers of Bantu finances the provision of essential services to plots in planned areas where Bantu may build their own homes. This new departure is still in its initial stages but there are signs that it will be an all-important factor in making up the backlog of 353,000 houses over the next ten years. It is expected soon to be solving the problems of 10,000 Bantu families each year in Johannesburg alone; and a Bantu trader in that city recently announced his intention to build a £1,000 "site-and-service" house.

Thus, by any standards, a vast programme of Bantu housing is being pushed ahead. Meadowlands, with its plan for 16,000 homes, is an important part of the pro- [**70/71**] gramme—however, it is only a part. But Father Huddleston sees only Meadowlands, and from the beginning this model township was for him a sinister thing. And why?—because it was to replace the Sophiatown which he had come to love so deeply.

*   *   *   *   *

There are many actions and attributes of Father Huddleston which most South Africans regard as unpardonable: but his attachment to the ugly, sprawling slum of Sophiatown is ·something different— moving, pathetic and difficult, though not impossible, to understand. Father Huddleston has invoked Freud in his judgment of South Africans, and his own attitude to Sophiatown can be explained only by some means such as this. Sophiatown is ugly, most of it horribly ugly. I have seen it and that is what ninety-nine out of every hundred people who have seen it would say.

But Father Huddleston writes of it in ecstatic phrases. Here are some of them, together with their contradictions:

"Sophiatown, how hard it is to capture and to convey the magic of that name! . . . . I cannot put my memories on paper, or, if I do so, they will only be like the butterflies pinned, dead and lustreless, on the collector's board . . . . And above it all you see the Church of Christ the King, its tower visible, north, south, east and west, riding like a great ship at anchor upon the grey and golden waves of the town beneath . . . . Why should we care so much to preserve what, on any showing, is two-thirds a slum area? I know Sophiatown at its worst: in all weather, under all conditions, as a slum living up to its reputation. I still love it and believe it has a unique value . . . . The overcrowded rooms of Sophiatown, wherein whole families must sleep and must perform all their human functions as best they may, do not make morality an easy thing . . . . So you have to be prepared if you live in the midst of it as a priest, for every conceivable problem at every hour of the day or night. How, then, can you fail to love it? . . . . You are home, your children are around you—ten of them, a hundred, a thousand: you belong to them and they will never let you forget it. How then can you fail to love the place where [**71/72**] such things happen? Its dusty, dirty streets and its slovenly shops, its sprawling and unplanned stretches of corrugated iron roof: its foetid and insanitary yards."

These are not the remarks of a man observing things on the normal plane: they are not the reactions of a reasoning man. Father Huddleston's views cannot be reconciled for a moment with logic. It is absurd to contend that because a man experiences love in a slum, that the slum is therefore beautiful. One might as well argue that because a nurse in a leper institute wins the love of her patients, leprosy is thereby justified.

Father Huddleston's attitude to Sophiatown cannot be explained in ordinary terms—his is the approach of the poet or the mystic. He sees ugliness as beauty (though the slum-dwellers don't), and the transforming agent *for him* is love. Love, as he himself so clearly illustrates, is the very essence of his relationship with Sophiatown. He tells how he won the love of the people there. And Meadowlands— the moving of them to another place— meant that he would lose it. It was the flock being led beyond the reach of the shepherd. The pastures there might be better, but nevertheless they were beyond his reach.

In some such terms as these one can understand Father Huddleston's attitude: but understanding it detracts little from the damage which he proceeded to do to goodwill among the races in South Africa and to the Union's name abroad. He had powerful friends in Britain and in the publicity world, and soon another sad chapter was being added to the misrepresentation of South African policy at home and abroad. The extent to which it is believed, is a measure of the degree in which public opinion towards South Africa has been poisoned. That is the real tragedy: that the romantic notions of this man could, and can, be taken seriously: for on the face of it, how can the removal of a slum be an oppressive action? But that is what the world was given to believe, and that is what it believed.

*   *   *   *   *

For weeks before the first families moved from Sophiatown to their new homes, feeling was being whipped up and the whole project was being represented as evidence [72/73] of a heartless, fascist tyranny. Newsmen and commentators converged on Johannesburg from far and near.

I went around Meadowlands one day with a Fleet Street man, and we had as our guide the official who was in over-all charge of the construction programme. The reporter asked him a lot of questions, and at one stage the official said, in more or less these words: "Now look, I want you to get one thing quite clear. I'm not a politician. I've never taken part in any politics—and I'm a member of the Anglican Church like Father Huddleston. But my main business is building houses for Natives. I've been doing it for years. When the Minister called me in and asked me if I'd take on this job I said yes. I said yes for one reason only—because I knew it was in the best interests of the Natives."

The official was asked whether he was expecting any difficulty when the move began. He said his main difficulty was that people not entitled to homes in Meadowlands were trying to get them: they were moving into Sophiatown and setting themselves up there so as to qualify. Later, soon before we parted, the correspondent asked him whether he expected any trouble—rioting and that sort of thing. The official said he didn't: numerous similar projects had been carried through without trouble.

"But *may* there be trouble?" the correspondent asked.

"Well of course there *may* be trouble. Anything *may* happen, especially after all this talk and publicity that's been going on."

The reporter turned on me. "You know what it is," he said. "You know what'll happen to my story if there's no suggestion of trouble in it. It'll be spiked."

As it happened there was no trouble when the families moved; and after all the fuss was over, a B.B.C. correspondent visited Father Huddleston and (according to *Naught For Your Comfort*) said: "But

after all, Padre, you must admit that Sophiatown was a slum. It was a jolly good
thing it was cleared away. And I've seen
Meadowlands: it's fine. They're quite
happy. What are freehold rights anyway?
Surely the principle isn't as important as
all that? And most of the property in Sophiatown was mortgaged too. Don't you
think all the fuss was a bit of a [**73/74**]
mistake? Was it fair? Is the Government
always wrong?"

Father Huddleston comments that he
would have liked to answer these questions over the air "but apparently that
was not considered desirable." Well, pre-
sumably after due thought, he has answered them now on pages 193 and 194 of
his book—and his answers do not make
convincing reading. His main arguments
appear to be that Sophiatown should have
been broken down but rebuilt in the same
place (though, I believe, he makes no
claim to be a town planner): that
Meadowlands may, in turn, one day be
moved (though there is not the slightest
evidence for this); that Sophiatown is
stolen property (though all properties ex-
propriated were generously paid for), and
that the Meadowlands people will not
own their houses (whereas, in fact, they
are given every encouragement to buy
them).

"Maybe," he writes, "it (the home in
Meadowlands) is a far better home than
the single room or the corrugated iron
shack that you have left. But beneath your
happiness you know, or perhaps you only
feel without knowing, a deeper uncertainty and more profound unrest." And
then: "They are happy in Meadowlands.
All right, all right, let us admit it."

What an admission! What a defence of
all the bitterness and commotion he created! What a sad figure, this influential
Priest blinded by love for a slum into a
common cause with agitators and rent
racketeers!

A Note on *Apartheid*, and the Colour Bar*

FRANCIS ADDINGTON SYMONDS emigrated from England to South Africa when he was seven and remained there for twenty-five years. He was on the staffs of the *Bulawayo Chronicle* and the *Cape Times* as well as a contributor to other newspapers and journals. On returning to England, he founded and was chief editor of a group of weekly periodicals. He has published numerous works of both fiction and non-fiction.

Of the variety of non-European races in South Africa, that which most closely concerns the Rand is the Bantu—the native, or African, as he is usually called.

The Bantu is the descendant of a number of barbaric tribes scattered over Africa—e.g. the Basutos, Zulus, Swazis, etc. These tribes were the original inhabitants of the country before the coming of the white man and have become subject to him as the result of wars and the enactment of laws framed alike by the Boer and the Englishman. These laws are based on the traditional assumption that the African is of an inferior race, uncivilised, uneducated, primitive; and on the fact that, being numerically superior to the white man in the ratio of four to one, there is always the danger that, if he is allowed too much freedom, he may swamp his white masters and gain control of the country.

There has always been a conviction of white supremacy, and therefore a rigid colour bar, in South Africa. In *Report on Southern Africa* (Cape, 1952), Basil Davidson quotes from the writings of a noted Afrikaner, Dr. E. G. Malherbe, Principal of the University of Natal, who referred to "the business man who sits at his office desk and rings the bell for Jim Fish, who is working in the yard, to bring his spectacles, which lie just beyond his reach on the desk; and the wife who, while sewing, drops her thimble and halloes in shrill tones for the little piccanin on the other side of the house to come and pick it up at her feet." The present writer, whose family emigrated from England to South Africa when he was a child, was brought up to look upon the native as "black trash" and the idea that he [225/226] had any rights, or even existed as an individual apart from the mass, was regarded as laughable. His part in life was to be ordered about, to wait on the white man. Such conditions have since been somewhat modified; but the essential spirit has not changed. The African is still the servant of the white man, treated at worst with indifference and cruelty and at best with a detached tolerance. Both British and Afrikaners agree broadly on principle as to how he should be governed, though there is a sharp division of opinion arising from the imposition of *apartheid*.

Apartheid (pronounced *apart-hate*) is the compulsory segregation of the European and non-European population and is the crystallisation in law of what has always been public opinion. But many Europeans in South Africa are opposed to it "not because they favour social equality or miscegenation but because they do not believe that such matters can, in the long run, be determined by legislation and regulation. They feel that popular sanction for social separation is so powerful

* F. Addington Symonds, "A Note on *Apartheid*, and the Colour Bar," *The Johannesburg Story* (London: Frederick Muller Ltd., 1953), pp. 225–232. Reprinted with the permission of the author.

that legislation is unnecessary and vexatious."*

The Nationalist Government reply by pointing to the facts and lessons of history. They insist that South Africa's racial problem goes deeper than a mere difference in the colour of a man's skin, that it has its roots in the white man's age-old conception of what is right and wrong as between himself and those of another and fundamentally different race. They emphasise that the position in South Africa differs sharply from that in any other country which has inter-racial problems. The whites in South Africa are not simply settlers, nor are they merely administrators or traders. South Africa is their homeland as much as it is the homeland of the Bantu; therefore they claim that they have as much right to live there as the Africans and the other non-Europeans. [226/227]

The Government also stress the fact that the Africans are a race set apart by their very nature—a race which, when it first came into contact with the white man late in the eighteenth century, had a civilisation more primitive than that of our European forebears in the time of Julius Caesar. Even today, they are still little more than a collection of tribes, speaking different languages, knowing a way of life utterly divorced from that of western civilisation and far behind it in knowledge, industry and culture. The two races differ in almost every conceivable respect and this, added to the fact that the whites are so overwhelmingly outnumbered, poses a racial problem unique in world history.

It is the aim of apartheid to try to solve that problem; and its protagonists insist that, as it is so far only in an experimental stage, subject to the methods of trial and error, it is unjust to pass judgment upon it. Broadly, its purpose is to help the African to become civilised, and this is something more than the provision of formal education. The Europeans have brought to South Africa a centuries'-old culture and the non-Europeans, especially the Africans, have found themselves caught up in this way of living without any preparation and therefore without any hope of understanding, much less assimilating it. They must be assisted to develop in their own way, to become useful citizens by following their own lines of thought and living. And—say the apartheid-ites—this can only be accomplished by segregation.

It is pointed out, however, that this policy of total segregation does not apply to the Africans employed on the Rand mines. Apart from the fact that it would lead to the collapse of the industry, the law does not affect them because the vast bulk of mine labour is migratory and forms no part of the "permanent" urbanised native community. Of the 360,000 Africans working in the gold-mines, forty per cent come from various parts of the Union, the remainder from territories as far [227/228] distant as Basutoland, Rhodesia, Nyasaland and Portuguese East Africa, and the conditions of labour are essentially of a temporary nature. The average length of contract is ten months and all must return home on the completion of that period. That many come back again to the mines after an interval of rest does not invalidate this rule. They are not "townsmen" but simply "temporary hands"; and apartheid is designed to apply only to the permanently resident population.

The conditions under which the African lives and works on the Rand are rigid and clear cut. In the first place, he has the choice of three methods of obtaining employment. He may come to Johannesburg as a recruit via the Native Recruiting Corporation, which pays his fare and allocates his work on such mines as are, at the moment, in need of labour; or he may join the Assisted Voluntary Scheme, which also pays his fare but makes it a condition that he must remain at work for ten months; finally, he may set out on his own to seek whatever job he can find and

* Peoples and Policies of South Africa, by Leo Marquard (Oxford University Press, 1952).

is at liberty to relinquish it after a month's service and return home.

The actual work is done in shifts, averaging 270 in ten months, and pay is at the rate of 2s. 5d. per shift (surface) and 2s. 9d. (underground). The men work in "gangs" under white supervision. They are forbidden to qualify for skilled labour because of the colour bar (which has *legal* force only in the mining industry) and the fact that, if they undertook such work, the white workers would immediately come out on strike—as, in fact, they did in 1922. The African's right to strike is effectively limited by the fact that, under the Native Labour Regulation Act, it is a criminal offence for him to refuse to obey an order or to break his contract; and he is prohibited from forming any trade union.

Before starting work, the African must submit to a rigorous medical examination, which is repeated at regular intervals. He is housed in compounds where he and his fellows live as [228/229] "bachelors" (as temporary employees, they are not allowed to have their wives or families with them). All food is based on a scientifically balanced diet to ensure good health. Recreation is provided in the form of African cinemas, athletics, tribal dances, etc., and in their off-duty hours, the natives mingle freely with the people in the city streets. They have their own shopping centres but may patronise the ordinary (European) shops if they wish.

Apart from mine-workers, there are some 200,000 Africans employed in secondary industries, about half of whom live in compounds. There are also those—chiefly women—engaged in domestic service, who live usually in huts or outside "lodgings" provided by their employers, who are also responsible for their food.

All Africans are subject to Government Pass Laws. They must have travel passes, to enable them to move from district to district; those in urban areas must also have a night pass permitting them to be "at large" in the European area after curfew hours. If an African enters an urban area to seek work or to visit friends,

he must have a local permit, and he is also required to carry his current poll-tax receipt, to be produced on demand. Failure to observe these regulations leads to immediate arrest, followed by a fine or imprisonment.

Such are the general conditions governing the movement of Africans today; but the Government have recently introduced reforms, via the Abolition of Passes Act of 1952, whereby some of these laws will shortly be rescinded and others simplified. Nevertheless, the colour bar, whether enforced by law or by social custom, remains substantially unaltered; and criticism of this, as a habit of thought as well as a national policy, is clamant among those who, rightly or wrongly, consider themselves to be of the enlightened minority. "South African national life," says Leo Marquard,* "is based on colour distinctions that are as [229/230] strong and rigid as the class and social distinctions that were characteristic of Europe until the nineteenth century. The immediate and obvious effect of this is that, economically, the whole country and all its people are suffering from the reckless waste of man-power and of land. Muscles and skills that could be harnessed to increase the prosperity of the country are kept untrained and idle. The mass of the population is unable to produce enough or to earn enough for sufficient food and housing and medical reports are unanimous in asserting the disastrous results in high mortality rates and susceptibility to deficiency diseases. . . . The policy of *apartheid* expressly excludes Africans from ever having political influence in Parliament. The effect of this is to induce anti-European African nationalism that cannot but weaken the country in peace and war. Failure to give the non-European an effective stake in the country and in sound government must, in the long run, lead to revolt."

Another critic* who, like Mr. Mar-

* In *Peoples and Policies of South Africa* (Oxford University Press, 1952).
* Lewis Sowden in *The South African Union* (Robert Hale, 1945).

quard, is a South African and has been resident in Johannesburg for many years, asserts that "the seven million Bantu of the Union are the most repressed class in the country. They do the bulk of the manual unskilled work on the farms, in the mines and in the industries. They are badly paid, badly fed, badly housed and, even for the limited scope of the work they are allowed to do, badly educated. They are largely the source of the cheap labour with which the mines have been developed, with which industries have been established, and which has enabled the European community to maintain a comfortable, sometimes a very comfortable, standard of living. . . . The Bantu are not a degenerate people. Living both beside and among European communities, often under the most depressing conditions, conducive to poor health, high mortality and a servile state of mind, they have yet shown remarkable vitality and resilience of [230/231] spirit. [They] possess the will to live in a fertile, fullblooded impulse, and nothing the European can do will destroy it. The white man has for long been conscious of the black man's power to survive and has tried to combat it by repressive legislation, by excluding him from work where he might compete with him, by denying him the benefits of the civilisation he has built upon his shoulders. The white man's line of conduct with the native has been and still is 'Keep him down,' and to the argument now rising in the land, 'The native cannot be kept down for ever,' his answer is: 'Keep him down as long as possible.' "

Are these criticisms justified? Or is the African so fundamentally separate from the white man in his way of life as to make it impossible for him ever to assume positions of importance in the labour market or to share in the responsibilities of government?

What sort of man is this African?

As an individual and as a race, experience has shown that, though there are good and bad among them, as among all other races, the average native is law-abiding and has a high sense of justice and morality. At heart he is a child, with a child's simple and direct notions of good and evil; and, like a child, he is on the whole malleable (allowing for tribal influences, which are now on the decline) and is therefore capable of being moulded into a useful and exemplary citizen. He is "uncivilised" in the sense that he is backward and uneducated (schools and universities notwithstanding, the majority of the natives remain illiterate); but he is intelligent, industrious and trustworthy and has that sense of wonder which makes for eagerness in learning. Moreover, he has a natural respect for authority and his loyalty to the head of the State, particularly to Royalty, is often both touching and inspiring. George VI was regarded by the native not only as a king but as a father and was held in the profoundest reverence. Queen [231/232] Elizabeth II, because she is his daughter, is similarly accepted as the fount of wisdom and the source of law.

But the civilised conditions of a great modern city, such as Johannesburg, are new and strange to the African and their effects are revolutionary; they are also in certain respects demoralising. He is rapidly shedding his ancient habits and traditions; his home life as he has always understood it is fast disappearing; and in the process of acquiring a Western "veneer" he is also developing a new outlook which fits lopsidedly upon his simple and unsophisticated character. His "re-education" is too rapid, too bewildering for him to comprehend it in its fullest implications, so that he tends to become an imitator without quite knowing what or why he imitates. Modern urban life is foreign to him; but though he is sent home at regular intervals, the lure of money in the shape of regular wages, and the novelties and excitements of the city, make him return again and again. Thus he is a kind of "displaced person," rootless in a society to which he does not belong, and without purpose other than his own immediate needs or desires. Inevitably he picks up some of the bad habits of his European masters—gambling, drinking, going with prostitutes—while poverty and overcrowding tempt him too frequently to violence and crime; and all this complicates the problem which government and people alike are called upon to face.

That the African has been and to some extent still is being treated with injustice cannot be denied by those with unprejudiced minds; but that the solution to the problem of his relationship with the white man lies merely in the righting of wrongs and the improvement of social and economic conditions, is too facile an answer. For the problem is not contemporary, it is historical; and, as such, it must continue to perplex and harass the most conscientious minds and hearts, probably for a long time to come.

No Easy Future*

ALAN PATON wrote his brief *Hope for South Africa* (London, 1958) immediately after the new Liberal Party, of which he is a member, had run its first candidates in the election of 1958—"the first time since Union (1910) that liberal and progressive ideas had ever been put before the electorate." After a concise summary of South African history, to explain the connotations of *liberal* in South Africa, he outlines what he sees as "No Easy Future" for the democracy he believes inevitable, however agonized in coming, if democracy continues in the rest of the world.

I hope this brief historical account has helped readers in other countries to understand why Afrikaner Nationalism has become what it is today, and how inflexible it appears to be in the matter of race relations. For some people African Nationalism is the irresistible force, and Afrikaner Nationalism is the immovable obstacle.

Further, this account should have made it clear that the liberal idea of a *common society* is repugnant and repellent to many Afrikaners, and the fact that the idea was introduced by the British administrator and missionary has made it even more so.

And now the Afrikaner Nationalist rules the country and there seems little possibility at the moment of unseating him. As a result of this his doctrines of *apartheid* have been powerfully reinforced, and there can be no doubt that just as in the past Afrikaners were subject to a process of anglicization, so now English-speaking people are subject to a process of Afrikanerization, more particularly in respect of these doctrines.

It is clear from the results of the 1958 elections that half of the white voters are in favour of white baasskap and Afrikaner supremacy, and that those 50% of the voters can win two-thirds of the seats; it would appear that of the other half of the voters, the great majority, though not in [52/53] favour of Afrikaner supremacy, are certainly in favour of white baasskap, although they do not like the phrase and prefer *white leadership*. It would appear that the white electorate is not in favour of any political concessions to non-white people and that the United Party has, since the deaths of Hofmeyr and Smuts, steadily drifted to the right, through fear of authority or through hopelessness, or even through a growing acceptance of the view that white and black interests are irreconcilable, and that all white people should stand together.

Furthermore it would appear that in Southern Rhodesia the white electorate is moving in the same direction; and might conceivably, after having fled bodily to Rhodesia for freedom, flee back spiritually to South Africa for protection.

These are ugly facts, and they must be faced. They are made still uglier by the possibility, seen so clearly by Hofmeyr, that white action would evoke black counteraction, and that every repressive act would make conflict more and more inevitable.* Hofmeyr said, 'Go forward in faith,' but today this would be regarded by the majority of white South Africans

* Professor McCrone, of the University of the Witwatersrand, is the outstanding exponent of this theme.

* Alan Paton, "No Easy Future," *Hope for South Africa* (London: Pall Mall Press Ltd., 1958), pp. 52–59. Reprinted with the permission of Frederick A. Praeger, Inc.

as highly unpractical, unrealistic and dangerous.

How does one escape from this predicament, if one really believes that to do justice and to do injustice are equally dangerous? There is one classical escape, and that is through total *apartheid,* the thoroughgoing division of South Africa into separate racial territories, in each of which the racial group in occupation will run its own affairs and pursue its own happiness. The arguments put forward to support total *apartheid* are, *first* that different racial groups cannot live in [**53/54**] harmony in a common territory, *second* that subordinate groups will never receive justice in a common territory. Nor do I doubt that fear of ultimate disaster is an important motive.

Professor B. B. Keet has called this the pipe-dream, and no name could be more appropriate, not merely because the dream is fanciful, but also because it can be dreamed even when every sign points, every event moves, in a contrary direction. There are I think four insuperable reasons why total *apartheid* is impossible; there is no land for it, there is no money for it, there is no time for it, there is no will for it.

Nevertheless the smokers of this pipe would argue that it is the liberal vision of a common society open to all that is in fact the true pipe-dream. There is nothing, they would argue, in the 300 years of our history to indicate that such an end is possible.

What is more, some of the frustrated opponents of the Government, after the still greater defeat of the 1958 elections, are inclined to say, 'Apartheid is too strong for us; it's a waste of time to fight it, let's try to work it.'

Finally, the total apartheider can say, 'I am a liberal too. I'm the Afrikaner liberal. I want *apartheid,* but I want a just *apartheid.* Why don't you support me? I at least am in contact with the sources of power.'

There are clear and emphatic reasons why liberals of my persuasion are totally unable to lend support to the forces of total *apartheid,* quite apart from the fact that there is no land, money, time or will for it.

To us *apartheid,* of whatever brand, is a rejection of one's fellow men, not those of Kamchatka and Patagonia, but those who are born and live and die in the same land. To make *apartheid* total does not fundamentally alter the fact that it is a rejection. Total *apartheid* is a device whereby one [**54/55**] can have in imagination rejection and justice simultaneously. Seen from a religious point of view, total *apartheid* is love of one's neighbour, provided he does not live next door.

Our present society has been the joint product of all South Africa; but some of these assets are quite indivisible; for example, our cities and harbours, our mines. How could there be any division of the country? On the contrary we believe that these new societies will be condemned forever to a poor and inferior life. Therefore we reject the proposition. Further, having seen the suffering and injustice inflicted by the preliminary measures of *apartheid,* how can we possibly believe that the final measures will be something quite different? *Apartheid,* whether partial or total, is essentially something done by someone with power to someone with none.

But we reject it even more emphatically because we believe that the vain pursuit of it will postpone still further the day when all South Africans share equally the duties, privileges and joys of living in South Africa. And to that we may add that the pursuit of this goal of fantasy will turn aside some of our best minds from consideration of the real problem of creating a common society under outstandingly difficult circumstances.

We have another reason for believing that total *apartheid* is a fantasy; for, supposing it could be achieved, how could the white State watch with equanimity the forging of alliances between the non-white State and other countries of Africa and the world?

This demonstrates the difficulty of our problem. The *apartheider* says that the idea of a *common society* is unthinkable, impossible, perhaps even disgusting. The liberal says that *apartheid* as domination is doomed to die, and *apartheid* as total separation is doomed never to be born. It is my [55/56] experience that the total *apartheider,* in whom reason and emotion struggle incessantly, sees the truth of the liberal argument, and is driven to a further and new argument, namely that so long as we do not know with certainty whether total *apartheid* or integration will be the solution, it is our duty to drive towards total *apartheid* rather than integration, because from the first there can be a turning-back, but never from the second. This is an interesting and significant argument.

It is my duty to place clearly before the reader the difficulties in the way of attaining either of these goals. It is also my duty to explain that there are many South Africans who, believing it impossible to reach either goal, are deeply pessimistic about the future. And it will be my duty a little later to contend that while total *apartheid* is impossible, a democratic society is inevitable, unless democracy dies out in the world. Just how we reach that society, and whether it will be reached without a bitter price, such as the ejection of most white persons or the suffering of an Algerian agony—those are the real questions. Whether one stays to work for that society regardless of the consequences, or whether one leaves the country fearful of the consequences, is to my mind as much a question of character and temperament as it is of being able to predict the future and to act upon that prediction.

There is another difficulty in the way of achieving a democratic and non-racial and liberal solution. One of the reasons why one supports the liberal solution is because one sees the danger of group irreconcilability. But the very growth of this group irreconcilability makes the liberal solution less likely and more difficult to bring about. My readers should by this time see quite clearly that the Government disapproves of inter-racial or non-racial association; it [56/57] has already taken certain *indirect* steps to make it impossible, and it has power in certain circumstances to take *direct* steps also. It does not wish however to say boldly, so that the world can hear, 'There must be no friendship or human communication between a white and a non-white person';* but it feels able to say, 'You, a white person, may not enter that area, because that area is set aside for black persons, so that they may live self-respecting, self-reliant, self-supporting lives, without let or hindrance from any person of any other group or race.' In fact, long before this Government came to power, no white person could enter a 'location' without permission; and a location superintendent would be incredulous if a white person sought a permit to pay a friendly call on a black person in a location. In other words, the increasing amount of enforced racial separation makes it more and more difficult to create that racial understanding on which any solution must be based.

Fortunately the road ahead is not completely blocked. S.A.B.R.A.,† at its most recent conference at Stellenbosch, was most outspoken on the subject of consultation between white and non-white people and decided to call a conference with non-white leaders in the near future. This is in direct conflict with the policy of Dr. Verwoerd, who told students at Stellenbosch that they should leave consultation to himself and his Department, and should not be carried away by so-called broadminded ideas. It was in fact strongly rumoured at the S.A.B.R.A. Conference that Dr. Verwoerd had resigned from the Bureau, but this fact has never been confirmed or denied. [57/58]

What is more, there are hopes that

---

* I have no doubt that Dr. Verwoerd, if he had sole power, would have no hesitation in framing a law which would say categorically 'no non-white person shall enter a white person's house except in the capacity of a servant.'

† I remind the reader that S.A.B.R.A., the South African Bureau of Racial Affairs, is a non-political organization supported largely by Nationalists of the total *apartheid* belief.

S.A.B.R.A. will really consult 'leaders,' and not the stooges that Dr. Verwoerd consults. By leaders I mean people like ex-Chief Luthuli and Professor Z. K. Matthews, both of whom were arrested on charges of high treason in December, 1956. Professor L. J. Duplessis, another S.A.B.R.A. man, bluntly called Dr. Verwoerd's consultants 'hirelings,' and that is precisely what they are.

Nevertheless, however cheering this may be, consultation between S.A.B.R.A. and non-white leaders is likely to be more palatable to the Government than consultation between liberals and non-white leaders, because S.A.B.R.A. is committed to a policy of total *apartheid*. One therefore cannot exclude the possibility that the law will be applied in such a way that only that kind of inter-racial association will be permitted which meets to promote racial separation.

A last question must be faced before we proceed to discuss the task of Liberalism and of the Liberal Party in the present situation. All of us hope that whatever difficult times must be endured, South Africa will eventually become a democracy; and by that we mean a country with parliamentary institutions based on universal suffrage, with a written constitution and a bill of rights, and a distribution of power and authority, not only in respect to parliament, cabinet and judiciary, but also in respect of national, provincial and local bodies.

This goal will almost certainly be reached if democracy does not retreat throughout the world. But it may be reached in one of two ways, either as an aftermath of violence and revolution resulting in a black racial domination, or by an evolutionary process of a massive kind.

To put it bluntly, the choice is not simply revolution or evolution, it is revolution or revolutionary evolution. If some readers [58/59] do not like that language, one can say the choice is between revolution and massive evolution. I do not know one liberal who believes that change will come about as a result of steady and quiet evolution. That particular fantasy is cherished only by those who think the change will or should take a thousand years (or some comparable time); it is often called the ostrich-fantasy, and it is held, I believe, by those whose vested interest depends on stability, and/or those who hope never to see such change. It is a common United Party view.

If we are fated to pass through a violent revolutionary period, it is clear I think that no liberal organization will survive it, and perhaps no liberal either. That there will be a task for liberalism in the period of aftermath, I have no doubt whatsoever, that is, if democracy still lives stoutly in the world. But that is a matter for the future. I shall concern myself rather with the task of liberals and a Liberal Party in a period of massive evolution. I believe in fact that we have already entered such a period, and it is clearly the duty of liberals, not only to themselves, but to every person in South Africa, to endeavour to ensure, in collaboration with all like-minded people, that the process is not allowed to enter a violent and chaotic phase, during which all liberty would be lost, with no guarantee as to when it would be found again.

This is no easy task; it is not unlike being required to guide safely to its destination a vehicle over whose steering one has control, but over whose speed one has not.

Suggested Topics for Controlled Research

This volume presents a complete novel and further materials to enlarge your view of the novel and provide sources for controlled research papers. Finding a topic for your paper on *Cry, the Beloved Country* will be easier if you ask yourself questions about the novel as you read it. Mark in the margin anything that seems significant, especially recurrences of any kind, until some one question begins to engross your curiosity. "Why does Paton so frequently repeat phrases, and even whole paragraphs?" you ask yourself. Well, now you have a topic: "Repetitions in *Cry, the Beloved Country*." And perhaps you can already formulate a tentative answer, which may serve as a thesis for your paper: "Paton repeats to emphasize underlying similarities between different classes of people and different situations." You will no doubt wish to adjust that thesis as you discover other reasons; perhaps you will change it altogether. But your topic, together with a tentative thesis if possible, will focus your further reading, and re-reading, as you collect your evidence, marking your book as you go. My own copy of the novel, for instance, has a whole series of numbers penciled in the margin referring me forward and back to mentions of *crying*, and the margins are also full of "up" and "down," with page numbers, from the time I began to gather ideas for the essay on Paton's moral geography. You will discover good possibilities for topics if you trace the recurrent theme of lamentation, the shifts from Zulu to English in the dialogue and Paton's way of showing them, the many voices through which the tale is unfolded and the attitudes they represent, the spiritual growth of Stephen Kumalo or James Jarvis, or the role of a minor character, like Msimangu or Mrs. Lithebe or Kumalo's unnamed friend in Ndotsheni.

After answering specific questions about the book's themes, language, structure, setting, characterization, or points-of-view, you may wish to consider larger topics about the novel: the interrelation of personal and social dilemmas, the connection between the landscape of the novel and the people who inhabit it, the plausibility of characters as against their function in representing abstract qualities or social types, the counterbalancing of fathers and sons, of country and city, the relationship of good to evil in the novel, and many others.

Reading the novel both responsively and critically, you will form your own impression of it, a base from which you may then challenge the critics and compare the sociological evidence in the rest of the volume. The critics offer a number of good possibilities for topics. First, you can either corroborate or challenge one of a critic's points, using evidence from the novel to support your case. Rolo, for instance, charges that the ending of the novel is too pat—that milk and water from High Place are too good to be true. To attack or defend that position, you should determine whether the motives behind the gift are sufficiently developed to make it plausible, or whether the author simply seems to reward Kumalo to make things end happily, whether other circumstances keep the success from seeming too simple and sweet—in short, whether you feel that Rolo has weighed all the evidence or read too lightly. You might consider the various instances of detribalization that Collins notes, as against any solution you think the novel as a whole suggests. You could explain or challenge Baker's assertion that the Zulu idiom as rendered by Paton "both represents and resolves, as does Kumalo himself, the black-white dilemma," or Rooney's that the novel conveys a message without propagandizing or preaching. Or you can join in the debate about the symbolic significance of the novel's setting, taking sides with either Gailey or Baker and bringing in further evidence to strengthen your mutual position—or knocking both their heads together from a third position that goes beyond both. Finally, you might write a paper on the five critics and their differences in attitude and approach.

Section III presents the South African setting, and here you can explore some of the historical, political, and social issues raised by the novel and compare the different ways in which these issues are conveyed in their fictional and nonfictional formulations. Lunt, for example, presents the history of South Africa and its "two streams," the Afrikaner and the British. You could write a paper on the way in which Paton includes the Afrikaner in *Cry, the Beloved Country,* how the Afrikaner's language comes into the novel both in dialogue and in the names of places and their significance, and how the Afrikaner fits into the social structure Paton indicates in the novel. Or you might study the Britishness of South African society as indicated in the novel, in the light of Lunt's description.

Similarly, you could examine the characterization of Gertrude, Absalom, the girl who becomes his wife, Baby Mkize, Johannes Pafuri, and others, along with the young dispossessed Africans described by Huddleston and Longmore, considering in what ways the characters in the novel are similar to and different from their social prototypes. You could also explain the relevance of the life Paton describes in "Through a Tribal Reserve" to the novel. Broader topics would include a consideration of how well the novel penetrates to the roots of the social problems in the light of the sociologists' explanations, or a consideration of how Paton's assertion that tribal religion can "restore . . . one of the great qualities of worship" to Christianity ("Through a

Tribal Reserve," p. 118) is worked out in the novel.

Paton has said that "the accounts of the boycott of the buses, the erection of Shanty Town, the finding of gold at Odendaalsrust, and the miners' strike, are a compound of truth and fiction. In these respects therefore the story is not true, but considered as a social record it is the plain and simple truth."[1] The paradox in this statement is based upon the special quality of the creative writer's representation of reality. All writers must order their work by selecting among facts; but the novelist extends, colors, and rearranges his material in such a way that his work will always be different, both in detail and in tone, from what we usually call "social records." What does Paton mean by "a compound of truth and fiction," and is there a truth of fiction, as he suggests? The two maps will furnish a set of facts against which you can check details of the novel. The accounts of the bus boycotts, the discovery of gold, and Oppenheimer's speech about housing for miners all provide means for exploring the difference between fictional representation and factual description. Comparing one or more of these documents with corresponding parts of *Cry, the Beloved Country* will turn up some significant differences in the kinds of detail chosen by the novelist and the reporter, which you could describe under a topic like "Fiction and Document: A Contrast of Detail." You can also speculate—with proper caution, since the document will by no means contain *all* the facts—as to what imaginary details Paton is adding to actual events.

The selections by Huddleston, Steward, Symonds, and Paton which conclude this volume carry the discussion of South African race relations a step in time beyond the novel, to the period after the policy of *Apartheid* was adopted by the Nationalist government; but the fundamental issues dividing South African

[1] "Author's Note," *Cry, the Beloved Country* (New York: Charles Scribner's Sons, 1950; Modern Standard Authors Series), p. vii.

opinion remain the same. By choosing a topic such as "Contrasting Attitudes Toward the Race Problem in South Africa," you could analyze the basic assumptions of each of these writers and then show how each viewpoint is represented (or misrepresented, or omitted) in the novel. You might also observe something of the differences in social and political involvement among these writers, and how these differences affect their selections and presentations of evidence. And you might come to an answer as to whether the novel transcends any individual view, and in what ways, and whether Paton's novel does convey, as Collins claims, " 'how it feels' to be a South African."

A comparison of Paton's "No Easy Future" with *Cry, the Beloved Country* will lead you to several interesting topics, arising from such questions as these: How are Paton's views in the essay conveyed in the novel? How does the novel portray the complexity Paton sees in the essay?— a study of Paton's stylistic devices, such as those he uses in presenting Shanty Town and the discovery of gold, will be helpful in answering this question. Is the mood of the novel similar to that of the essay, or has the situation, or Paton's attitude, changed significantly in the decade between? What hope for the future does each indicate?

A study of the ways in which characters portrayed in the novel influence and are influenced by their society might shed light upon what Paton is saying about South Africa. Does Kumalo seem a successful bridge between two cultures? How relevant is Christianity to South Africa's problems? Is Kumalo something of "a white man's dog . . . a trick to hold together something that the white man desires to hold together" (p. 35), as John Kumalo accuses the tribal chief of being, and as Stephen Kumalo himself wonders (p. 265)? Is John Kumalo's way less or more effective than his brother's?—a comparison of these two brothers, each a preacher in his own way, would be very interesting in itself, and might provide a good test of the plausibility of Paton's characters. Alternatively, you could examine Arthur Jarvis's program for social reform and decide whether the ideals he represents are effectively dramatized in the novel.

Finally, you might choose as a topic a single problem that runs through all the selections in this volume, the novel as well as the accompanying materials: the problem of cultural differences, for instance, thoroughly analyzed in the documents and illustrated in the novel in a myriad of chance remarks, such as that of the man who tries to describe buildings as higher than the hill behind his father's kraal, when nobody knows his father's kraal nor the hill behind it, or the differing attitudes toward Sibeko's daughter, who has lost her job at uSmith's daughter's house. Similar problems can be found in South Africa's diversity of languages, the poverty of the countryside, the discrepancies in wealth, the splitting of families, the dependence of the economy on unskilled labor, the problems of crime and of justice, and many more.

Suggested Topics for Library Research

The selections in this volume have probably already tempted you toward research in the library. Indeed, any one of the books from which I have excerpted would shed further light on *Cry, the Beloved Country*—its accuracy in characterization, its presentation of Christianity in South Africa, its adequacy in presenting such problems as detribalization, agricultural erosion, poverty, and cultural differences. You could write a valuable paper, for instance, on Jan Hofmeyr's contribution to Paton's thought as indicated in Paton's *South African Tragedy*, or you could look up Theodore Gregory's book on Oppenheimer and see if Oppenheimer fulfilled the expectations expressed of him in *Cry, the Beloved Country*.

Arthur Jarvis's library (Chapter 20) also offers tempting possibilities for research papers. In this room, Paton is surely endowing Jarvis with something of his own intellectual background. Any one of the books may provide clues to *Cry, the Beloved Country*: F. V. Engelenburg's book on Botha (London, 1929), or Sarah Gertrude Millin's biographies of Rhodes (New York, 1933) and Smuts (Boston, 1936). You could also compare Mrs. Millin's *The People of South Africa* (London, 1951) with Paton's *The Land and People of South Africa* (Philadelphia, 1955).

Abraham Lincoln is expressly important to *Cry, the Beloved Country*. You might succeed in turning up the actual book on Lincoln that James Jarvis takes from the shelf (one with a chapter headed "The Famous Speech at Gettysburg," some preliminary pages, then the speech itself). You could detail the specific relevance to the novel of Lincoln's Gettysburg Address and Second Inaugural Address, or you might try a more elusive and speculative topic: "The Significance of Arthur Jarvis's Four Pictures." The picture of Lincoln provides an embarrassment of riches, but "Vergelegen" is hard to identify. My own efforts failed completely, until an inquiry to Mr. Paton brought this response:

> The "white gabled house of Vergelegen" is an actual place, and it was built by Adrian van der Stel about the year 1700. It is 30 miles from Cape Town and lies under the Hottentots Holland Mountains. It is a massive building with tremendously thick walls and is shaded by giant Camphor trees, which must be the oldest exotic trees in South Africa.

With this much to go on, you might be able to find further details about van der Stel and his house to suggest why they should rank with Christ crucified and Lincoln in Jarvis's mind. "Leafless willows" are also elusive, though perhaps just simply and obviously their weeping selves. A book such as R. S. Adamson's *The Vegetation of South Africa* (London, 1938) might tell you where willows are indigenous in South Africa, and Stith Thompson's *Motif-Index of Folk-Literature* (Bloomington, 1932–1936) will give you some notion of their literary and traditional symbolism.

Another line of research is suggested by Arthur Jarvis's library. One bookcase is full of books in Afrikaans, whose titles convey nothing to James Jarvis, and doubtless would convey as little to us. But clearly they meant something to Arthur Jarvis—and to Paton, who contributed an article on the contemporary Afrikaans novel to *English Studies in Africa* (September, 1959). Even if these novels have not been translated into English and are unavailable to you, Paton's remarks on those that would have been contemporary with Arthur Jarvis would shed light on Jarvis's attitudes.

Another book of great significance for *Cry, the Beloved Country* is the Bible. When, at the end, Kumalo cries out "My son, my son, my son," we know that Paton's naming the son "Absalom" was not inadvertent. You could describe how the story of David and Absalom (II Samuel xiii ff.) is, and is not, relevant to *Cry, the Beloved Country*. Similarly, the parable of the prodigal son (Luke xv. 11–32) has explicit, and ironic, relevance.

If you are familiar with the Bible, or the Book of Common Prayer, you could point out verbal and stylistic echoes of the Bible in *Cry, the Beloved Country* and show how Biblical language has reinforced Paton's rendering of the Zulu language in English, as several critics have remarked. For example, in Chapter 13 Msimangu reads from the Zulu Bible; phrases from the Twenty-Third Psalm spring from Kumalo's lips in Chapter 10; Father Vincent makes a point "in that symbolic language that is like the Zulu tongue" (p. 108), telling a little figurative story that is very like a Biblical parable. And you can find a number of similar Biblical allusions, direct and indirect.

Paton's other creative works, of course, also furnish excellent possibilities for papers. The influence of the Bible on *Too Late the Phalarope* as compared to that on *Cry, the Beloved Country* would be interesting to trace, as would the theme of fathers-and-sons, the picture of the Afrikaner, of the Britisher, of the black African, and so forth. Almost every one of Paton's *Tales from a Troubled Land* suggests a paper on its particular connections with *Cry, the Beloved Country*. And you could study the differences between narrative and dramatic writing by comparing *Sponono: A Play in Three Acts* with the three *Tales* from which it draws, or by seeing how Maxwell Anderson adapted *Cry, the Beloved Country* for the stage in *Lost in the Stars*.

Paton's "The Negro in America Today" (*Collier's,* October 15, October 29, 1954) offers several opportunities for papers. First, you could spell out the differences between the American and the South African racial situations that Paton only implies, combining evidence from Paton, Longmore, Huddleston, Steward, and others concerning differences between the two countries in social structures, customs, history, economics, ideology, constitutional framework, democratic representation, proportions of white to black, and so forth. Or you could search out another description of the American Negro contemporary with Paton's for comparison—bearing in mind that the year is 1954, the year of the Supreme Court's declaring "separate but equal" schooling unconstitutional. You could also find an article of the present time, affording you an analytic look back to Paton's vision of the future. The chapter on the Negro in Nathan Glazer and Daniel Patrick Moynihan's *Beyond the Melting Pot* (Cambridge, 1963), and Daniel Patrick Moynihan's *The Negro Family: A Case for Action* (Washington, 1965) are valuable sources.

Two autobiographies offer several fine topics: Martin Luther King's *Stride Toward Freedom: The Montgomery Story* (New York, 1958) and Albert Luthuli's *Let My People Go* (New York, 1962). Both men are Christians, advocates of nonviolence, and leaders of their people, one in America, the other in South Africa. King's book, furthermore, describes a bus boycott in America so similar to that in *Cry, the Beloved Country* that it appears to have been inspired by it, until we discover that the two boycotts were entirely unrelated. Side by side, the two offer many similarities as they reveal differences in the two societies. You could also use King's book to check Paton's description of the Negro in America. A comparison between King and Luthuli would be equally fruitful. Finally, you could examine Paton's Kumalo in terms of Luthuli's self-portrait, since both represent similar reconciliations of the Zulu and the white worlds.

A number of novels offer profitable comparisons with *Cry, the Beloved Country*. You could follow out the leads that Collins has suggested. You could work out at length the parallel, mentioned by Rooney, with *The Grapes of Wrath*, which we know to have been an immediate stimulus to Paton. And you could choose any number of comparisons as to how the Negro appears in literature, beginning with Mrs. Aphra Behn's *Oroonoko, or The Royal Slave* (1688), the first anti-slavery novel. Harriet Beecher Stowe's famous *Uncle Tom's Cabin* (1851–52) provides a wealth of contrasts with *Cry, the Beloved Country*. How are the authors alike in their aims, and how different? How, in what they assume a novel to be? How, in what they assume about society and attitudes, Negro and white? The African novels of Sarah Gertrude Millin, Nadine Gordimer, and Joyce Cary are good possibilities for comparison with *Cry, the Beloved Country*, as are the American novels of James Wright, Ralph Ellison, James Baldwin, and others. Two instructive essays in this area are Blyden Jackson's "The Negro's Negro in Negro Literature" and Boyd M. Berry's "Another Man Done Gone: Self-Pity in Baldwin's *Another Country*," *Michigan Quarterly Review*, IV (Fall, 1965), 290–295, and V (Fall, 1966), 285–290.

Any number of interesting historical and sociological studies could start from the materials in this volume. The history of Sophiatown, as suggested by Paton and filled out by Longmore, Huddleston, and Steward, leads on to general questions about renovating slums anywhere, about private ownership and public housing, about privilege and underprivilege, about law and defying law. You might also like to follow the developments of South African politics since 1948.

For such topics of social history, the *Index* to The London *Times* will prove invaluable. Under "South Africa," you will find the important news stories, day by day, concerning politics, mining, agriculture, social and racial strife, prominent people, and so forth. The similar *New York Times Index* is less helpful for South Africa, but will nevertheless lead you to important news of America and the world. The London *Economist*, indexed quarterly, consistently treats South African economics, gold-mining, and trade. You will find a useful bibliography at the end of the article on South Africa in *The Encyclopædia Britannica*, itself an excellent summary of the history, literature, sociology, climate, vegetation, and topography of that country. Other useful aids to research are *The World Almanac and Book of Facts*, *The Reader's Guide to Periodical Literature*, the *Social Science and Humanities Index* and the annual *PMLA Bibliography* (for scholarly articles), the *Essay and General Literature Index* (for subjects within books of essays and criticism), the *Biography Index*, and the *Book Review Digest*.

This last reference work brings us back to *Cry, the Beloved Country* and its impact. Look up the 1948 reviews and write a review of the reviews, indicating how Rolo compares with other reviewers, what sort of things were said, what overlooked, and who may have been echoing whom.

The Principal Works of Alan Paton

Cry, the Beloved Country: A Story of Comfort in Desolation
First edition: New York: Charles Scribner's Sons, 1948.
British edition: London: Jonathan Cape, 1948.
Hardbound text edition: New York: Charles Scribner's Sons, 1950; Modern Standard Authors Series, with an introduction by Lewis Gannett.
Paperbound edition: New York: Charles Scribner's Sons (Scribner Library, SL 7), 1960.

South Africa Today
New York: Public Affairs Committee (Public Affairs Pamphlet No. 175), 1951.

Too Late the Phalarope
First edition: New York: Charles Scribner's Sons, 1953.
British edition: London: Jonathan Cape, 1953.
Paperback text: New York: New American Library (Signet Books, S 1290), 1956.
Paperbound edition: New York: Charles Scribner's Sons (Scribner Library, SL 79), 1963.

"The Negro in America Today: A Firsthand Report"
Collier's, October 15, 1954, October 29, 1954.
Reprinted: Washington: Civil Rights Committee and Education and Research Department, Congress of Industrial Organizations, 1954.

The Land and People of South Africa
First edition: Philadelphia: J. B. Lippincott Co., 1955; Portraits of Nations Series.
British edition, entitled *South Africa and Her People*: London: Lutterworth Press, 1957; Portraits of Nations Series.
Revised edition: Philadelphia: J. B. Lippincott Co., 1964.

South Africa in Transition
New York: Charles Scribner's Sons, 1956; Photographs by Dan Weiner.

Hope for South Africa
London: Pall Mall Press, 1958.

220

Tales from a Troubled Land

First edition: New York: Charles Scribner's Sons, 1961.
Paperbound edition: New York: Charles Scribner's Sons (Scribner Library, SL 131), 1966.

Hofmeyr

First edition: London: Oxford University Press, 1964.
American edition, entitled *South African Tragedy: The Life and Times of Jan Hofmeyr;* abridgement by Dudley C. Lunt: New York: Charles Scribner's Sons, 1965.

Sponono: A Play in Three Acts. By Alan Paton and Krishna Shah.

New York: Charles Scribner's Sons, 1965. Based on three stories by Alan Paton from the collection, *Tales from a Troubled Land.*